A Course in Organic Chemistry

edited by

SIR ROBERT ROBINSON, O.M., F.R.S.

ADVANCED SECTION · VOLUME XXVI

THE ISOQUINOLINE ALKALOIDS
A Course in Organic Chemistry

The Isoquinoline Alkaloids

A COURSE IN ORGANIC CHEMISTRY

BY

K. W. BENTLEY

PERGAMON PRESS

OXFORD · LONDON · EDINBURGH · NEW YORK
PARIS · FRANKFURT

112564

547.72
B 477

PERGAMON PRESS LTD.
Headington Hill Hall, Oxford
4 & 5 Fitzroy Square, London, W.1

PERGAMON PRESS (SCOTLAND) LTD.
2 & 3 Teviot Place, Edinburgh 1

PERGAMON PRESS INC.
122 East 55th Street, New York 22, N.Y.

GAUTHIER-VILLARS ED.
55 Quai des Grands-Augustins, Paris 6

PERGAMON PRESS G.m.b.H.
Kaiserstrasse 75, Frankfurt am Main

FEDERAL PUBLICATIONS LTD.
Times House, River Valley Road, Singapore

SAMCAX BOOK SERVICES LTD.
Queensway, P.O. Box 2720, Nairobi, Kenya

Set in 10 on 12 pt. Times Roman and printed in
Great Britain by Spottiswoode, Ballantyne & Co. Ltd.
London and Colchester

Contents

Preface

I<small>T WAS</small> with pleasure that I accepted the invitation of Sir Robert Robinson to prepare this volume, since it was at his suggestion in 1947 that I began the investigation of the phenyldihydrothebaine problem, and so made my first acquaintance with that remarkable alkaloid, the study of which has occupied most of my research time since that date. On a number of occasions since then it has appeared that the chemistry of the morphine alkaloids, and of thebaine in particular, has been fully explored, but this has always been followed by a burst of further activity, and the recent demonstration of the amazing pharmacological properties of some of the derivatives of thebaine make it clear that the bases of this group still have their parts to play in medicine.

My work with the alkaloids of the isoquinoline group over the last seventeen years has been sometimes difficult, sometimes frustrating, but always immensely interesting, and it is in the hope that some of this interest may be communicated to others that this volume has been written.

Reckitt & Sons Limited,   K. W. B<small>ENTLEY</small>
Hull, 1965

NOTE BY THE EDITOR

The volumes in the Advanced Section of this Course in Organic Chemistry have an independent value as short monographs by experts in the respective fields treated. They are therefore offered in advance of the General Sections of the Course, even though this implies a greater prior knowledge on the part of the student.

CHAPTER 1

Introduction

For many centuries opium, the dried latex exuded from the cut seed capsule of the opium poppy, *Papaver somniferum*, has been greatly valued on account of its ability to alleviate pain and also to induce a euphoric state when eaten, or smoked. One particular chemical substance is responsible for both of these effects of opium, although the material contains a number of other compounds as well. Morphine, the euphoric and analgesic agent, was first isolated in 1805, and was the first nitrogenous base to be isolated from living sources. Although of considerable structural complexity, the complete constitution of the base was not elucidated until 1925, morphine belongs to a large general class of natural bases, to which the term alkaloid is applied, and to a smaller though still large sub-group all based on the isoquinoline structural unit.

The alkaloids of the isoquinoline group may be further sub-divided into families, all of which are clearly related structurally and by their mode of formation in the plant. In this work an attempt has been made to order the presentation of each sub-group on the basis of a rational relationship to those first described. The account is not intended to be exhaustive, rather it is intended to indicate the methods used in the elucidation of the structures of new organic compounds, and for this purpose representative members of each sub-group of alkaloids are selected for discussion and the relationships of other members of the group to the selected compound are given. In the case of the alkaloids of the morphine group where great interest centres on the complex rearrangements that the alkaloids may be made to undergo, the chemical properties of the compounds are discussed at greater length. The rest of this chapter is devoted to a discussion of a few of the most important chemical processes used in the degradative studies necessary for the elucidation of the structures of the alkaloids.

The chemical structures of the alkaloids have been deduced by the classical methods of organic chemistry, namely the degradation of the bases to simpler fragments, the structures of which are more readily determined and the assembly of a satisfactory molecular formula from these fragments from a knowledge of the nature of the reactions used. In these days when the structures of complex natural products may be elucidated with scarcely a reaction done at the bench, by the application of the modern tools of ultraviolet, infrared, nuclear magnetic resonance and mass spectrometry, and X-ray crystallography greatly facilitated by modern high-speed computing techniques, it is easy to forget or belittle the impeccable work done with poor (by present standards) equipment by the pioneers in this field. It should be remembered that even catalytic reduction was only introduced as a new technique in the early 1920's, at a time when the major researches of Hesse, Pschorr, Knorr, Wieland and Perkin had been completed and Robinson had been working for almost twenty years. While the chemist should never scorn new methods as if there was an inherent virtue in clinging to the more lengthy methods of the past, it should be remembered that the modern techniques of structure elucidation have only become of value because they have been built up on the massive foundation of knowledge gained so impressively by the classical techniques. The final proof of the correctness of any structure deduced from a complex of data, however, remains the total unambiguous synthesis of material of that structure and comparison of the product with material from natural sources, and this can only be done at the bench by drawing on the whole accumulated store of chemical knowledge and theory.

In the work described in the following chapters it will be found that two general processes have been repeatedly utilised for the degradation of alkaloids of the isoquinoline group to recognisable compounds, namely oxidation and exhaustive methylation and related processes for the removal of the nitrogen atom, and some space is here devoted to an explanation of these processes.

Oxidation

All of the alkaloids of the isoquinoline group contain aromatic nuclei bearing as substituents methoxyl, methylenedioxy, hydroxy or aryloxy groups and saturated or unsaturated carbon side-chains. Oxidation of such compounds with alkaline permanganate results in the destruction only of phenolic nuclei and the carbon side-chains, the products being methoxy, aryloxy or methylenedioxy-substituted aromatic acids of generally easily determined structures, in which the positions of the carboxyl groups indicate the positions of the carbon side-chains of the parent alkaloids since they are the residue of such chains. For this purpose a phenolic nucleus linked directly to a non-phenolic aromatic ring is regarded as a side-chain since the phenol is oxidised away to a carboxyl group; a phenolic nucleus not directly linked to another aromatic ring leaves no residue.

It is usually more instructive to methylate a phenol to its *O*-methyl ether before oxidation since the aromatic nucleus then survives and can be isolated as an acid from the products of the reaction. Still more instructive is oxidation after *O*-ethylation of the phenol since the position of the phenolic hydroxyl group in the original base, frequently in the presence of one or more OMe groups, can be deduced from the position of the ethoxyl group in the acid or acids obtained during oxidation.

Examples of these processes are given in formulae (1)–(12). Sometimes intermediate oxidation products are obtained, e.g. the amide corydaldine (2) may be isolated from the oxidation of tetra-hydropalmatine (1) and separately oxidised to *m*-hemipinic acid (4), and the restriction of the amount of permanganate used in the oxidation of berberine $C_{20}H_{19}O_5N$ to considerably less than is

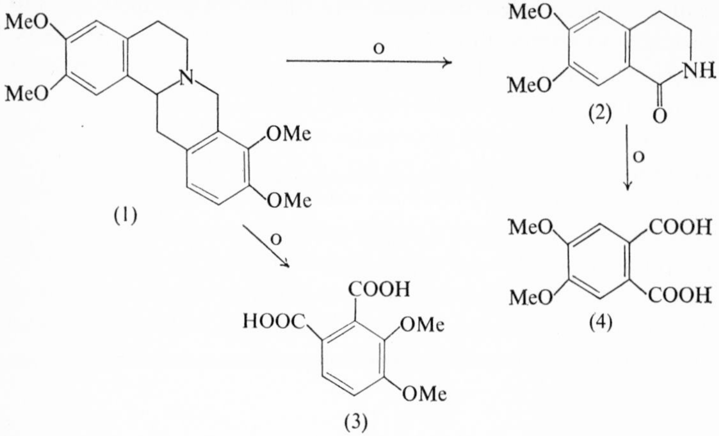
MeO
MeO
N
OMe
OMe
(1)
O
MeO
MeO
NH
O
(2)
O
COOH
HOOC
OMe
OMe
(3)
MeO
COOH
MeO
COOH
(4)

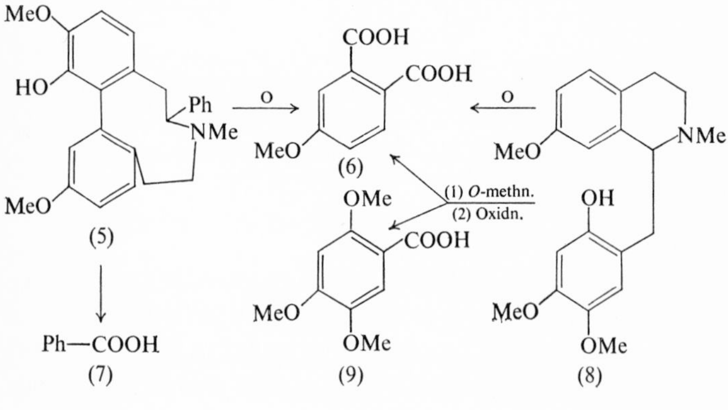
MeO
HO
Ph
NMe
MeO
(5)
O
COOH
COOH
MeO
(6)
O
MeO
NMe
(1) O-methn.
(2) Oxidn.
OMe
COOH
MeO
OMe
(9)
OH
MeO
OMe
(8)
Ph—COOH
(7)

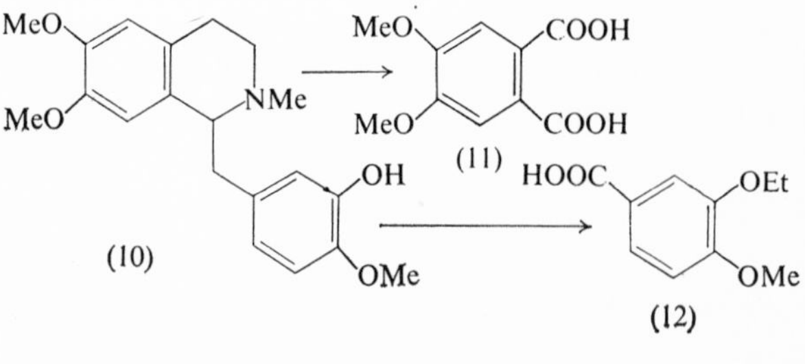
MeO
MeO
NMe
OH
OMe
(10)
MeO
COOH
MeO
COOH
(11)
HOOC
OEt
OMe
(12)

required for complete destruction to stable end-products leads to products of composition $C_{20}H_{17}O_5N$, $C_{20}H_{17}O_6N$, $C_{20}H_{17}O_7N$, $C_{20}H_{17}O_8N$ and $C_{20}H_{19}O_9N$ from the natures of which important conclusions could be drawn (see Chapter 8).

In some cases it has proved more informative to oxidise the alkaloids after one or two stages of Hofmann degradation (see below) as the double bonds introduced into the molecule during such degradations increase the ease of oxidation, and the nature of the products so obtained usually throws light on the position of the newly introduced double bonds and hence of the nitrogen atom. This is illustrated by the degradations of apomorphine dimethyl ether set out in formulae (13)–(15).

(13)   (14)   (15)

Exhaustive methylation

The Hofmann degradation, in which pyrolysis of a quaternary ammonium hydroxide leads to an olefine and a tertiary base, is one of the most widely used processes in degradative studies of alkaloids. The results of the reaction, often clear and unambiguous, must, however, not infrequently be interpreted with some care. The reaction basically involves attack of a hydrogen atom on the carbon β to the quaternary nitrogen by a base, generally a hydroxyl ion, and elimination of a tertiary base and water.

When no β-hydrogen is present the reaction takes a different course involving attack by the base at one of the carbon atoms attached to the nitrogen.

$$\begin{matrix} \text{C}-\text{C}-\overset{+}{\text{N}}\text{R}_3 \\ \text{HO}^{\ominus} \end{matrix} \longrightarrow \begin{matrix} \text{C}-\text{C} + \text{NR}_3 \\ \text{OH} \end{matrix}$$

When the quaternary salt is the salt of an open chain amine one degradation results in the elimination of the nitrogen, whereas if the nitrogen is bound in a ring the first step affords an open chain olefinic amine and a repetition of the process is necessary for complete elimination of the nitrogen atom, and in cases where the nitrogen is the point of union of two rings three Hofmann degradations are required for its removal as shown in formulae (16)–(19). The sequence of *N*-methylations and Hofmann degradations leading to removal of the nitrogen is generally referred to as exhaustive methylation. The number of stages involved in the process, before examination of the products, clearly gives some information about the environment of the nitrogen atom.

(16)   (17)   (18)   (19)

Where more than one product could be formed as a result of Hofmann degradation on alternative sides of the nitrogen atom the product actually obtained depends on the ease of removal of the β-hydrogen atom. In the isoquinoline alkaloid series all the bases have an aromatic nucleus attached also to one of the β-carbon atoms and fission to a styrene is accomplished very easily. In the case of hydrohydrastinine (20) fission can only occur on one side

(20)

(21)

(22)

(23)

(24)

(25)

(26)

(28)

(27)

(29)

of the nitrogen, to give (21) as on the other side there is no β-hydrogen atom, whereas when such an atom is present, as in laudanosine (22) fission occurs to give the stilbene (23) in preference to the styrene. In the morphine (24) series of the styrene, e.g. (25), is always formed in preference to the unconjugated olefine (26), but in the aporphine series fission occurs on both sides of the nitrogen atom, e.g. isothebaine methyl ether (27) gives both the optically active isomethine base (28) and the inactive methine (29). (The term "methine" is generally applied to the first basic product of exhaustive methylation of an alkaloid.)

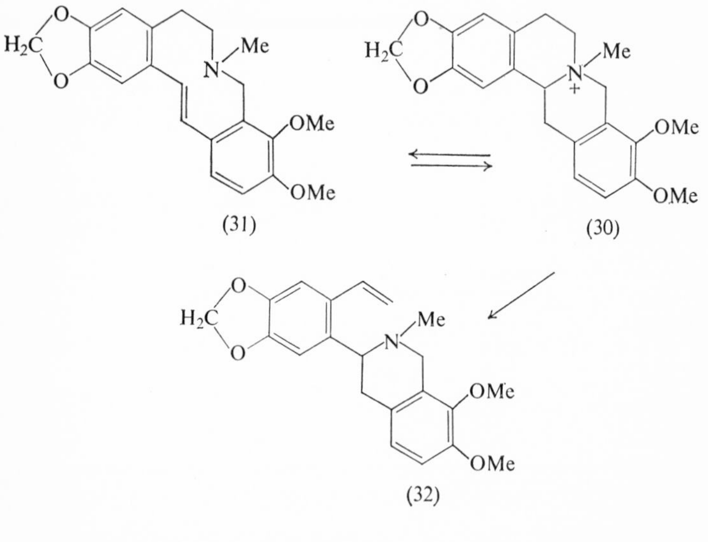

(31)   (30)

(32)

Recombination of a methine base to the original quaternary salt has been recorded only in three cases. One of these is provided by (−)-canadine methiodide (30) which on degradation affords a mixture of the two methines, inactive (31) and (−)-(32) together with (±)-canadine methiodide and (±)-methine (32). The racemic salt (30) must arise by recombination of the inactive symmetrical base (31) and clearly the racemic methine (32) arises by subsequent degradation of racemic quaternary salt. In this case the recombination is presumably facilitated by the holding of the *N*-methyl group in close proximity to the double bond.

The presence of a carbonyl group attached to the β-carbon atom (giving a "Mannich base") results in exceptionally rapid elimination of amine, for example dihydrothebainone-C methiodide (33) is split to the methine base (34) under the influence of such mild reagents as aqueous sodium bicarbonate.

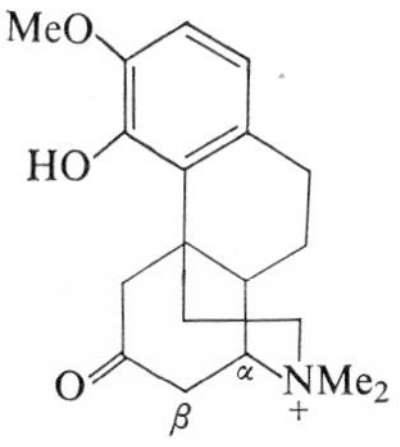

(33)

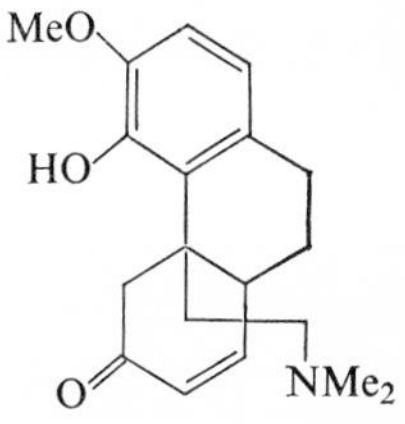

(34)

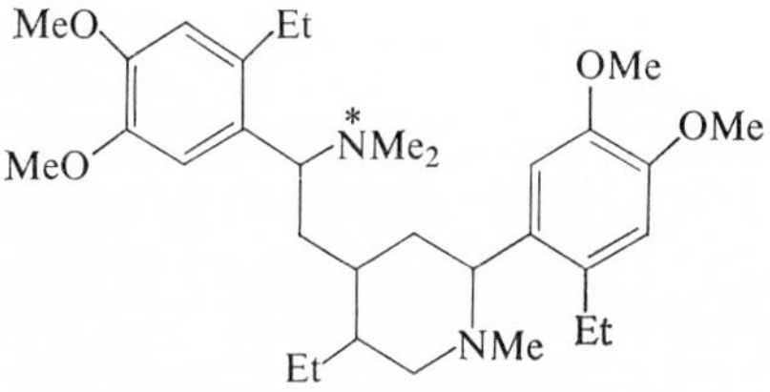

(35)

When two quaternary nitrogen atoms are present in the same molecule both centres are usually affected by the Hofmann degradation, e.g. the bisbenzylisoquinoline alkaloids, in which the environments of the two nitrogen atoms are virtually identical, yield bis-methines very readily, but when the environments of the tertiary centres differ it is often possible to prepare a mono-methiodide and thus effect degradation at one centre only, e.g. the emetine derivative (35) may in this way be degraded only at the centre marked with an asterisk.

It occasionally happens that the position of the double bond or double bonds in the product of Hofmann degradation of a quaternary salt is not what would be expected, since the newly introduced double bond may, under the influence of the strongly alkaline conditions, move into conjugation with a double bond or aromatic nucleus already present, e.g. the degradation of the de-*N*-(*a*)-emetinehexahydrobismethine (36) affords the conjugated diene (37) not the unconjugated elimination product. Also unconjugated double bond systems present in the starting material may be conjugated during the vigorous conditions of the reaction and dihydrothebaine-ϕ (38) on degradation yields not the related methine base but the fully conjugated triene (39).

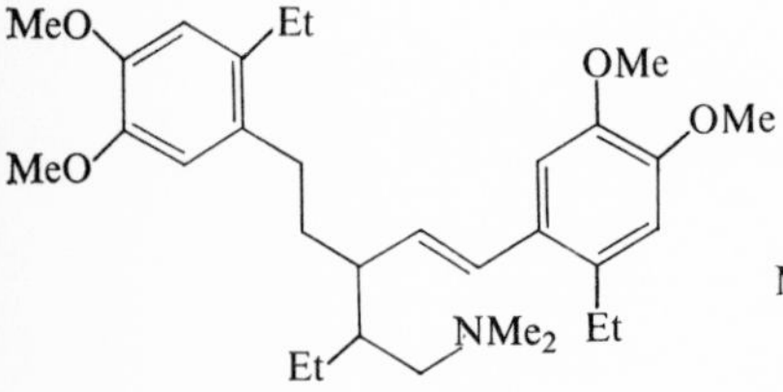

(36)

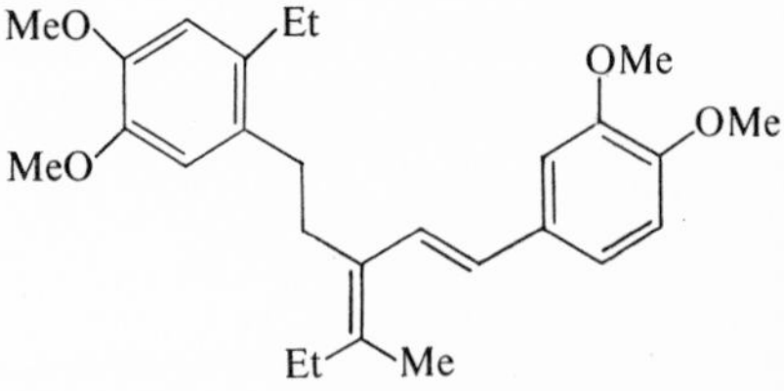

(37)

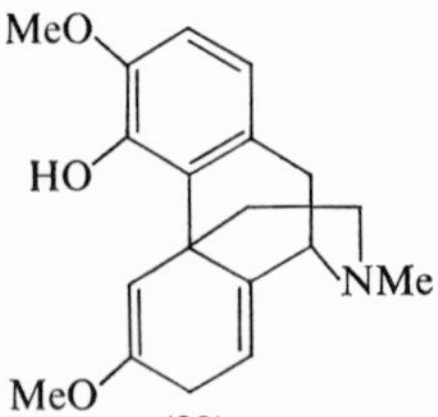

(38)

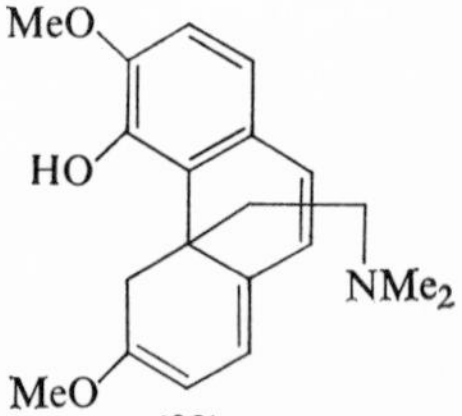

(39)

The formation of an olefine is, however, not the only process that can result in the production of a tertiary base from a quaternary salt. The reaction can proceed by direct attack of base at the α-carbon atom rather than at the hydrogen attached to the β-carbon to give a tertiary base together with an alcohol or an ether, in the following ways, all of which are variants of essentially the same reaction.

I. Displacement of methanol

$$-CH_2-CH_2-\overset{+}{N}\!\!\underset{Me\;\;:OH^{\ominus}}{\overset{Me}{\diagup}}\!\!-Me \longrightarrow -CH_2-CH_2-NMe_2 + MeOH$$

II. Displacement of an alcohol

$$-CH_2-CH_2-\overset{+}{N}\!\!\underset{Me}{\overset{Me}{\diagup}}\!\!-Me \longrightarrow -CH_2-CH_2OH + NMe_3$$
$$^{\ominus}HO:$$

III. Ether formation

$$\left\{ \begin{array}{l} -CH_2-CH_2-\overset{+}{N}Me_3 \\ \\ -C-O-H\;\;:OH^{\ominus} \end{array} \right. \longrightarrow \left\{ \begin{array}{l} -CH_2-CH_2 \\ \quad\quad\quad\mid \quad + NMe_3 \\ -C-O \end{array} \right.$$

OR

$$\left\{ \begin{array}{l} -CH_2-CH_2-\overset{+}{\underset{|}{N}}\overset{Me}{}-Me \\ \quad\quad\quad\quad\; Me \\ -C-O-H\;\;:OH^{\ominus} \end{array} \right. \longrightarrow \left\{ \begin{array}{l} -CH_2-CH_2-NMe_2 \\ \\ -C-O-Me \end{array} \right.$$

In the absence of β-hydrogen this general process is frequently the only one by which a tertiary base may be formed, and even in the presence of β-hydrogen a displacement reaction generally competes with elimination. The degradation of γ-tetrahydro-codeimethine methohydroxide (40) provides a most interesting example of the competing processes.

Simple Hofmann elimination affords the olefine (41) and competing displacement of methanol yields the parent tertiary base (42). Cyclic ether formation occurs by process III (a) involving the alcoholic hydroxyl group to give codiran (43), whereas the process

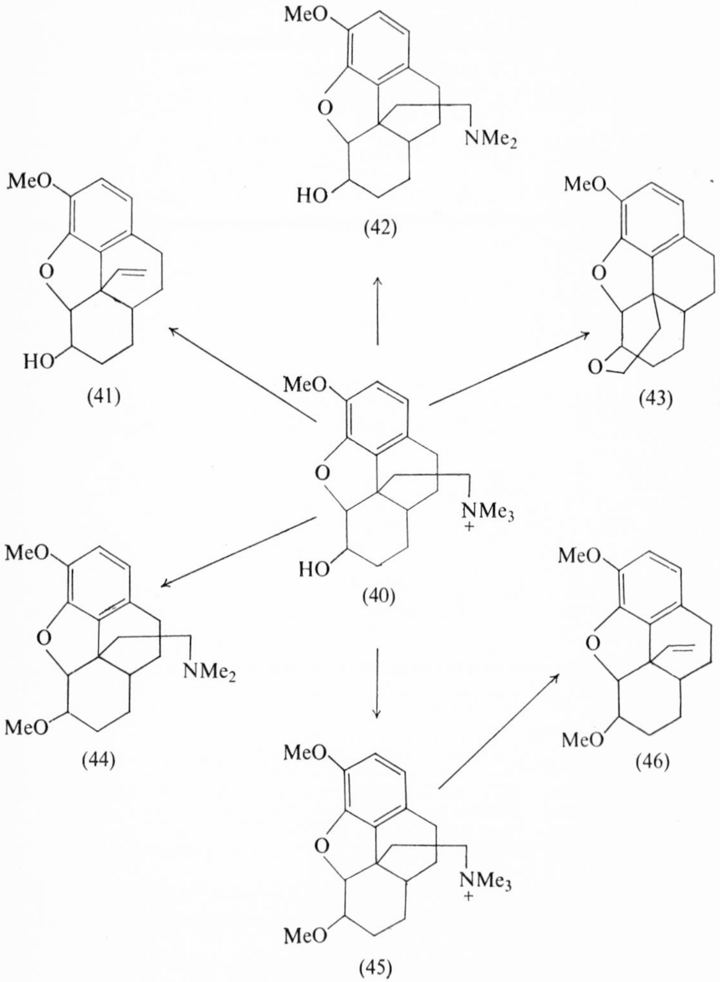

(42)

(41)

(43)

(44)

(40)

(46)

(45)

III (b) involving the quaternary centre of one molecule and the alcoholic hydroxyl of another leads to the base (42) and the *O*-methylated quaternary salt (45), which may suffer subsequent Hofmann elimination to yield the olefine (46) or the *O*-methylated tertiary base (44). The base (44) could arise also by an intra-molecular process of type III (b) but on steric grounds a sufficiently close approach of the alcoholic oxygen atom to one of the *N*-methyl groups is unlikely.

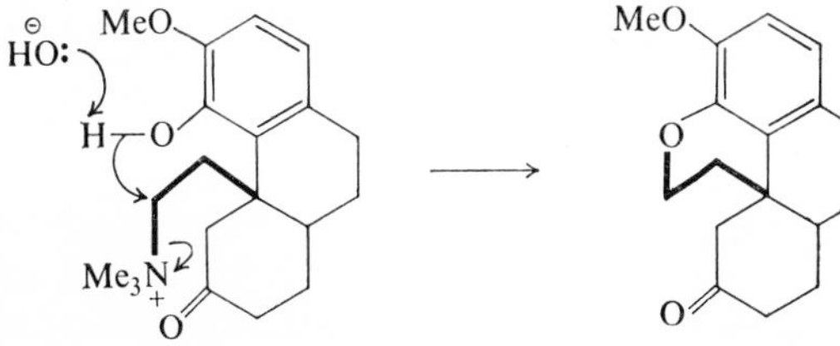

(47)   (48)

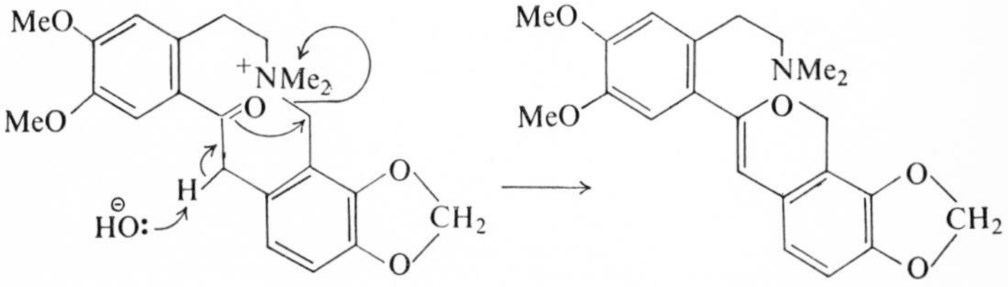

(49)   (50)

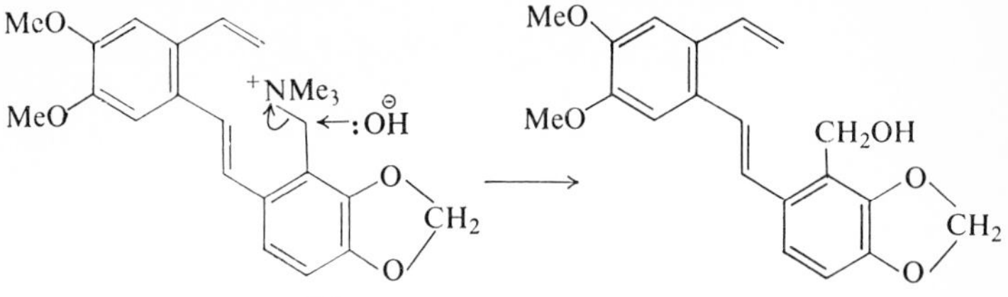

(51)   (52)

For cyclic ether formation by the process III (a) a suitable disposition of the hydroxyl group and the quaternary nitrogen atom is necessary to permit close approach of the oxygen atom to one of the few carbon atoms attached to nitrogen, and it may be noted that α-tetrahydrocodeimethine, the alcohol diastereoisomeric with the γ-compound (40), affords no cyclic ether analogous to codiran (43) on degradation, though methyl ethers diastereoisomeric with the olefine (46) and the base (44) are obtained as well as the simple elimination product.

In cyclic ether formation the oxygen atom may be part of an alcoholic group as above, a phenolic group as in the degradation of dihydrothebainone dihydromethine (47) to thebenone (48), or an enolisable carbonyl group as in the formation β-methyl-cryptopine (50) during the degradation of cryptopine methosulphate (49). In the last of these reactions the main product is the styrene derivative resulting from normal Hofmann elimination.

Displacement of an alcohol other than methanol, i.e. reaction II above, which is simply a special case of attack by hydroxyl ion at one of the four α-carbon atoms, may be exemplified by the conversion of the cryptopine degradation product (51) into α-isocryptopidol (52).

Abnormal reactions

It is sometimes found that the products of a Hofmann degradation bear little apparent resemblance in structure to the tertiary base from which they are derived, since under the strongly alkaline conditions of the reaction other reactive centres in the molecule may become involved and a pathway may be opened for elimination of tertiary base with prior or concomitant molecular rearrangement, or fission and loss of a fragment of the molecule. The morphine group of alkaloids, particularly the derivatives of flavothebaone, provides a number of examples of such abnormal reactions and the mechanisms of the processes involved are discussed in the relevant sections of Chapter 7, but one characteristic example may be given here, namely the degradation of α-codei-

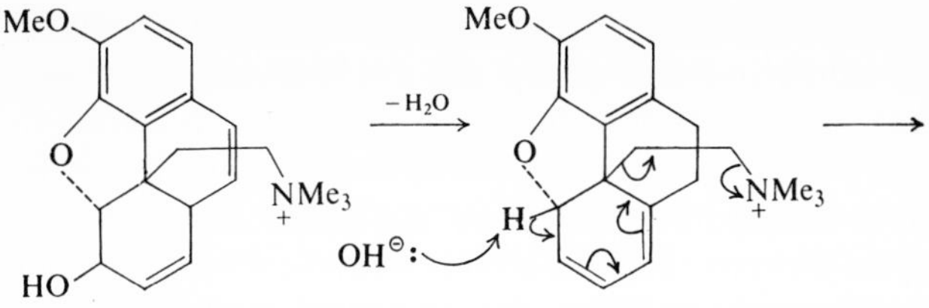

(53) $-H_2O$ (54)

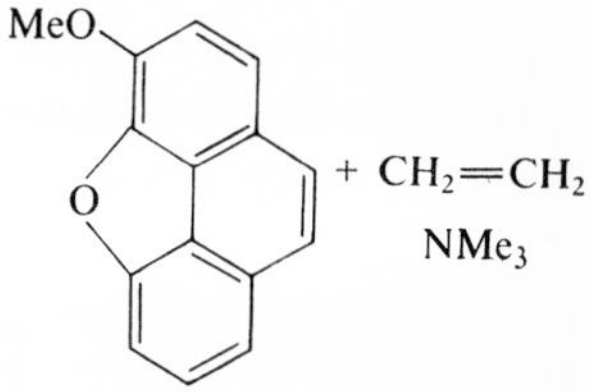

$OH^{\ominus}:$

(55) $+ CH_2{=}CH_2$ NMe_3

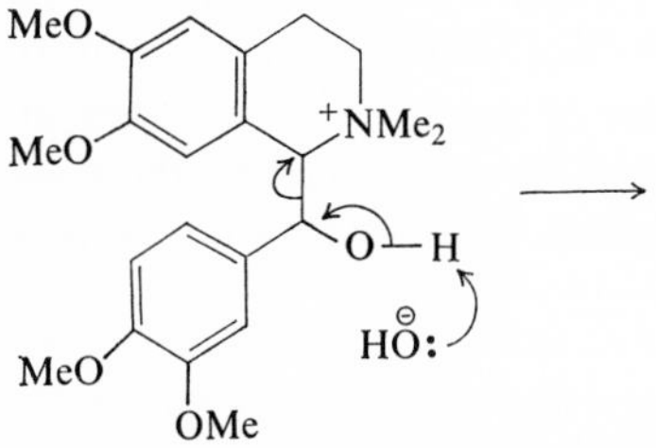

(56)

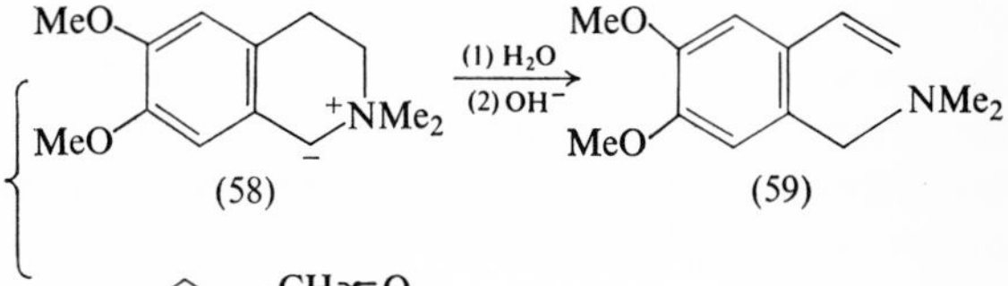

$HO^{\ominus}:$

(58) $\xrightarrow[(2)\,OH^-]{(1)\,H_2O}$ (59)

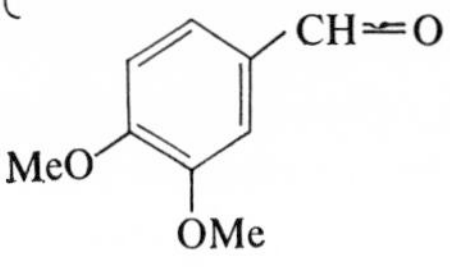

(57)

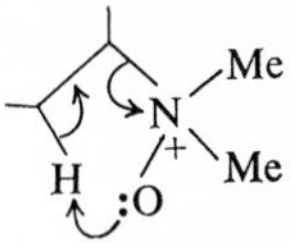

(60)

methine methohydroxide (53) to methylmorphenol (55) by dehydration to the intermediate (54) followed by elimination of water, ethylene and trimethylamine.

In the degradation of hydroxylaudanosine (56) fission of the molecule occurs under all conditions, the products of the reaction being veratraldehyde (57) and the base (59). These presumably arise as shown in (56) by attack of the most acidic proton, followed by fission to the aldehyde (57) and the transient ylide (58) which is subsequently transformed into the normal elimination product, the base (59). As explained in Chapter 11, when the alcoholic hydroxyl group is bound up in a lactone ring, as in the phthalideisoquinoline alkaloids, normal Hofmann degradation occurs.

Pyrolysis of amine oxides

When amine oxides are dry distilled a cyclic elimination reaction can take place, unless prevented by steric factors, analogous to the Hofmann degradation, to give an olefine and a dialkylhydroxyl-amine. The cyclic nature of this reaction, which is essentially as set out in formula (60), tends to limit attack to the β-hydrogen atom leaving unaffected other reactive centres, the involvement of which with free hydroxyl ions not infrequently complicates the Hofmann degradation. In this way almost all of the olefines in the morphine–thebaine–flavothebaone group that are inaccessible by the Hofmann degradation may be prepared, e.g. the N-oxides of α-codeimethine (61, $R = CH_2CH_2NMe_2$) and 14-hydroxydihydrocodeinone meth-ine (61, $R = CH_2CH_2NMe_2$) afford the related vinyl compounds (62, $R = CH{=}CH_2$) and (62, $R = CH{=}CH_2$) respectively, whereas Hofmann degradation of the corresponding quaternary salts yields methylmorphenol (55) and the cyclic ether (63) respectively. Other examples of the utility of the process in this series are given in Chapter 7. The degradation of the N-oxide of dihydrothebainone dihydromethine, however, affords thebenone (63) identical with the product of Hofmann degradation, the reaction presumably proceeding as shown in (64).

The reaction is not applicable in cyclic systems when for steric reasons the β-hydrogen atom is held beyond the range of the negative oxygen, but in the benzylisoquinoline series the *exo*cyclic β-hydrogen atom is readily involved and laudanosine *N*-oxide (65) can be degraded to the olefine (66). The degradation of the *N*-oxide of β-hydroxylaudanosine however follows the same course as the Hofmann degradation of the corresponding quaternary salt, with attack of the hydrogen of the hydroxyl group and subsequent molecular fission.

(61)   (62)   (63)

(64)   (65)   (66)

Emde degradation

In the simple tetrahydroisoquinoline series Hofmann degradation of the quaternary salt (67) affords the styrene (68) by normal attack of the β-hydrogen atom, but this styrenoid base, having no β-hydrogen, is stable to further degradation. The original salt (67) is, however, the quaternary salt of a benzylamine and undergoes very rapid hydrogenolysis on reduction catalytically (Emde reduction) or with sodium and liquid ammonia, to the tertiary base (69) which may then be subjected to normal Hofmann degradation to obtain the nitrogen free product (70). This reaction, which is of general application in the isoquinoline series, is a useful variant of the Hofmann degradation. Sodium and liquid ammonia is, however, liable to effect other reactions such as fission of ether linkages during the same reaction, for example reduction of thebaine methiodide (71) yields the base (72) the methiodide of which may be reduced (less readily) to the nitrogen-free product (73).

(68)   (67)   (69)   (70)

(71)   (72)   (73)

The von Braun degradation

One other method of degradation of amines has been employed in alkaloid work, namely the von Braun degradation with cyanogen bromide. When a tertiary amine is treated with cyanogen bromide the products are an *N*-cyano-compound and an alkyl bromide

$$R^1{\diagdown}N{-}R^3 + CNBr \longrightarrow R^1{\diagdown}N{-}CN + R^3Br$$
$$R^2{\diagup} \qquad\qquad\qquad R^2{\diagup}$$

If R^1—R^3 or R^2—R^3 in this reaction is a ring then the ring is split and all the carbon atoms are retained, otherwise R^3 is lost. In general the cleavage occurs with loss of the smallest alkyl group, which is usually methyl in alkaloid work, and the process affords a useful method of *N*-demethylation since the *N*-cyanocompound is generally easily hydrolysed to a secondary amine. If, however, there is a benzylamine or allylamine system in the molecule, fission usually occurs wholly or predominantly to give the benzyl or allyl halide, and this can be used as a method of detecting such systems in alkaloids, for example diacetyl morphine (74, R = Me) with cyanogen bromide gives diacetylcyanonormorphine (74, R = CN) but hydrohydrastinine (75) gives the bromide (76).

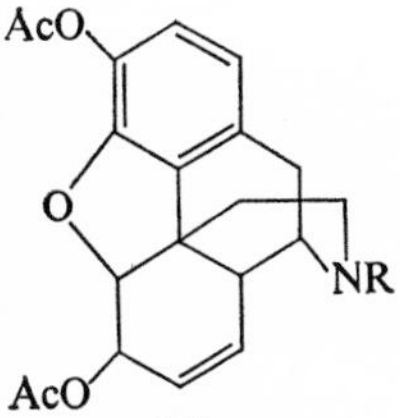

(74)

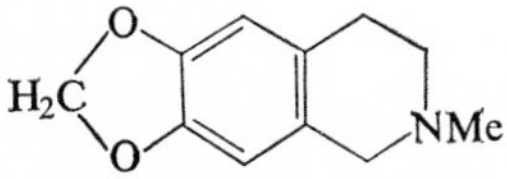

(75)

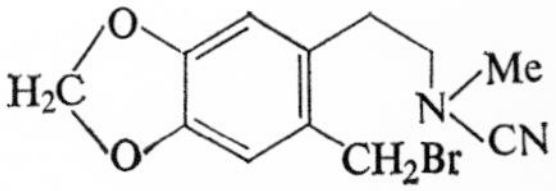

(76)

β-Phenylethylamines and Simple Isoquinolines

THE simplest isoquinoline alkaloids found in plants are derivatives of tetrahydroisoquinoline bearing always oxygen substituents at positions 6 and 7 and frequently at position 8. These oxygen substituents may be hydroxyl, methoxyl or methylenedioxy groups. The bases which may be secondary or tertiary may also bear a methyl group at position 1. They are generally believed to arise in nature by the condensation of β-phenylethylamines with formaldehyde or acetaldehyde or their equivalents, the amines themselves being derived from amino-acids. This may be illustrated essentially

(1)   (2)   (3)

as in formulae (1)–(3) starting from dihydroxyphenylalanine (1), which appears to be the fundamental building block from which all the bases in the whole isoquinoline series are derived. The β-phenylethylamines may conveniently be discussed with these bases although they are not actually isoquinolines and though derivatives of monohydroxyphenylethylamine occur naturally.

Hordenine (4)

This base, which has been isolated from the cactus *Anhalonium fissuratum* Engelm., is a phenolic tertiary amine of composition

20

$C_{10}H_{15}ON$. On *O*-methylation and Hofmann degradation it gives *p*-methoxystyrene and trimethylamine and must thus be α- or β-(4-hydroxyphenyl)ethyldimethylamine and that it is in fact the β-compound (4) was demonstrated by synthesis. Several syntheses have been recorded, the most unambiguous being the demethylation of the base (5) prepared by reduction and *N*-methylation

(4)   (5)   (6)

of the nitrostyrene (6), itself obtained by the condensation of *p*-methoxybenzaldehyde and nitromethane.

3-*Hydroxytyramine* (2)

This base is one of the hypertensive agents of the common broom, *Cytisus scoparius*. Its structure is clear from its formation by the decarboxylation of 3,4-dihydroxyphenylalanine (1) on heating above its melting point. It is one of the fundamental units from which all isoquinoline alkaloids may be regarded as being built.

Mescaline

The cactus *Anhalonium lewinii* Hemmings, or pellote, dried pieces of which form the well-known "mescal buttons", has been used for many generations by the Mexican indians to produce a form of intoxication during certain religious ceremonies and the alkaloid responsible for the curious hallucinatory effects of this plant, which are reported to take the form of vivid coloured images frequently of an abstract form, has been identified as mescaline. This has the composition $C_{11}H_{17}O_3N$ and contains one primary amino and three methoxyl groups, although the presence of an —NMe— group appears to be indicated by the normal Herzig–

Meyer method. As mescaline can be oxidised to 3,4,5-trimethoxy-benzoic acid, 3,4,5-trimethoxybenzylmethylamine was prepared but found not to be identical with the alkaloid, which was later proved to be β-3,4,5-trimethoxyphenylethylamine by synthesis. A number of such syntheses have been recorded. Two start from 3,4,5-tri-methoxybenzaldehyde (7) and proceed through the ω-nitrostyrene (8) or the cyanhydrin (9), reduction of which affords the desired

amine (10), which is also obtained by the reduction of the oxime of trimethoxyphenylacetaldehyde (11), the product of ozonolysis of the naturally occurring elemicine (12).

N-Dimethylmescaline is the alkaloid trichocereine.

Isomers and analogues of mescaline have been synthesised but none has been found to produce the euphoric state induced by mescaline.

The anhalonium bases

The cactus *Anhalonium lewinii* also contains besides mescaline a number of other bases that were quickly shown to be structurally different from mescaline, but on the assumption that they were

derivatives of this alkaloid Spath synthesised the tetrahydroisoquinoline (15, R = H) by Bischler–Napieralsky cyclisation of
N-acetylmescaline (13), followed by reduction of the resulting
dihydroisoquinoline (14). *N*-Methylation of the secondary base
(15, R = H) eventually yielded the quaternary methiodide which
was shown to be identical with the alkaloid derivatives, *O*-methyl-
pellotine methiodide and *O*,*N*-dimethylanhalonidine methiodide;
O-methylpellotine is thus the tertiary base (15, R = Me) and
O-methylanhalonidine is the secondary base (15, R = H).

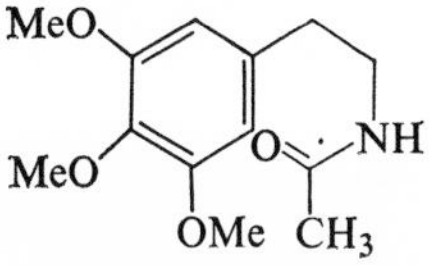

(13) 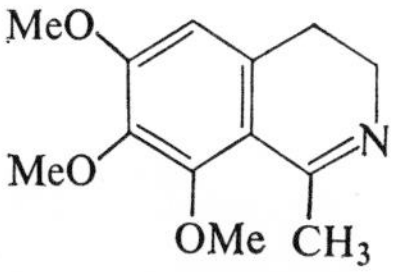   (14) 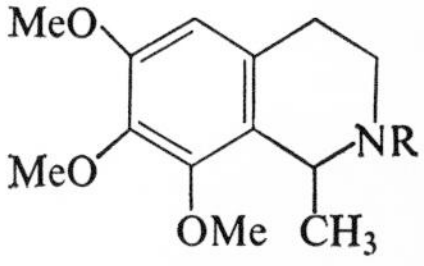   (15)

A synthesis of anhalonidine and pellotine was then accomplished
by the same Bischler–Napieralsky process starting from the
N-acetyl derivative of 3-acetoxy-4,5-dimethoxyphenylethylamine,
but this did not define the position of the phenolic hydroxyl groups
in the bases, since isoquinoline ring closure could occur *para* or
ortho to the acetoxy group giving structure (16) or (17) for anhalonidine (R = H) or pellotine (R = Me). That structure (17) is
correct was clearly demonstrated by the production of 3-ethoxy-
4,5-dimethoxyphthalic acid on oxidation of pellotine ethyl ether.

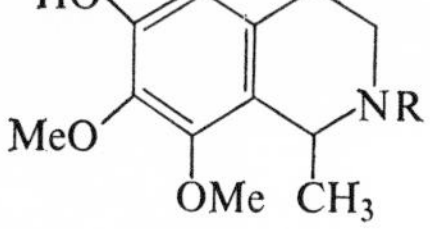

(16) 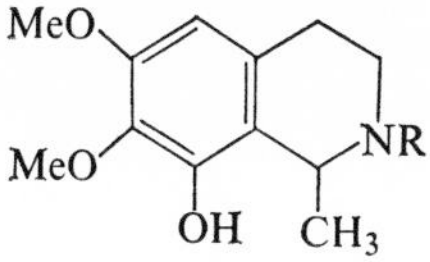   (17) 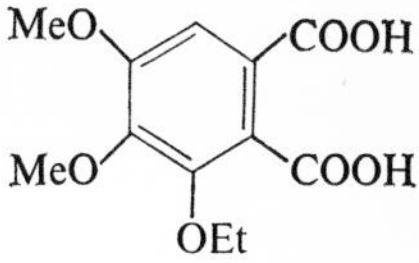   (18)

The two bases anhalonine and lophophorine have the same
relationship of secondary and tertiary bases as anhalonidine and

pellotine. They are nonphenolic but contain a methylenedioxy group and one methoxyl. Assuming that the common origin of anhalonidine and anhalonine implies a similar orientation of substituents in the bases only two structures (19) and (20) need be considered for these two alkaloids. The base (20, R = Me) was prepared by the action of methylmagnesium iodide on the quaternary cotarnine iodide (21) but was found to be isomeric not identical with lophophorine, which must therefore have the structure (19, R = Me) and this has been confirmed by synthesis by the general process outlined above (13)–(15).

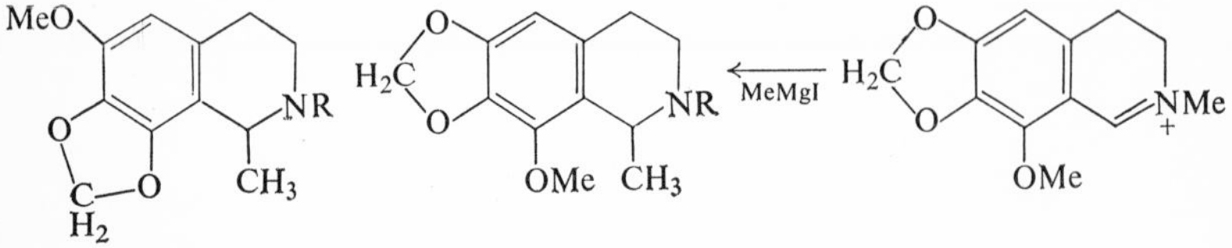

(19) (20) (21)

Salsoline

This alkaloid occurs in the desert plant *Salsola arbuscula*, has the composition $C_{11}H_{15}O_2N$ and contains one phenolic hydroxyl, one methoxyl and one imino group. On *O*-methylation with diazomethane it gives the alkaloid salsolidine, which yields *m*-hemipinic acid (22) on oxidation and is therefore probably the base (23, R = Me) assuming the presence of a C-1 methyl group. The structure (23, R = H) has been determined for salsoline by synthesis

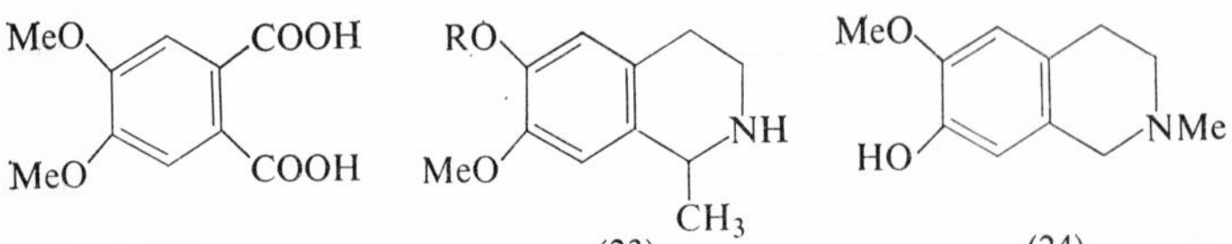

(22) (23) (24)

from 3-hydroxy-4-methoxybenzaldehyde (isovanillin) through the *O*-benzyl-ω-nitrostyrene and β-phenylethylamine using the processes already described above.

Corypalline

This alkaloid, from *Corydalis pallida*, is isomeric with salsoline and also contains one methoxyl and one phenolic hydroxyl group, but as it also contains an *N*-methyl group the *C*-methyl group cannot be present. The structure (24) for the base was proved by synthesis from vanillin (4-hydroxy-3-methoxybenzaldehyde) by a method analogous to that used in the synthesis of salsoline.

CHAPTER 3

Benzylisoquinolines

THE benzylisoquinoline alkaloids (3) may be regarded as being formed by the condensation of 3,4-dihydroxyphenylethylamine (1) with 3,4-dihydroxyphenylacetaldehyde (2) (or rarely the *p*-hydroxy-aldehyde). They are not very widely distributed in Nature and only a few alkaloids of the group are known. The first of these to be

discovered was papaverine, which occurs as a minor constituent of opium, and the elucidation of the structure of this base constituted a major advance in the knowledge of alkaloids.

Papaverine

Papaverine has the composition $C_{20}H_{21}O_4N$ and contains four methoxyl groups. Although it behaves as a tertiary base it contains no *N*-methyl group and as it can be reduced to a secondary amine with the addition of four atoms of hydrogen it was soon recognised as a derivative of pyridine, with the heterocyclic ring fused to a benzene ring to account for the addition of only four atoms of hydrogen during reduction. Such a fusion of pyridine and benzene can be accomplished in two ways, to give isoquinoline (4), from which the alkaloids are in fact derived, and quinoline (5), and as the earlier workers in this field were more familiar with the latter than the former it was from quinoline that papaverine was first

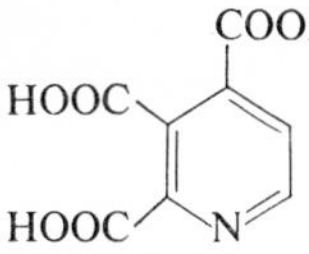

(6) 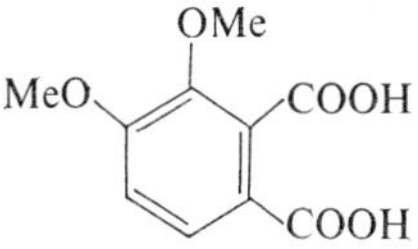   (7) 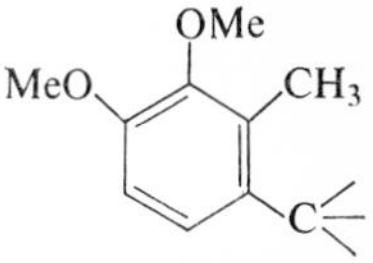   (8)

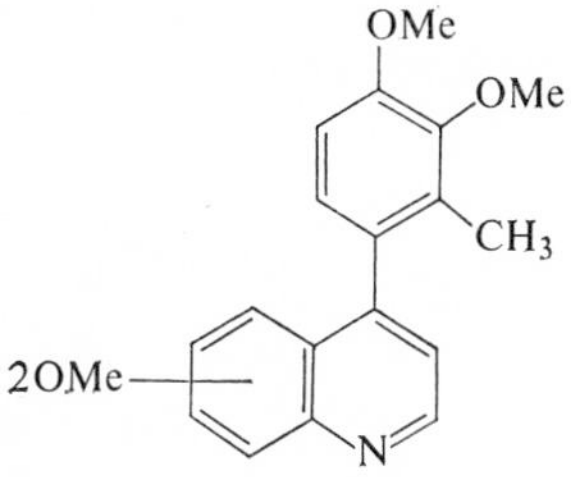

(9)

thought to be derived. This view was strengthened by the production of a dimethoxyphthalic acid, veratric acid and pyridine-2,3,4-tricarboxylic acid (6) and papaverinic acid on oxidation of the alkaloid. The dimethoxyphthalic acid was initially believed to be identical with the then known hemipinic acid (7) and as it was initially supposed to arise from a unit of type (8) in papaverine the alkaloid was assigned the part-structure (9).

The mild oxidation of papaverine results in the conversion of —CH_2— to —CO— and this was interpreted on the basis of the structure (9) as oxidation of —CH_3 to —CHO and the product was named papaveraldine. Such a formulation leads to the aldehydic structure (10) for papaverinic acid, which is at variance with its failure to suffer further oxidation to a tricarboxylic acid.

Oxidation of papaverine ethobromide, a quaternary salt, was found to give a dimethoxy-*N*-ethylphthalimide (11) which could not possibly arise from a quinoline system, but could arise from an isoquinoline system such as (12) or (13) and, as both of these systems could also give hemipinic acid (7) by destruction of the pyridine ring, it was no longer necessary to postulate the presence in the papaverine molecule of the system (8). The ketonic structure (14), which would resist oxidation to a tricarboxylic acid, thus became possible for papaverinic acid leading to the structure (15) for papaverine, which satisfactorily accounts for all the oxidation products of papaverine, namely papaverinic acid, veratric acid and the acids (6) and (7).

The dimethoxyphthalic acid obtained during these oxidations was identified with hemipinic acid on the basis of its melting point, but, as a result of anhydride formation, the melting points of such acids vary with the rate of heating and are not, therefore, good criteria of identity. The acid was finally identified as *m*-hemipinic acid (16) as on demethylation it gives a phenol that gives only *one* mono-ethyl ether (17), whereas hemipinic acid gives two compounds (18) and (19) when treated in the same way.

MeO\ /COOH

MeO^ ^COOH

(16)

EtO\ /COOH

HO^ ^COOH

(17)

OEt

HO\ /COOH

^COOH

(18)

OH

EtO\ /COOH

^COOH

(19)

Other work being carried out at the same time led to similar conclusions about the structure of the alkaloid. Fusion of papaverine with potassium hydroxide affords a base $C_{11}H_{11}O_2N$ and a neutral substance $C_9H_{12}O_2$ which between them account for all of the carbon atoms of the alkaloid. The base $C_{11}H_{11}O_2N$ contains two methoxyl groups and on oxidation affords the same *m*-hemipinic acid (16) as is obtained from papaverine and as demethylation of the base and subsequent distillation of the product with zinc dust yields isoquinoline it may be assigned the structure (20). This was confirmed by comparison of the base with material of that structure prepared by synthesis by Friedländer's process from veratric aldehyde (22) and amino-acetal (23) via the intermediate (21).

The neutral substance $C_9H_{12}O_2$ from the potash fusion is readily oxidised to veratric acid $C_9H_{10}O_4$ and can thus only be homo-veratrole (24). The mode of linkage of the two units in papaverine, already deduced to be as in structure (15), was revealed by the oxidation of the alkaloid to an acid $C_{12}H_{11}O_4N$, which can only be the isoquinoline 1-carboxylic acid (25) since it may be oxidised to a mixture of *m*-hemipinic acid and pyridine-2,3,4-tricarboxylic acid; the carboxyl group of the acid (25) must represent the same carbon atom as the methyl group of homoveratrole, and papaverine must accordingly be assigned the complete structure (26).

MeO. ... N ... MeO (20) ... $\xrightarrow{H_2SO_4}$ ... MeO. ... CH(OEt)$_2$ ... N ... MeO ... (21) ... $\leftarrow$ ... Me O ... MeO ... CHO ... (22) ... + ... CH(OEt) ... NH$_2$ ... (23)

CH$_3$ ... OMe ... OMe ... (24) ... MeO. ... MeO ... N ... COOH ... (25)

This structure has been confirmed by several unambiguous syntheses, and since papaverine has achieved some importance in medicine as an antispasmodic and, since it is present in opium in very low concentration, commercially useful methods of synthesis are of importance.

The first successful synthesis was achieved in 1909 by Pictet and Gams who acetylated veratrole to acetoveratrone (27), nitrosated this to the oximino-ketone (28) and reduced the product to ω-aminoacetoveratrone (29) with tin and hydrochloric acid. This amine on acylation with homoveratroyl chloride yielded the amide (30), which was reduced to the secondary alcohol (31) and this alcohol afforded papaverine when subjected to Bischler–Napieralski isoquinoline ring closure with simultaneous dehydration.

Interesting modifications of this method have been made, for example homoveratrylamine (32) has been used in place of the amine (29) in which case cyclisation of the related amide (33) affords 3,4-dihydropapaverine which may be dehydrogenated to

papaverine. Both homoveratrylamine and homoveratric acid (34)
are readily available from the nitrile (31a), itself preparable by the
action of potassium cyanide on the product of chloromethylation
of veratrole. A variant of this reaction involves the use of the
cheaper veratric acid in place of homoveratric acid since the
diazoketone (35), obtained by the interaction of diazomethane and
veratroyl chloride, reacts with homoveratrylamine (32) in the
presence of silver oxide to give the amide (33) as a result of Arndt–
Eistert homologation reaction; the over-all yield in the process is
reported to be good.

The addition of methanol to ω-nitrostyrenes under the influence
of bases has also been used as a convenient method of preparation
of the requisite β-arylethylamines, e.g. 3,4-dimethoxy-ω-nitro-
styrene will add methanol to give a nitro-compound that may be
reduced to an amine giving an amide analogous to the amide (31)
but bearing a methoxyl in place of the hydroxyl group. This amide
behaves like the hydroxy-compound on cyclisation.

An interesting commercial synthesis has as starting material
3,4-dimethoxyphenylpyruvic acid (37), prepared by alkaline
hydrolysis of the azlactone (36) from veratraldehyde and hippuric

acid. This acid with ammonia under pressure at 100° gives the
diamide (38, R = NH$_2$) convertible through the acid (38, R = OH)
and methyl ester (38, R = OMe) into 3,4-dihydropapaverine-3-
carboxylic acid which can be decarboxylated and dehydrogenated
in one reaction. The over-all yield in this process is reported to be

one part of alkaloid from every four parts of vanillin used to make the initial veratraldehyde.

Papaverine is easily nitrated and acetylated (with acetic anhydride and sulphuric acid) to give the 6′-substituted bases (39, R = NO₂) and (39, R = COCH₃) and of these the former is reducible to the amine and the latter, which is a neutral pseudobase, rearranges slowly in aqueous solution to a strong quaternary, berberine-like base (see Chapter 8) coralyn (40). The tetrahydrobases α-coralydine (41, R = Me) and norcoralydine (41, R = H)

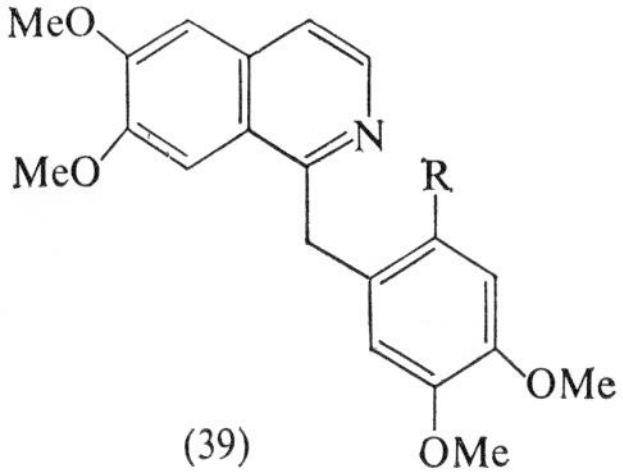

(39)

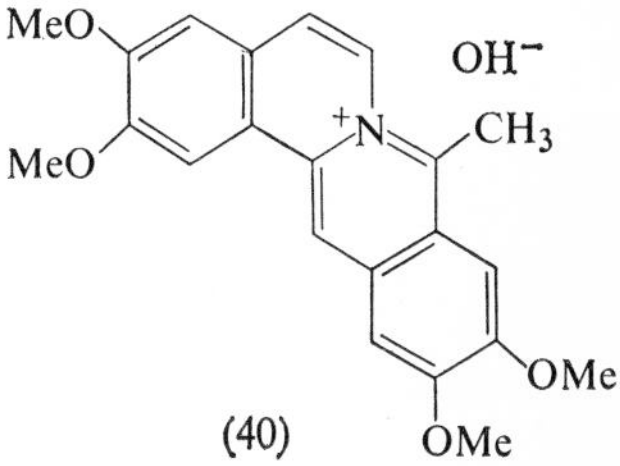

(40)

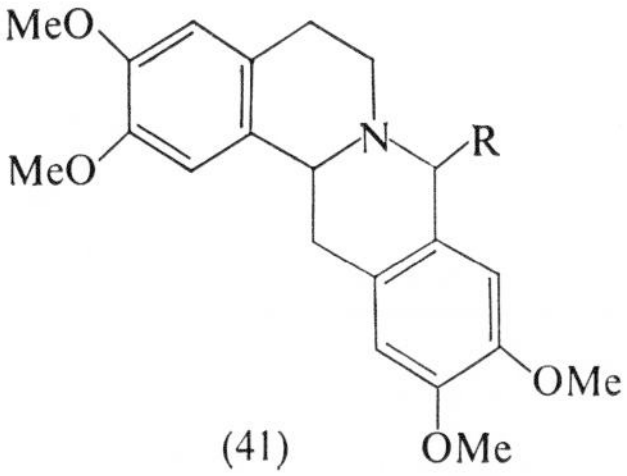

(41)

are obtainable by the condensation of tetrahydropapaverine with acetaldehyde and formaldehyde respectively in sulphuric acid.

Papaverine quaternary salts (42) do not suffer typical Hofmann degradation, instead they are converted by concentrated alkali into coloured anhydro-bases, the *N*-alkylisopapaverines (43), which dissolve in water to give the alkaline quaternary hydroxide or with acids to give quaternary salts. These anhydro-bases may be

oxidised to *N*-alkyl-6,7-dimethoxyisoquinolines and veratric acid
(44). The action of dilute alkalis on the quaternary salts, however,

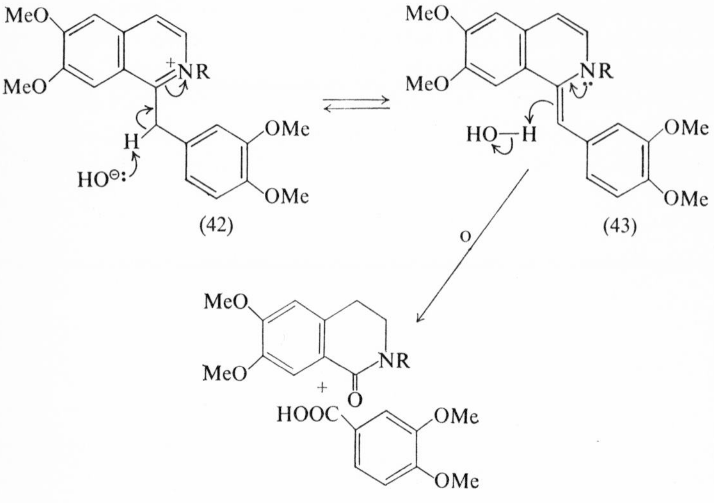

(42)   (43)

(44)

is to effect demethylation of the 6-methoxyl group, the resulting
phenol quaternary salt betaine can then be ethylated to a 6-homo-
papaverine quaternary salt.

Laudanosine

This alkaloid is found in very small quantity (about 0·008 per
cent) in opium. It has the composition $C_{21}H_{27}O_4N$ and contains
four methoxyl groups; like papaverine it is a tertiary base but
unlike that alkaloid it contains an *N*-methyl group. The nitrogen
atom is lost after two successive Hofmann degradations indicating
that it is contained in a ring. The product of the first stage degradation gives veratric acid on oxidation. It was early suggested as a
result of the origin and composition of laudanosine that this base
is *N*-methyltetrahydropapaverine, and this was confirmed by

reduction of papaverine methochloride with tin and hydrochloric acid. Reduction of the quaternary salts of papaverine (45) in aqueous or alcoholic solution with sodium borohydride is now regarded as being the most convenient method of preparation of laudanosine (46). The structure (46) has also been confirmed by independent total synthesis, using generally the same methods as given above for the synthesis of 3,4-dihydropapaverine, the methochloride of which (47) on reduction affords laudanosine.

The products of Hofmann degradation of laudanosine are thus seen to have the structures (48, R = Me) and (49), and it is of interest that the pyrolysis of laudanosine *N*-oxide involves degradation to the hydroxylamine (48, R = OM), since the exocyclic β-carbon bears a hydrogen that can participate in the cyclic transition state (50).

Catalytic reduction of the methochloride of papaverinol, the secondary alcohol (51) corresponding to papaveraldine, yields two diastereoisomeric hydroxylaudanosines, presumably differing in orientation of the newly introduced hydrogen atom at C-1 relative to the hydroxyl group. The quaternary salts of these two bases do not suffer normal Hofmann degradation but undergo molecular fission on heating with alkali to give the base (53) and veratric

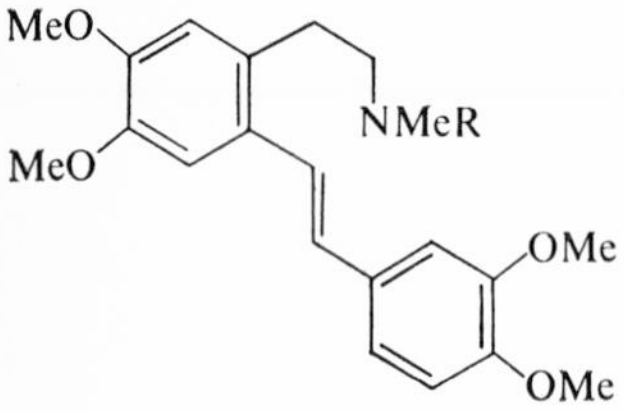

(48)

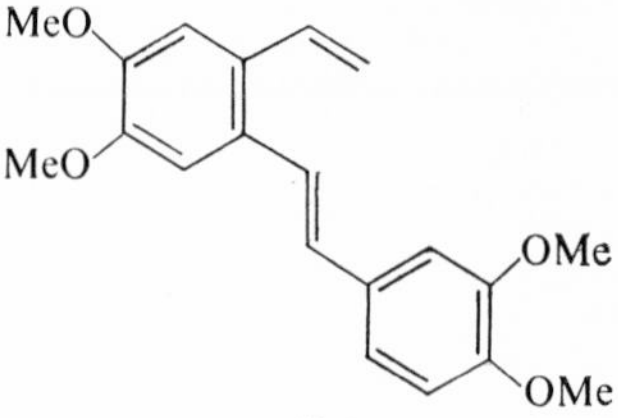

(49)

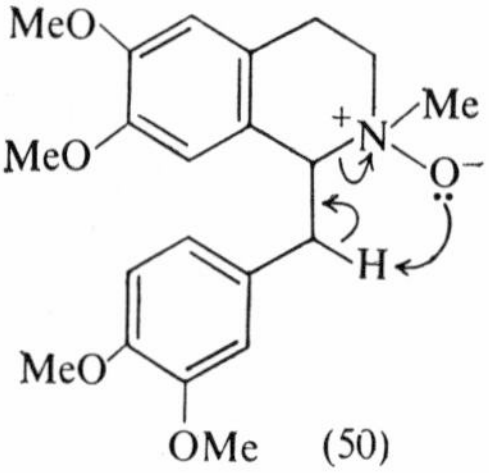

(50)

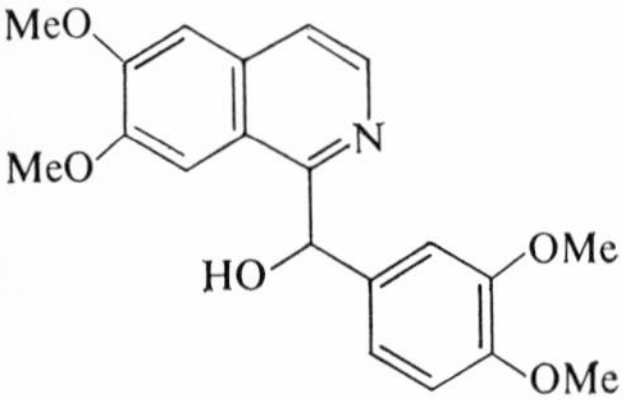

(51)

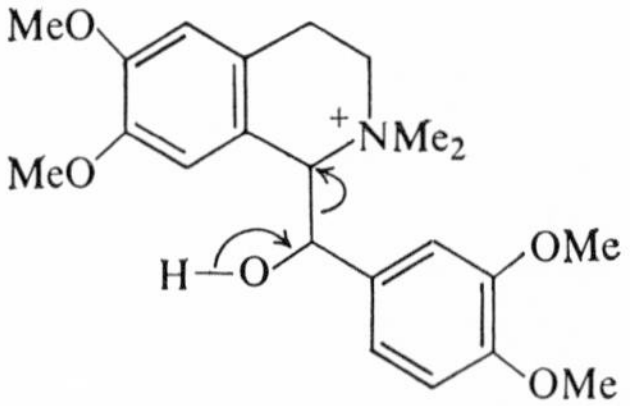

(52)

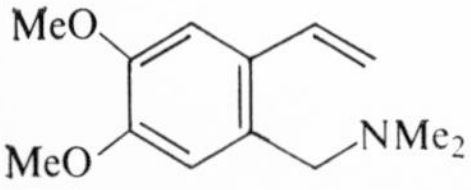

(53)

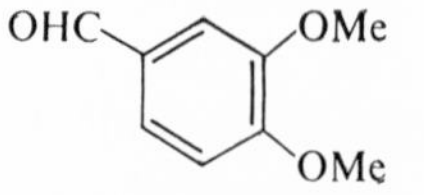

(54)

aldehyde (54). Presumably in this case the most easily removed proton is not either of those β to the nitrogen but that of the hydroxyl group, the result of this being fission of (52) to veratric

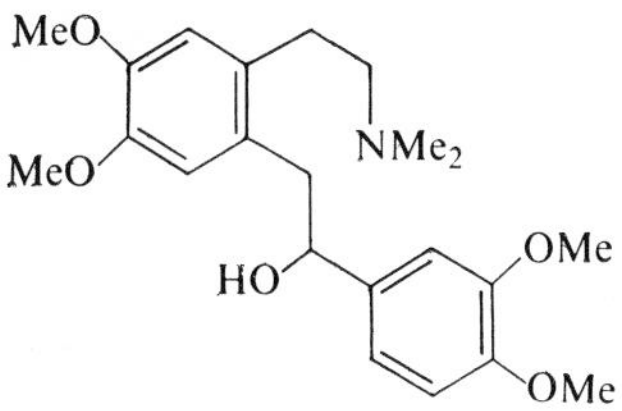

(55)

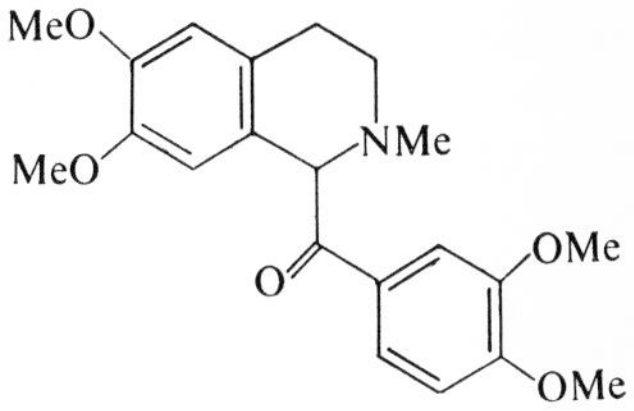

(56)

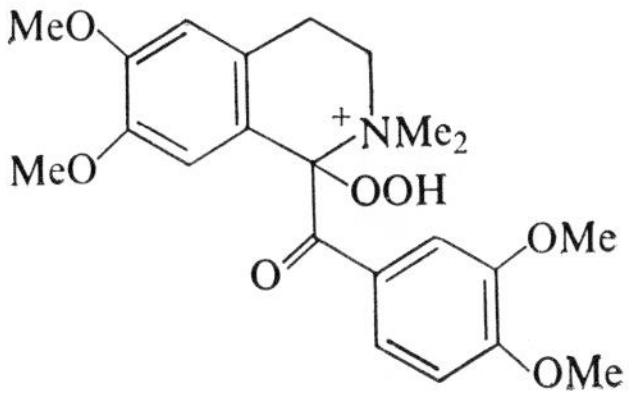

(57)

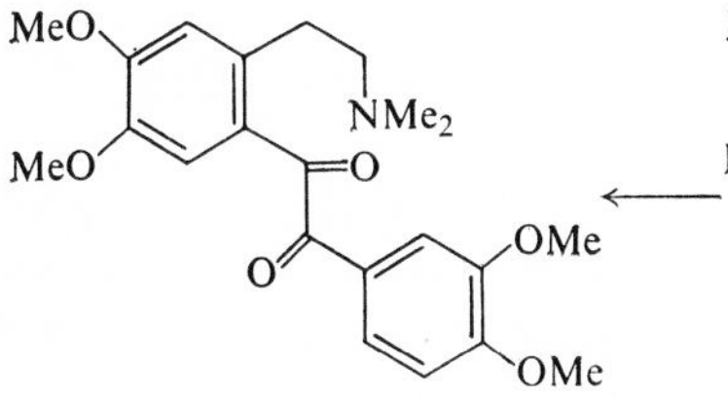

(58)

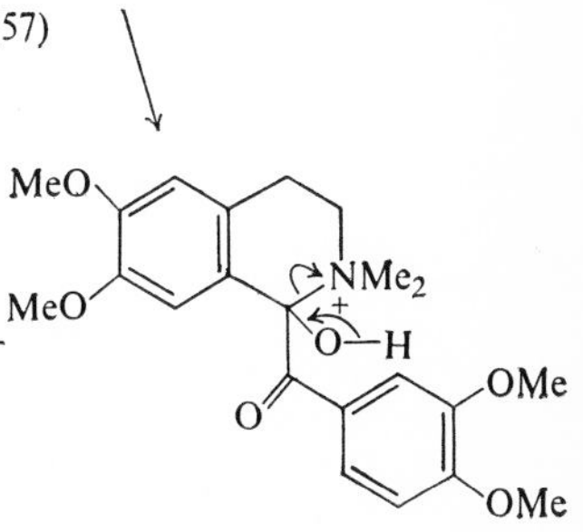

(59)

aldehyde and a quaternary salt that suffers further degradation to (53). A similar process is operative in pyrolysis of the corresponding amine oxides but reduction of the quaternary salts with sodium and liquid ammonia affords hydroxylaudanosine dihydromethine (55) in good yield.

Although the oxidation of papaverine can be made to give papaveraldine, laudanosine is resistant to such oxidation, presumably because the methylene group lacks the powerful activation of isoquinoline tertiary nitrogen. Ketolaudanosine (56) can, however, be prepared either by sodium borohydride reduction of papaveraldine methosulphate or Oppenauer oxidation of hydroxylaudanosine. Like the last-named base ketolaudanosine does not suffer normal Hofmann degradation, instead it gives veratric acid and the base (53); with sodium and ammonia, however, the methiodide gives the ketone analogous to the alcohol (55). Ketolaudanosine methiodide undergoes rapid aerial oxidation to the hydroperoxide (57) which is quickly reduced by the iodide ions to the carbinolamine salt (58) (not isolated) and this is transformed into the tertiary base (59).

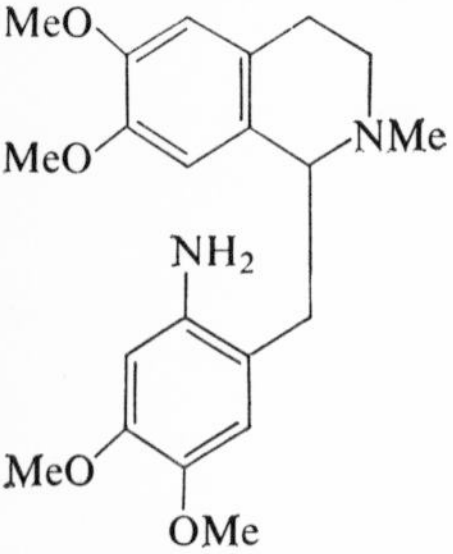

(60)

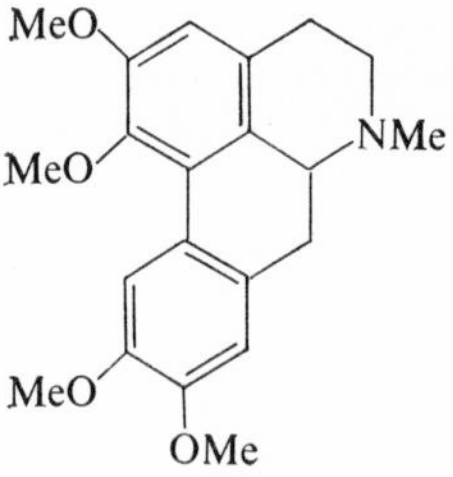

(61)

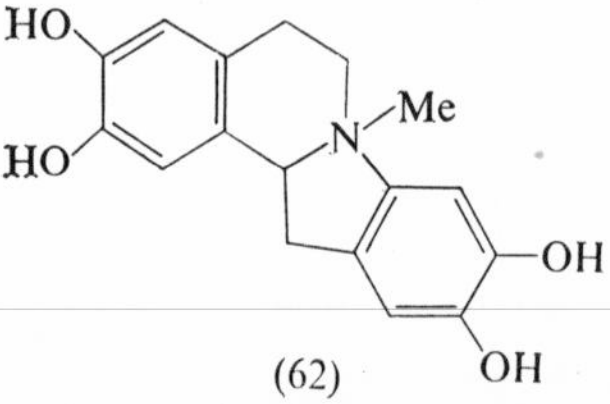

(62)

Reduction of 6'-aminopapaverine methochloride gives 6'-aminolaudanosine (60) and this on diazotisation and Pschorr phenanthrene ring closure with copper powder, is converted into

($\pm$)-glaucine (61). The aporphine alkaloids of which glaucine is a representative are believed to arise in nature by oxidation of laudanosine-like compounds, and, in an attempt to simulate this, laudanosoline has been oxidised with a variety of reagents, but at the time of writing the only recognisable product of these reactions is the benzopyrrocolinium salt (62).

Other alkaloids of this group are analogues of laudanosine, namely laudanine (3'-hydroxy-compound), codamine (7-hydroxy-compound), coclaurine (6-methoxy-7,4'-dihydroxybenzyltetrahydroisoquinoline), armepavine (6,7-dimethoxy-4'-hydroxy), corpaverine (6,7,4'-trimethoxy-8-hydroxy).

Pavine

The reduction of papaverine with tin and hydrochloric acid affords 1,2,3,4-tetrahydropapaverine and a second base, pavine,

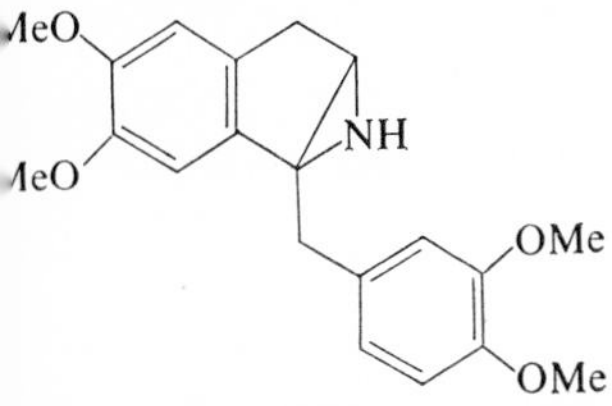

(63)

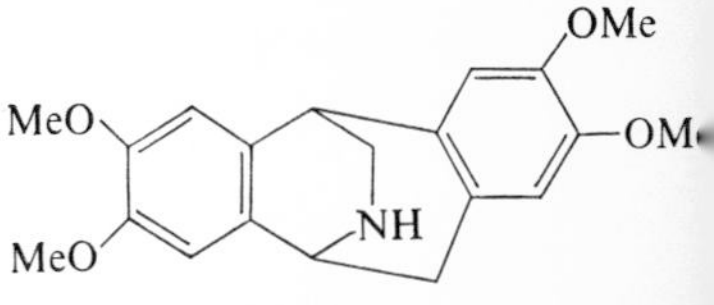

(64)

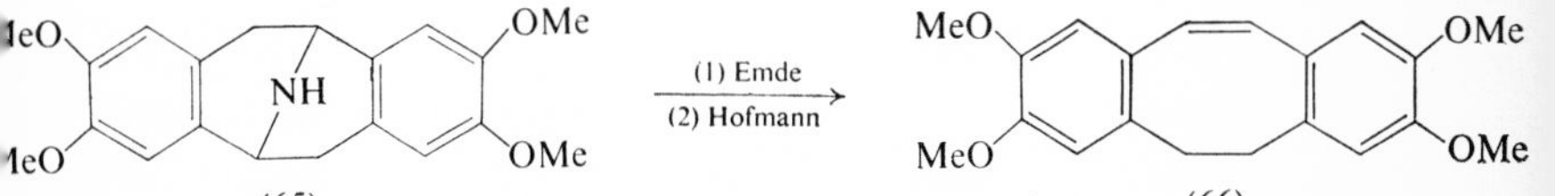

(65)

$\xrightarrow[\text{(2) Hofmann}]{\text{(1) Emde}}$

(66)

(67)

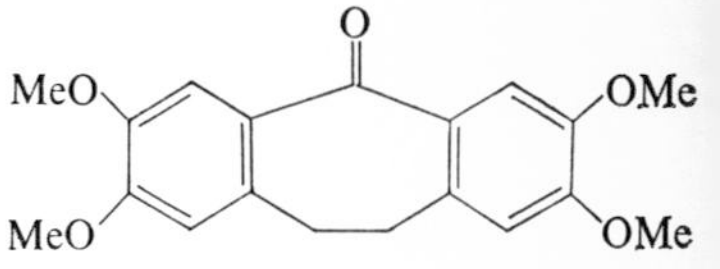

(68)

which is a secondary base having the composition of a dihydro-papaverine. It is not identical with 3,4-dihydropapaverine and as it cannot be further reduced or oxidised back to papaverine cannot be 1,2-dihydropapaverine. The structure (63) was originally assigned to pavine, but no veratric acid has ever been isolated from the products of oxidation of pavine as would be expected on the basis of such a structure. When *N*-methyl-1,2-dihydropapaverine (from the lithium aluminium hydride reduction of papaverine methiodide) is demethylated by boiling with hydrobromic acid a saturated phenolic base is obtained and this may be methylated to *N*-methylpavine, and pavine clearly must arise by addition to the double bond of 1,2-dihydropapaverine of some part of the molecule, of which only the aromatic nucleus of the benzyl group need be considered. Two structures (64) and (65) are thus possible for pavine and of these the latter has been shown to be correct by degradation to (66) and oxidation of this to the dibasic acid (67), identical with material prepared by synthesis. The oxidation of the *N*-free product from a base of structure (64) would have afforded the ketone (68). *N*-Methylpavine has recently been shown to be a naturally occurring alkaloid.

CHAPTER 4

Bisbenzylisoquinolines

THE alkaloids of this group are believed to arise in plants by the oxidation of phenolic bases of the benzylisoquinoline group, and in particular all can be represented as being derived from coclaurine (1, R = Me) or norcoclaurine (1, R = H). The oxidation process

may be represented as in (2)–(5), in which one electron is removed from the phenate anion to give the free radical which may be represented by either canonical structure (3) or (4) and the pairing

41

of the radicals in these two forms could afford the dienone (5), enolisation of which would lead to the hydroxydiphenyl ether (6).

When oxidative coupling of this type occurs with norcoclaurine, bases containing one, two and three diphenyl ether linkages are formed as shown in formulae (7)–(14). Coupling in position 12/11′ (7) produces the mono-ether structure (8) inside which further coupling can afford the di-ether (9) and the tri-ether (10) while dehydration of the di-ether (9) can lead to a second type of tri-ether, namely (11). If the initial coupling to a mono-ether occurs between positions 12 and 8′ the product (12) can then couple further to a di-ether in two ways, either by 7/11′ or 8/12′ union to give the systems (13) and (14) respectively, but for steric reasons in neither of these can further oxidative coupling to a tri-ether occur.

In fact all of the possible arrangements (8)–(14) except the mono-ether (12) occur more or less methylated as alkaloids in Nature. The alkaloids are widely distributed in plants of the *Menisperm-aceae* and related species, and the bisquaternary salts of some of them are the physiologically active constituents of tube curare, one of the South American indian arrow poisons.

The molecular weights and compositions of the bisbenzyliso-quinoline alkaloids quickly reveal their bimolecular nature, and once this is appreciated the structures of individual bases may be revealed by the following reactions:

1. Oxidation of the fully methylated base to a mixture of carboxylic acids.
2. Hofmann degradation of the methylated base and oxidation of the resulting methine base or nitrogen-free product.
3. Fission of the molecule at the diphenyl ether link or links to give simple benzylisoquinolines whose structures and stereo-chemistry can be determined.

From the information provided by these reactions the structure of the fully methylated alkaloid may be assembled, and the positions of free hydroxyl groups in the alkaloid itself can be determined by repetition of some of the reactions using the ethyl instead of the

Structures (13), (12), (14), (7), (8), (9a), (9), (11), (10) with coupling arrows labelled 7/11′, 8/12′, 12/8′ coupling, 12/11′ coupling, 8/7′, 7/8′, 8′/7, 7′/8, − H₂O methyl ether. The application of these methods of structure determination may be illustrated by reference to work on examples of each of the distinct series of bases set out in formulae (8)–(14).

BASES CONTAINING ONE DIPHENYL ETHER LINKAGE

Magnoline

This alkaloid occurs in the leaves of *Magnolia fuscata* Andr., has the composition $C_{36}H_{40}O_6N_2$ and contains two methoxyl and three hydroxyl groups. Oxidation of the trimethyl ether gives the acid (15, R = Me) and the isoquinoline (16, R = Me), whereas oxidation of the triethyl ether gives the corresponding ethoxy compounds

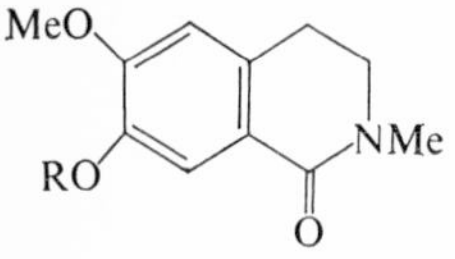

(16)

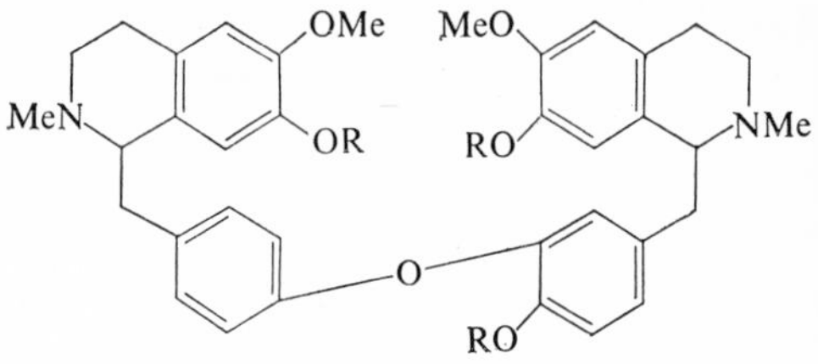

(17)

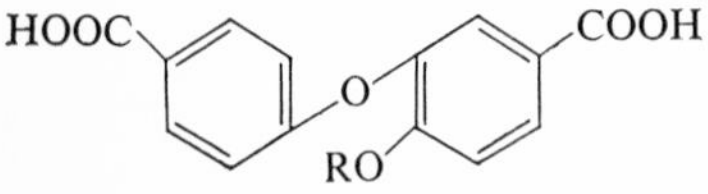

(15)

(15, R = Et) and (16, R = Et). Assuming that the carbonyl and carboxyl groups of (16) and (15) represent the residues of fission of benzylisoquinoline systems the structure (17, R = H) follows logically for magnoline.

Dauricine

Dauricine, $C_{38}H_{44}O_6N_2$ from *M. dauricum* D.C., contains four methoxyl groups and one phenolic hydroxyl group, but the C_{38}

structure was only finally indicated by careful methoxyl determinations of the methyl ether and its derivatives, the results of molecular weight determinations in camphor being equivocal. Exhaustive methylation of dauricine methyl ether and oxidation of the nitrogen free product gave *m*-hemipinic acid (18) and the dicarboxylic acid (15, R = Me), suggesting the structure (17, R = Me) for the alkaloid methyl ether, which was confirmed by synthesis of the methine base (19) by Hofmann degradation of the base (20) obtained by a laudanosine-type synthesis from homoveratrylamine (21) and the dicarboxylic acid (22).

The position of the phenolic group in dauricine is indicated by the exhaustive methylation of the ethyl ether to an *N*-free product oxidisable to the acid (15, R = Et) obtained from magnoline triethyl ether.

Fission of dauricine methyl ether with Na + liquid ammonia

affords the (−)-base (23, R = Me) and (−)-base (23, R = H) and thus the stereochemistry of both halves of the molecule is known. This alkaloid ether has recently been synthesised by the Ullmann reaction between the bromo-compound (24) and the base (23, R = H).

(23)

(24)

BASES CONTAINING TWO DIPHENYL ETHER LINKS

Oxyacanthine and berbamine

These two bases are isomeric and both contain three methoxyl groups and one hydroxyl group. The methyl ethers when subjected to Hofmann degradation give isomeric methine bases and these on ozonolysis afford the same pair of products, namely the neutral dialdehyde (25) and the dibasic dialdehyde (26). The neutral aldehyde was identified as (25, R = Me) by oxidation to the acid (15, R = Me) and the basic aldehyde must have structure (26) since further degradation and reduction give successively the neutral products (27) and (28). Repetition of these reactions on the ethyl ethers of the two alkaloids affords the aldehyde (25, R = Et) in both cases. The positions of the formyl groups in the degradation products (25) and (26) reveal the positions of the double bonds in the two methine bases, and it must be concluded that the two parent alkaloids are represented by the pair of structures (29) and (30). Sodium and liquid ammonia fission of the diphenyl ether links of berbamine methyl ether affords (−)-1-(4′-methoxybenzyl)-*N*-methyl-6,7-dimethoxytetrahydroisoquinoline, and (+)-1-(4′-hydroxybenzyl)-*N*-methyl-7-hydroxy-6-methoxytetrahydro-isoquinoline. Since the production of these two bases can only be rationalised on the assumption that berbamine methyl ether has the structure (30, R = Me) and is split as shown by the dotted lines, berbamine must be represented by (30, R = H) and oxyacanthine by (29, R = H).

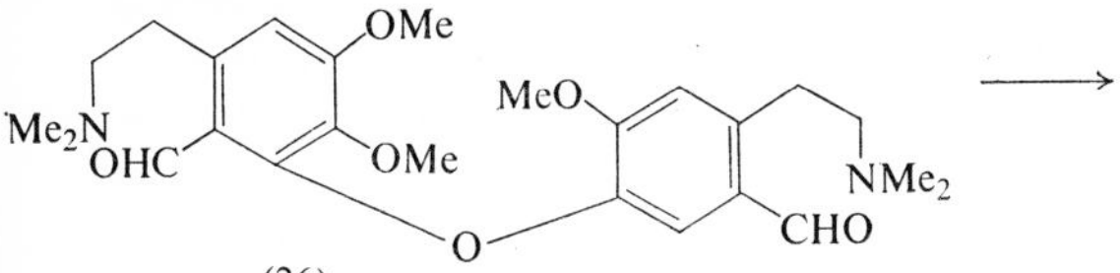

(26)

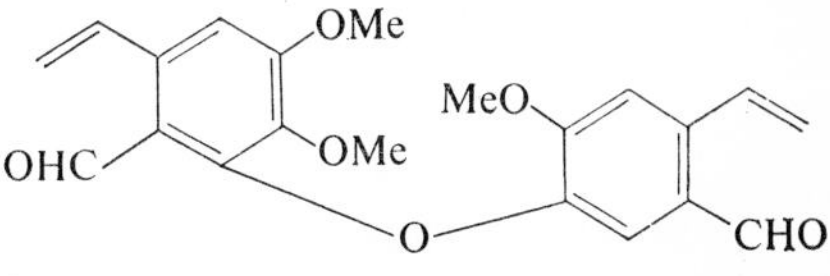

(27)

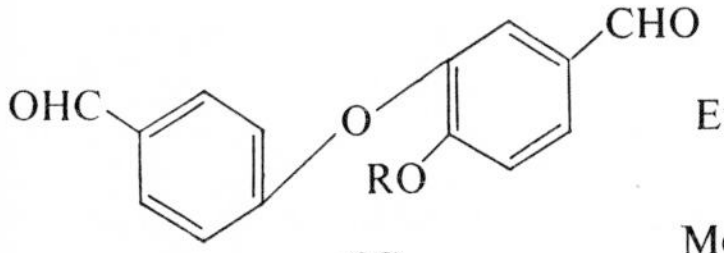

(25)

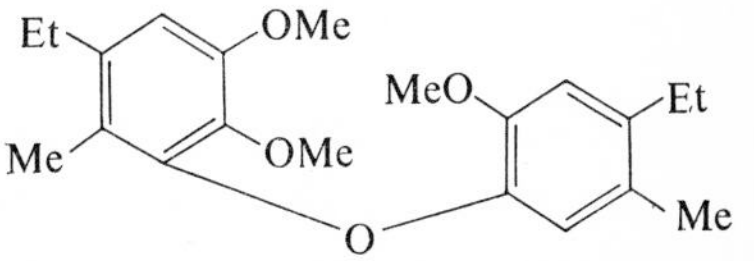

(28)

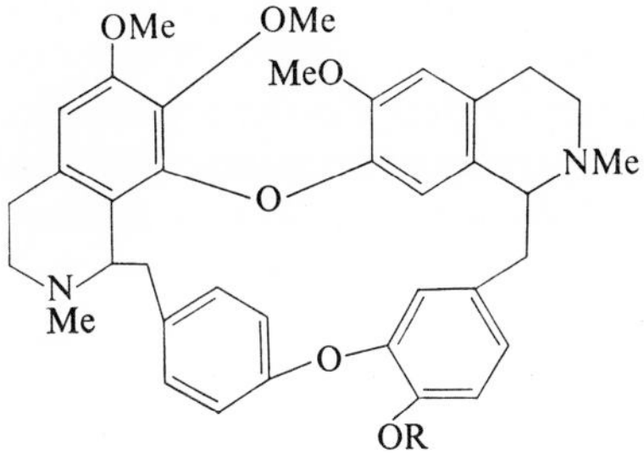

(29)

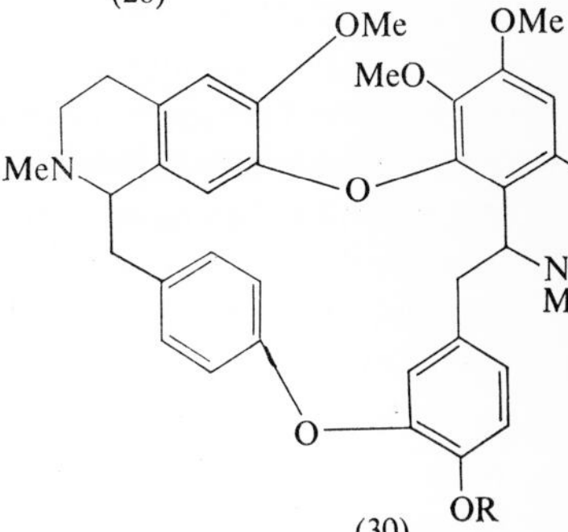

(30)

Isochondodendrine

Isolated from a number of *Chondodendron* species, this base was first formulated as a $C_{18}H_{19}O_3N$ base on the basis of cryoscopic measurements in camphor, but the cryoscopic study of several derivatives in dibromopinene gave a double value corresponding to $C_{36}H_{28}O_6N_2$. Methylation of the phenolic group and Hofmann degradation yielded two isomeric methine bases (presumably by fission on either side of the nitrogen atom) which afforded a common nitrogen-free product on further degradation. This on oxidation yielded a single tricarboxylic acid, finally identified by synthesis as the diphenyl ether (31). On the assumption that the

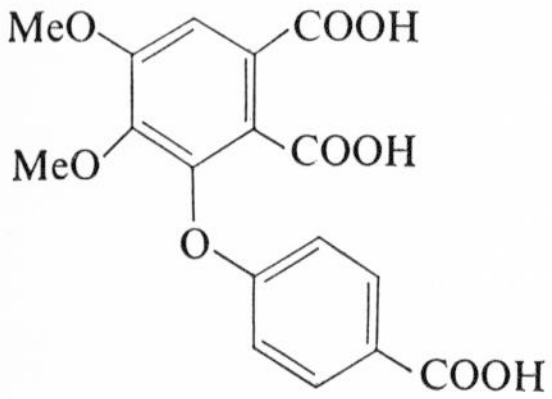

(31)

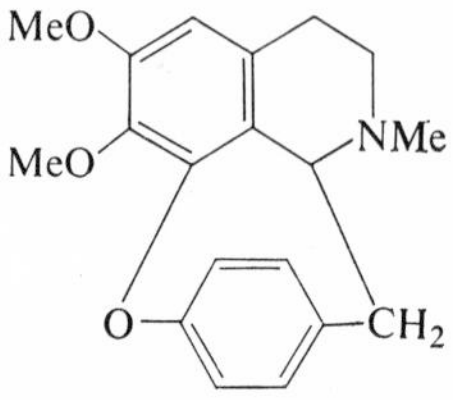

(32)

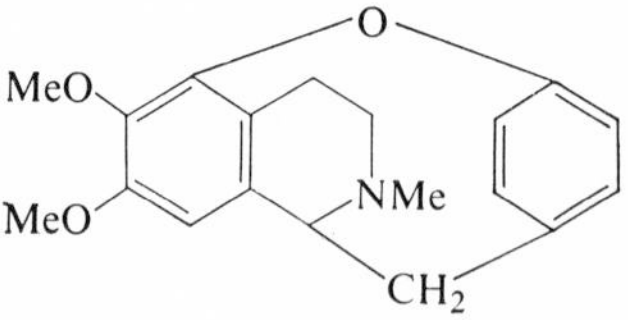

(33)

m-hemipinic acid system of (31) represents the residue of a tetra-hydroisoquinoline system and that the third COOH group arises from oxidation of a methylene group, the structures (32) and (33) were advanced for the alkaloid. Such structures are, however, impossible on steric grounds, and were found to be unnecessary when the correct composition of the alkaloid was finally deduced from a series of MW determinations in systems other than camphor. The carboxyl groups still originate from the same structural units

(34)

(35)

(37)

(36)

(38)

(39)

but from different halves of the molecule, so that isochondodendrine dimethyl ether may be formulated as (34, R = Me). Confirmation of this structure follows from the degradations outlined in formulae (35)–(38). Of the two isomeric methine bases that which is optically inactive (which must be 35) on ozonolysis gives the dialdehyde (36) which may be oxidised and degraded to the nitrogen-free product (37). The last of these on decarboxylation and oxidation gives the acid (38). Isochondodendrine methyl ether, which also occurs naturally, may be split at the diphenyl ether linkages to give a single base of structure (39). The assignment of the position of the free hydroxyl group in isochondodendrine (34, R = H) is made on the basis of an assumed origin from coclaurine (1, R = H).

Chondodendrine (bebeerine)

This base is isomeric with isochondodendrine and was originally formulated as the other half of the isomeric pair (32)–(33), until careful MW determinations of a number of derivatives revealed the

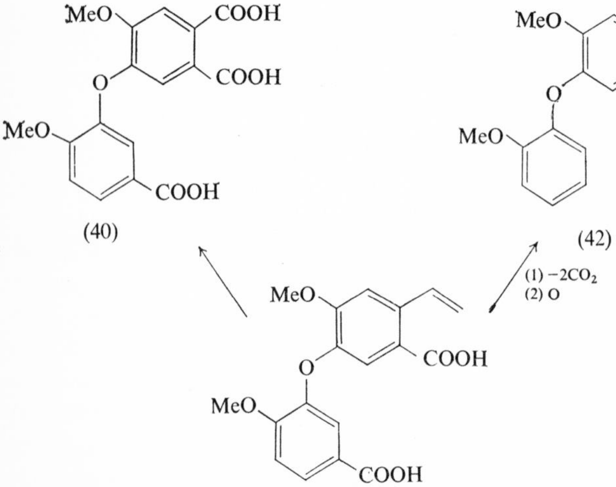

(40)

(41)

(42)

(1) $-2CO_2$
(2) O

correct C_{36} composition. When the alkaloid is methylated, degraded to a nitrogen-free product and then oxidised it gives, unlike isochondodendrine, two isomeric tricarboxylic acids. One of these is identical with the acid (31) from isochondodendrine and the other, which gives 2,2'-dimethoxydiphenyl ether on decarboxylation, has the structure (40). Degradation of the alkaloid

dimethyl ether by the Hofmann method followed by ozonolysis and oxidation and then by a second Hofmann elimination as in the case of isochondodendrine, affords the vinyldicarboxylic acid (41). The structure of this acid is unambiguously proved by oxidation to the acid (40), and by decarboxylation and oxidation to the monocarboxylic acid (42), both of the acids (40) and (42) being identified by synthesis. Assembly of the chondodendrine dimethyl ether structure from these oxidation products leads to the formula (43, R = Me) and, since exhaustive methylation of the related diethyl ether followed by oxidation of the nitrogen-free product leads to a mixture of the acids (44) and (45), the positions of the two phenolic hydroxyl groups is made clear. Chondodendrine may thus be assigned the structure (43, R = H).

The bis-quaternary methochloride of (+)-chondodendrine is a diastereoisomer of (+)-tubocurarine chloride, one of the most powerful curarising agents of tube curare.

BASES CONTAINING THREE DIPHENYL ETHER LINKS

Two types of base, corresponding to structures (10) and (11) may be distinguished in the group, one derived by formal dehydration of the structure (8) (it is highly unlikely that such a process actually occurs in the plant) and one derived by oxidative coupling of the same sort of precursor.

Trilobine and isotrilobine

These two bases which occur in *C. trilobus* D.C., were originally thought to be isomers of composition $C_{36}H_{36}O_5N_2$ but trilobine is now known to contain one NMe and one NH group and isotrilobine is its *N*-methyl derivative. The structure of isotrilobine has been elucidated using essentially the same processes as for the isomeric bases oxyacanthine and berbamine. Hofmann degradation leads to the methine base and ozonolysis of this affords a mixture of the neutral dialdehyde (46, R = Me) (obtained from oxyacanthine and berbamine) and a dibasic dialdehyde showing the properties of a diphenylene dioxide. This base on further Hofmann degradation yields trimethylamine and a divinyl-dialdehyde, the structure (47) for which was only proved by the synthesis of its reduction product (48) after the correct structure for trilobine had been proposed by Faltis, on the basis of a hypothetical origin from a precursor of the oxyacanthine type. From this it may be deduced that the dibasic aldehyde obtained together with the neutral aldehyde (46) during the ozonolysis of the methine base must have the structure (49). Combination of this

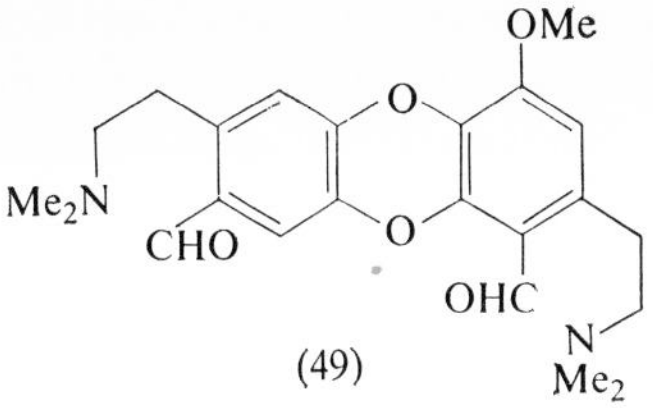

(49)

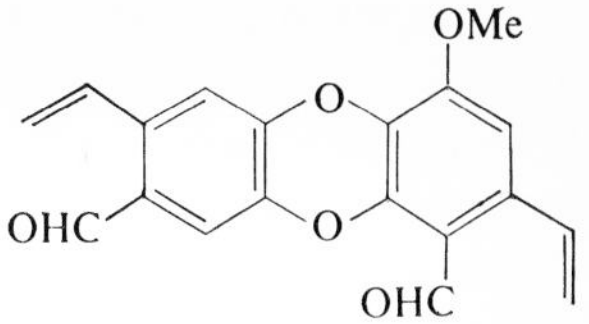

(47)

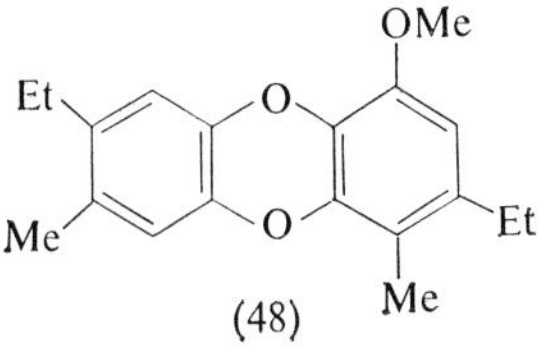

(48)

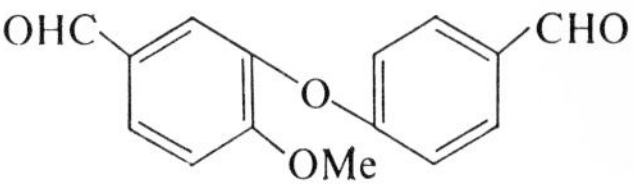

(46)

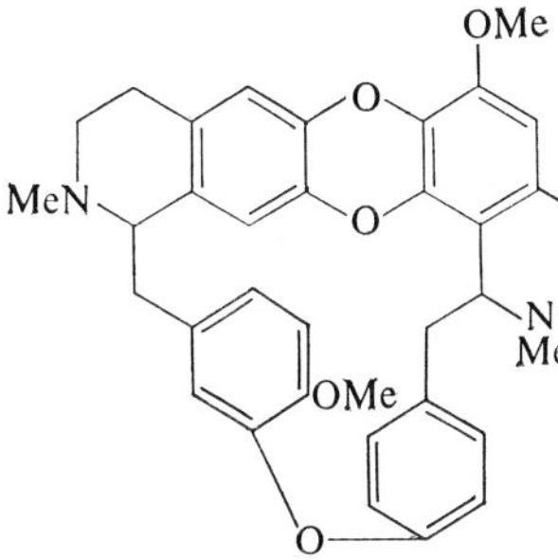

(50)

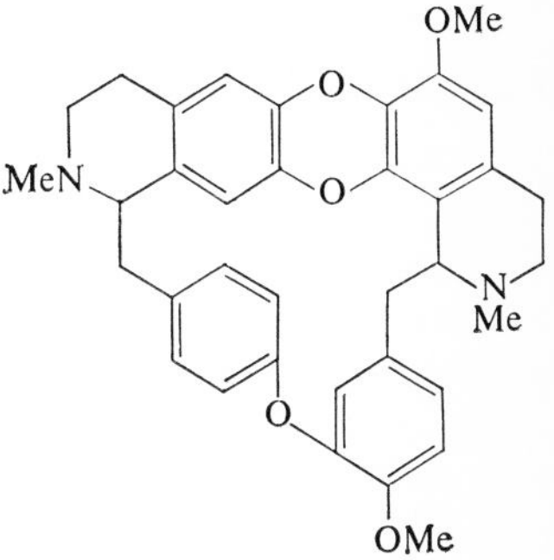

(51)

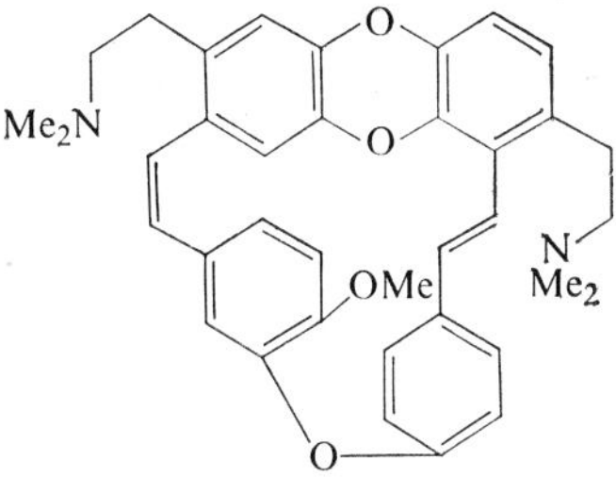

(52)

with the aldehyde (46) in both possible senses leads to the structure (50) or (51) for isotrilobine. Oxyacanthine, known to have the structure (29, R = H), can be *O*-demethylated and finally dehydrated by heating with hydrobromic acid at 130° to a diphenolic diphenylenedioxide base, and this on *O*-methylation affords a diastereoisomer of isotrilobine, which gives isotrilobine methine (52) on Hofmann degradation. Accordingly isotrilobine must have the structure (50).

Micranthine and menisarine

Micranthine from *Daphnandra micrantha,* is a diphenolic base of composition $C_{34}H_{32}O_6N_2$ containing one methoxyl group and one

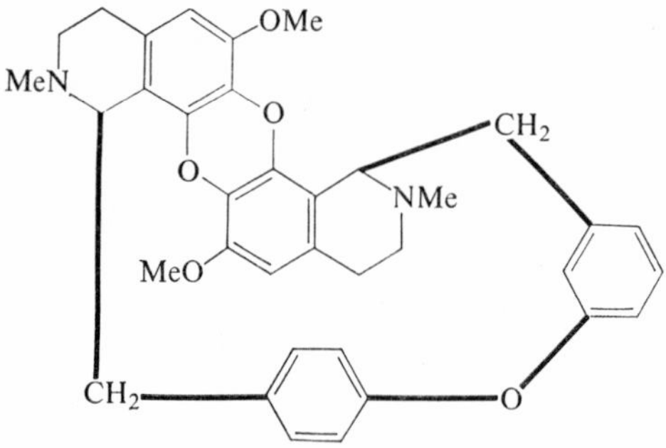

(53)

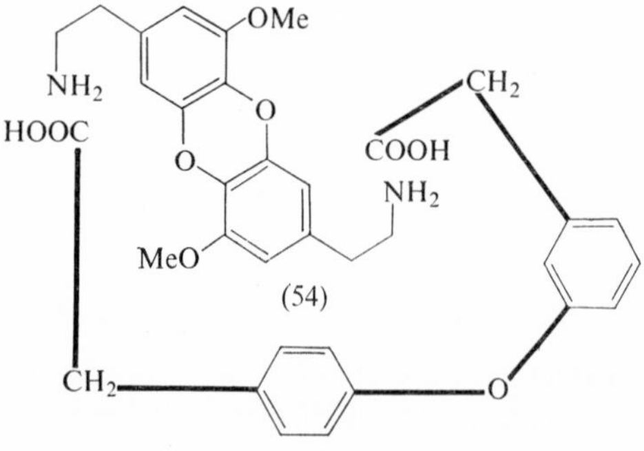

(54)

(55)

secondary nitrogen, and gives colour tests characteristic of di-phenylene dioxides. Complete methylation of oxygen and nitrogen atoms and Hofmann degradation to a methine base, followed by ozonolysis, yields the neutral dialdehyde (46) and a basic aldehyde. The last of these on further Hofmann degradation yields a di-methoxydiformyldivinyldiphenylenedioxide. On the assumption that the alkaloid arises from an oxyacanthine or berbamine analogue by further oxidative coupling, and, assuming that coupling does not occur at position 5 of the isoquinoline system (since no isoquinoline alkaloid is known with an oxygen substituent at such a position), the structure (53) emerges for *O,O,N*-trimethyl-micranthine. This has been confirmed by the synthesis of a base of this structure by a standard laudanosine type synthesis from the diamine (54) and the dicarboxylic acid (55); the product of this synthesis is a diastereoisomer of trimethylmicranthine, and both bases give the same optically inactive methine (56) on Hofmann degradation.

(56)

Since the degradation of *N*-methyl-*O,O*-diethylmicranthine affords the dialdehyde (25, R = Et) the position of one of the phenolic groups is known; the positions of the second phenolic hydroxyl and of the —NH— group have not been determined.

A Mixed Bisbenzylisoquinoline Alkaloid

Thalicarpine

This alkaloid, from *Thalictrum dasycarpum* Fisch. and Lall, very recently discovered, is the only example so far of a bisbenzylisoquinoline alkaloid composed of one benzylisoquinoline and one aporphine unit. It has the composition $C_{41}H_{48}O_8N_2$ and the

(57)

(59)

(60)

(58)

(61)

(62)

(63)

nuclear magnetic resonance spectrum indicates that its molecule contains two *N*-methyl groups, seven methoxyl groups and seven aromatic hydrogens, indicating the presence of seven unsubstituted aromatic nuclear positions. Sodium and liquid ammonia fission of the alkaloid yields (−)-6′-hydroxylaudanosine (57) and (+)-3,6-dimethoxyaporphine (58). Of these the structure of the aporphine was determined by the general methods of degradation and synthesis of aporphine alkaloids set out in Chapter 6, while the structure of the other base was deduced by Hofmann degradation of the ethyl ether ethiodide to the methine base (59) and *N*-free product (60), and oxidation of the last compound to 2-ethoxy-4,5-dimethoxybenzoic acid.

During the course of the sodium–ammonia fission of the alkaloid one methoxyl group is lost and one diphenyl ether group is split. All known aporphine alkaloids contain oxygen substituents at positions 5 and 6 and accordingly either the missing methoxyl group or the diphenyl ether linkage in the thalicarpine must be at position 5 of the aporphine and, by analogy with almost all other aporphine alkaloids, the other oxygen function is most likely located at position 2 or 4. The precise structure of thalicarpine (61) was revealed by its synthesis by heating (−)-6′-bromolaudanosine (62) with the alkaloid isocorydine, which is shown in Chapter 6 to be (+)-4-hydroxy-3,5,6-trimethoxyaporphine (63).

A Trimeric Isoquinoline Alkaloid

Pilocereine

This base, isolated from the giant Mexican cacti *Lophocereus schottii* Britton and Rose, and *Pachycereus marginatus* B. and R., was originally believed to be a bisisoquinoline alkaloid $C_{30}H_{44}O_4N_2$ and was assigned the structure (64, R = H) on the basis of fission of its methyl ether (64, R = Me) into the four possible fragments (65)–(68) by potassium and liquid ammonia.

3

Further work, however, particularly nuclear magnetic resonance studies, molecular weight determinations and acetyl estimations on the base and its *O*-acetyl ester indicated that the alkaloid contains

three not two isoquinoline units, and a more careful examination of the products of potassium–ammonia fission revealed the presence among these of two other bases. One of these was isomeric with the phenol (66) and was shown to have the structure (69), and the other was the so-called isopilocereine which was shown to be the dimeric base (64, R = H) by NMR and MW studies and by fission of its methyl ether to the four bases (65)–(68). Pilocereine must thus have the structure (70). Piloceredine, which occurs with pilocereine, is also trimeric and may be a stereo-isomer of pilocereine (70).

CHAPTER 5

Cularine

CULARINE, which has been isolated from a number of *Dicentra* species and from *Corydalis claviculata*, is an unusual base. It has the composition $C_{20}H_{23}O_4N$ and contains an *N*-methyl group and three methoxyl groups. The fourth oxygen atom is not present in any functional group and was early assumed to be part of an ether system. Exhaustive methylation requires two steps for removal of the nitrogen, which then appears as trimethylamine and accordingly the nitrogen atom must be part of a single ring. The nitrogen-free product of exhaustive methylation $C_{19}H_{18}O_4$ contains two reducible double bonds and two benzene rings, and can be oxidised to a tricarboxylic aromatic acid $C_{18}H_{16}O_{10}$ indicating that the ether oxygen must join the two aromatic nuclei. The production of a tricarboxylic acid rather than a mono or dicarboxylic acid in the final oxidation indicates also that in the nitrogen-free product the aromatic nuclei are also joined by an olefinic system. Since the two double bonds arise from fission of the nitrogen-containing ring, and since molecular weight determinations of all cularine derivatives rule out the possibility that the alkaloid is a bisbenzylisoquinoline, the part structures (1), (2) and (3) may be advanced for the base, the *N*-free product and the tricarboxylic acid respectively; the ether link cannot be placed except as shown without introducing impossible strain into the molecule.

Fission of the diphenyl ether system by sodium and ammonia, in a manner similar to that used in the study of the bisbenzylisoquinoline alkaloids, gives a single phenolic product and this on oxidation (with destruction of the phenolic ring) affords 4-methoxyphthalic acid (4). Methylation of the phenolic hydroxyl group, however, followed by Hofmann degradation and oxidation gave 4-methoxy-phthalic acid (4) and 2,4,5-trimethoxybenzoic acid (5), and these results indicate that cularine must have the structure (7) and that its sodium–ammonia fission product must be the phenol (6), any

arrangement with the ether oxygen linking other positions being sterically impossible. The alternative structure (7a) equally compatible with the chemical evidence was considered to be unlikely since all alkaloids containing two oxygen substituents in one aromatic nucleus have them in the *ortho* relationship.

Confirmation of this structure (7) for the alkaloid has recently been obtained by the synthesis of (±)-cularine by the Pomeranz–Fritsch synthesis of the isoquinoline (10) from the ketone (8) via the amino-acetal condensation product (9); the reduction of the methiodide of the base (10) by sodium borohydride afforded racemic cularine, the infrared spectrum of which in solution was identical with that of the natural alkaloid. The final stage of this synthesis is exactly analogous to the reduction of papaverine methiodide to racemic laudanosine (Chapter 3).

Of the other alkaloids of this group cularimine is known to be the related secondary amine, giving cularine on *N*-methylation, and

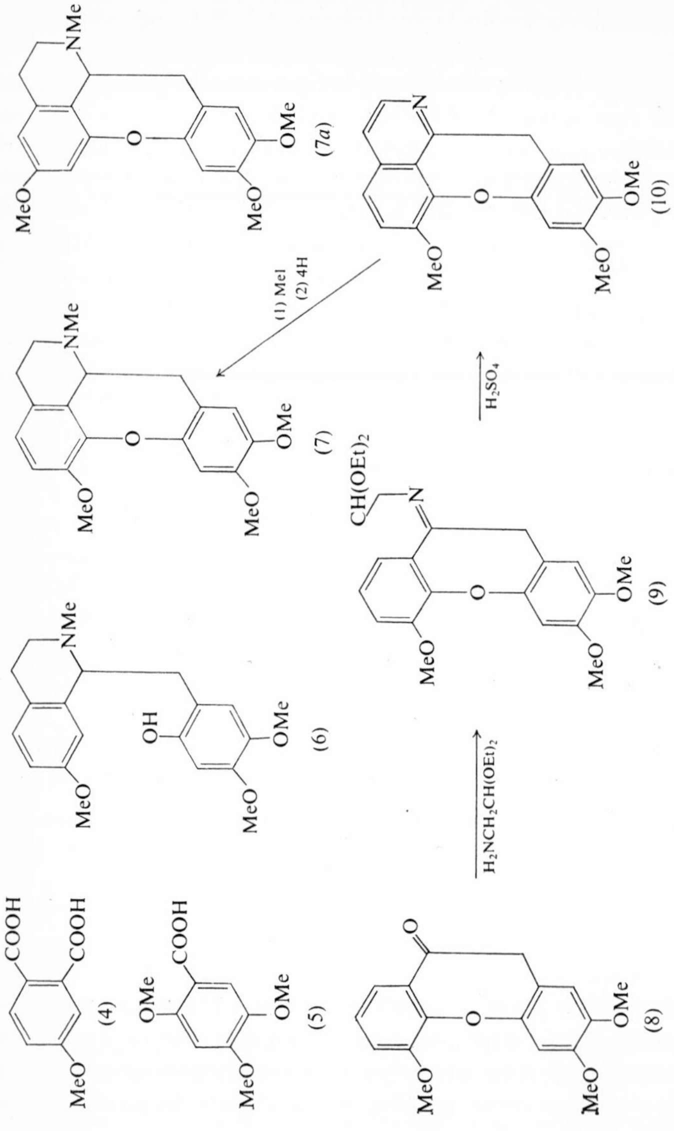
(4)
(5)
(6)
(7)
(7a)
(8)
(9)
(10)
H2NCH2CH(OEt)2
H2SO4
(1) MeI
(2) 4H

the phenolic cularidine is one of the possible *O*-desmethylcularines, since it gives cularine on methylation with diazomethane.

The bases of the cularine group are unusual in that they are the only representatives of the internal ethers analogous to the bis-benzylisoquinolines, and also because their oxygen substitution pattern is anomalous. All other known alkaloids of the benzyl-isoquinoline and derived groups (aporphines, protoberberines, cryptopines and phthalide-isoquinolines) have oxygen substituents in positions 6 and 7 of the isoquinoline system, whereas cularine is 7,8 substituted. It could arise by radical-oxidation and *O*-methyla-tion of either of the diphenols (11) or (12), but each of these has an unusual substitution pattern, and its origin from a base substituted as in (13) with subsequent removal of the additional substituent in the isoquinoline ring is much more likely. Bases with a substitution pattern analogous to (13) are known, e.g. narcotine (14) and

(11) Cularine (12)

capaurine (15) and in these the oxygen at C-8 is believed to be introduced at a stage after construction of the benzylisoquinoline system. The removal of one or more oxygen substituents in the aporphine series appears to occur quite frequently during

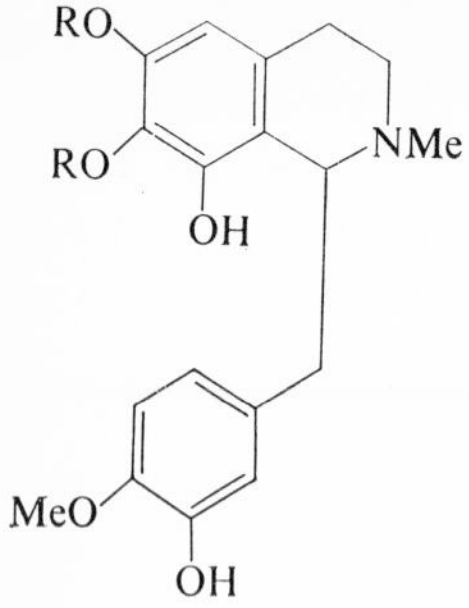

(13)

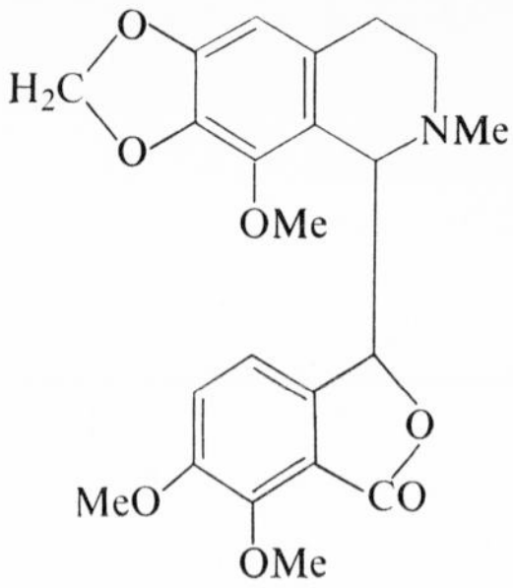

(14)

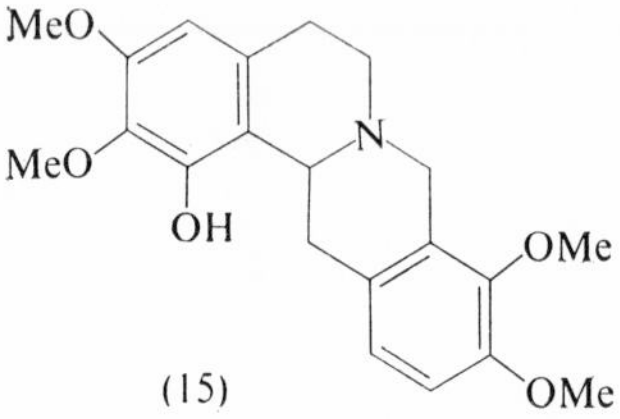

(15)

biosynthesis, but only in the "benzyl" portion of the molecule, the
substituents in the isoquinoline portion being unaffected, and in
this respect, therefore, cularine remains unusual.

CHAPTER 6

The Aporphines

THE alkaloids of this group arise naturally by oxidation of phenols of the benzyltetrahydroquinoline series through the pairing of free radicals, essentially as in formulae (1)–(4) and (6). The patterns represented in structures (4) and (6), are the only sterically possible products of this type from bases having the oxygen substitution pattern of the known benzylisoquinoline alkaloids. These patterns, however, are not universally found in the natural alkaloids. Although all bases so far known in this series have oxygen substituents in positions 5 and 6, some have only one substituent in the other aromatic nucleus; where this is at position 2, 3, or 4 the base must be assumed to arise by a reductive removal of the second substituent from a base of substitution pattern (4) or (6), and the bases anonaine and reomerine which contain no oxygen function in that nucleus must have lost both of these after the internuclear coupling (see p. 154). The bases crebanine (1,2-dimethoxy) and stephanine (1-methoxy) must arise by oxidation of the primary coupled phenol followed by removal of one or both of the oxygen substituents originally present in that aromatic nucleus.

The methods by which aporphine alkaloids may be degraded were worked out by Pschorr during investigation of the structures of the first representative bases of the group, apomorphine and morphothebaine, the products of acid-catalysed rearrangement of morphine and thebaine respectively. Although these bases do not occur naturally, and differ from the natural alkaloids in not having oxygen substituents at positions 5 and 6, they present a convenient and instructive introduction to the series.

Apomorphine

Apomorphine is obtained when morphine is heated with mineral acids at temperatures in the range 140–160°. It contains two phenolic hydroxyl groups, and is a tertiary base containing one *N*-methyl group. The phenol itself is very readily oxidised and is too sensitive in alkaline solution to survive Hofmann degradation in a clean condition, but the dimethyl ether is stable to oxygen and the investigations were limited to this base. Two Hofmann degradations are necessary for elimination of the nitrogen atom, which must accordingly be in a ring. In the first of these degradations two methine bases are obtained from apomorphine dimethyl ether methiodide, one optically active and the other inactive, as a result of the fission of the ring on alternative sides of the nitrogen atom; both bases on further degradation yield the same nitrogen-free product, $C_{18}H_{16}O_2$ which has the properties of a vinyl-phenanthrene.

Oxidation of the nitrogen-free product affords a carboxylic acid $C_{17}H_{14}O_4$, as a result of destruction of the vinyl group, and the conversion of the acid through the amide into the amine by the Hofmann rearrangement yields an aromatic amine easily converted

(7)   (8)   (9)

(12)   (11)   (10)

into the corresponding phenol methyl ether. The product of this sequence of reactions is 3,4,8-trimethoxyphenanthrene (7), identical with material prepared by the Pschorr phenanthrene synthesis. The sensitivity of apomorphine to aerial oxidation in alkaline solution indicates that it is probably a derivative of catechol and accordingly of the methoxyl groups present in 3,4,8-trimethoxy-phenanthrene those at positions 3 and 4 must be present in the parent base and that at position 8 must represent the one introduced during the degradation, at the site of the vinyl group present in the

N-free product, which must therefore be 3,4-dimethoxy-8-vinyl-phenthrene (8).

The double bond of the vinyl group is generated during degradation, and to account for the optical inactivity of one of the methines the nitrogen atom in this base (9) must be attached to the terminal atom of the chain. As apomorphine does not show the properties of a phenanthrene or naphthalene the 9,10 double bond in the methine must have been generated during degradation, and apomorphine methyl ether may be assigned the structure (10), which is greatly to be preferred on steric grounds to the alternative (12); the optically active methine may then be given structure (11).

Morphothebaine

This base is obtained by the action of hot concentrated hydrochloric acid on thebaine (see Chapter 7); it has the composition $C_{18}H_{19}O_3N$ and contains one methoxyl, one *N*-methyl and two

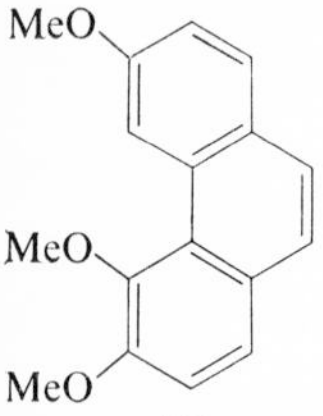

(13) 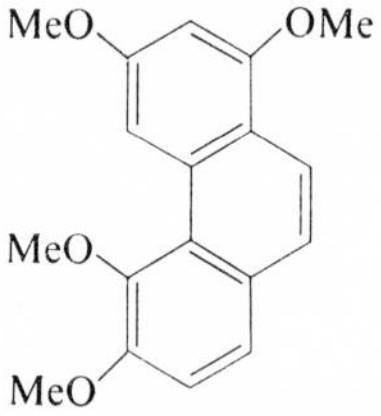   (14) 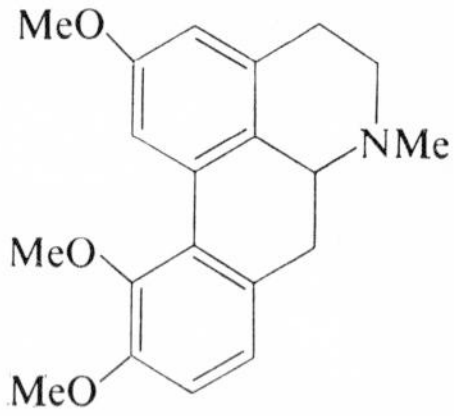   (15)

phenolic hydroxyl groups. Exhaustive methylation of the dimethyl ether affords in the first step one optically active and one inactive methine and, in the second step, a single *N*-free product $C_{19}H_{18}O_3$, which is oxidisable to a carboxylic acid $C_{18}H_{16}O_5$. This acid on decarboxylation yields 3,4,6-trimethoxyphenanthrene (13) and, when converted through the amide, amine and phenol into the phenol methyl ether, gives 3,4,6,8-tetramethoxyphenanthrene (14). The production of the trimethoxyphenanthrene (13) indicates the oxygen substitution pattern of the parent alkaloid, while the production of the tetramethoxy-compound (14) reveals the point of attachment of the vinyl group in the *N*-free product, and as a result the structure (15) may confidently be assigned to morphothebaine dimethyl ether.

The structures (10) and (15) for apomorphine dimethyl ether and morphothebaine dimethyl ether respectively have been confirmed by unambiguous synthesis as follows. The amide (18), prepared

from the amine (16) and the acid chloride (17), on Bischler–Napieralsky isoquinoline ring closure yields the nitro-base (19), the methiodide of which (20) on reduction is converted into the amino-base (21), which gives the aporphine (22) on diazotisation and cyclisation by heating with copper powder. The last stage of this process is analogous to the Pschorr phenanthrene cyclisation, developed during earlier work on morphine and thebaine. In formulae (16)–(22) R = H gives rise to apomorphine dimethyl ether and R = OMe to morphothebaine dimethyl ether. Of the parent bases apomorphine is clearly 3,4-dihydroxyaporphine and, since thebaine contains a non-hydrolysable methoxyl group at the phenanthrene position 3, morphothebaine is 4,6-dihydroxy-3-methoxyaporphine.

A further reaction characteristic of the aporphine bases was discovered during the course of this work, namely the easy degradation of the bases to aromatic phenanthrene derivatives with fission of the carbon–nitrogen bond on heating with acetic anhydride or benzoyl chloride, e.g. apomorphine dimethyl ether with benzoyl chloride on heating gives the non-basic amide (23). This is a reaction by which aporphine alkaloids may be readily recognised.

Glaucine and corytuberine

Although the degradative work reported above preceded the elucidation of the structures of the natural aporphine bases, the syntheses of the dimethyl ethers of apomorphine and morphothebaine were only achieved after the route had been worked out during the syntheses of certain natural bases. The first of these to be prepared was glaucine. This alkaloid and corytuberine dimethyl ether are two bases of composition $C_{21}H_{25}O_4N$, which equals (laudanosine − 2H). As both bases contain four methoxyl groups like laudanosine (24, R = H), Gadamer made the intelligent supposition that both were derived from the last-named base by the abstraction of two hydrogen atoms with the coupling of the two aromatic nuclei, on the basis of which theory only two structures (25) and (26) could be considered for them. By application of the Pschorr phenanthrene ring closure to 6′-aminolaudanosine (24, R = NH$_2$) (±)-glaucine (25) was prepared and resolved, when the (+)-form was shown to be identical with the natural base.

The isomeric tetramethoxyaporphine (26) has also been synthesised and the (+)-form of this has been identified with corytuberine dimethyl ether. Corytuberine itself contains two phenolic hydroxyl groups, and from it by partial methylation two monomethyl ethers, identical with the alkaloids corydine and isocorydine, can be prepared, and the elucidation of the structures of these three bases presents an interesting problem, solved as follows.

Corytuberine may be ethylated to a diethoxydimethoxy-analogue of the base (26), and this on oxidation yields 3-ethoxy-4-methoxy-phthalic acid, and hence corytuberine must have the structure (27) or must be the 6-hydroxy-5-methoxy isomer of (27). Three

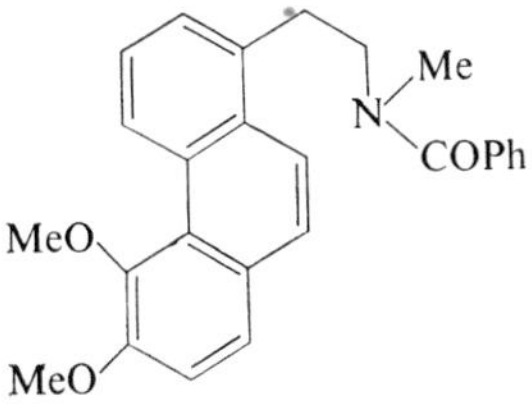

(23)

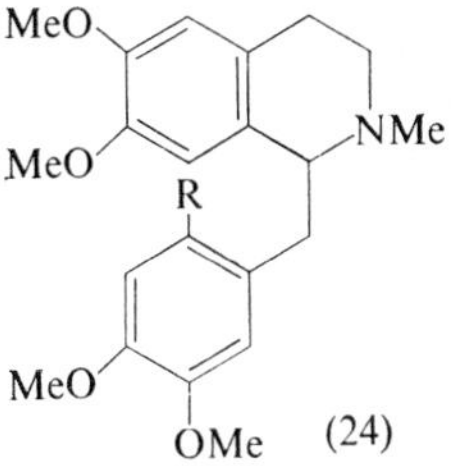

(24)

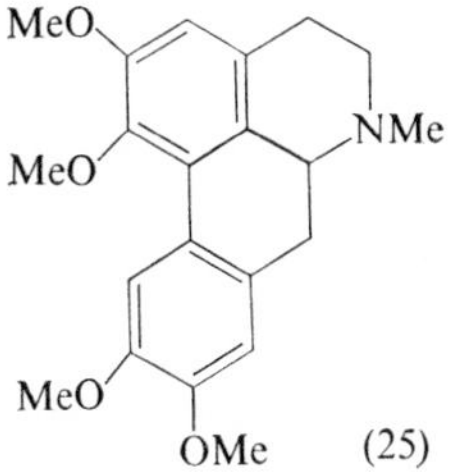

(25)

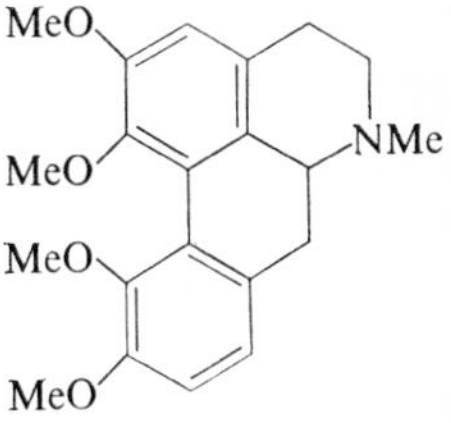

(26)

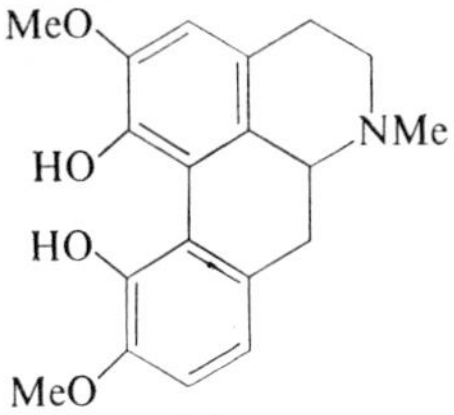

(27)

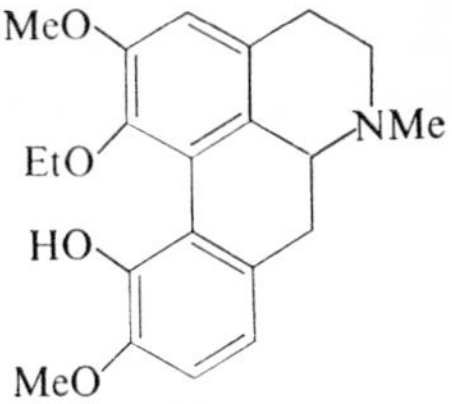

(28)

possible structures thus remain for the two monomethyl ethers corydine and isocorydine. The corresponding mixture of mono-ethyl ethers of corytuberine on oxidation affords a mixture of 3-ethoxy-4-methoxyphthalic acid and 4-ethoxy-5-methoxyphthalic acid from which it may be deduced that one of the ethers has the structure (28), which can only be derived from (27). Corytuberine must therefore have the structure (27) and corydine and isocorydine must be represented by the pair of structures (29) and (30). Since

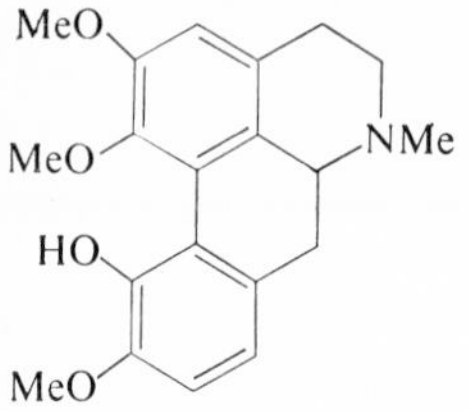

(29)

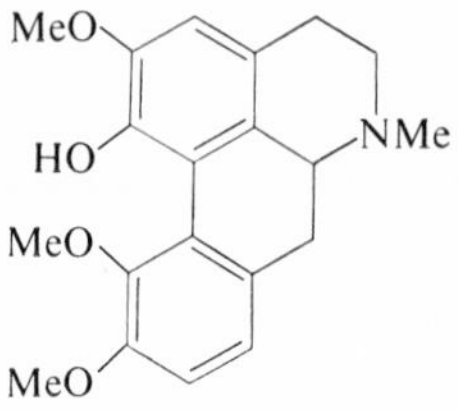

(30)

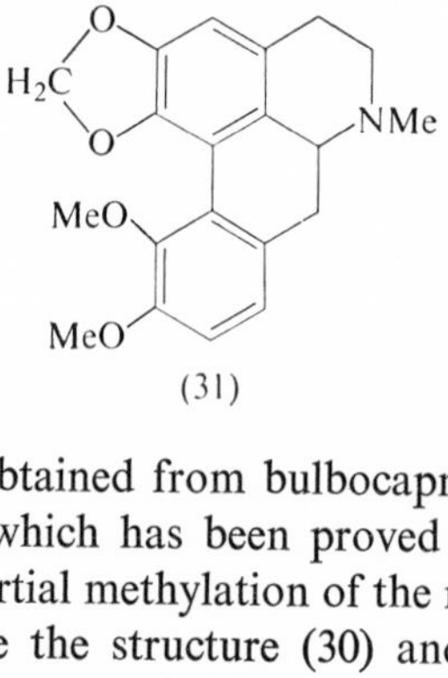

(31)

corydine (29) may be obtained from bulbocapnine methyl ether (the structure (31) for which has been proved by synthesis) by demethylenation and partial methylation of the resulting catechol derivative, it must have the structure (30) and isocorydine by elimination must be represented by (29).

Isothebaine

As will be seen from the discussion so far the degradation of morphothebaine dimethyl ether to a trimethoxyphenanthrene carboxylic acid and the decarboxylation of this to 3,4,6-trimethoxyphenanthrene gives information about the orientation of oxygen substituents on the dihydrophenanthrene system of the parent base, but that, since the nitrogen-containing ring is completely destroyed during this process, no conclusions about the position of this ring in the base can be made. It is only the formation of 3,4,6,8-tetra-methoxyphenanthrene by a sequence of changes ensuring the appearance of an additional methoxyl group at the point of attachment of the carbon end of the nitrogen ring that establishes unambiguously the orientation of substituents on the aporphine ring system in the base. Failure to obtain definite evidence of the point of attachment of the ring in this way can lead to an erroneous assignment of structure to a base, as the following discussion of isothebaine illustrates.

Isothebaine is isolated from the oriental poppy, together with thebaine (32, see Chapter 7) and, as their names imply, these two bases both have the composition $C_{19}H_{21}O_3N$, and both contain two methoxy groups; the third oxygen function in the two bases differs, however, being a phenolic hydroxyl group in isothebaine and a cyclic ether group in thebaine. The oriental poppy was reported to produce almost exclusively thebaine during the period of active growth, but withering of the plant was reported to be accompanied by a steady decrease in the amount of thebaine and a corresponding rise in the isothebaine content, and these findings were interpreted as indicating a conversion of thebaine into isothebaine and hence a close structural relationship between the two bases. This assumption evidently led the early workers on isothebaine to pay too little attention to the interpretation of their degradative work on the alkaloid.

Exhaustive methylation of isothebaine methyl ether, as in the case of the other aporphine alkaloids, leads in the first step to two isomeric methine bases, one optically active and one inactive, and in the second step to a single N-free substance. This end-product is a trimethoxyvinylphenanthrene and on oxidation to a carboxylic acid and decarboxylation of this gives 3,4,5-trimethoxyphen-anthrene (33), identical with material prepared from morphine (see Chapter 7) and by synthesis. On this evidence only a structure was assigned to isothebaine and this remained unchallenged for over forty years. As thebaine (32) is readily converted in the

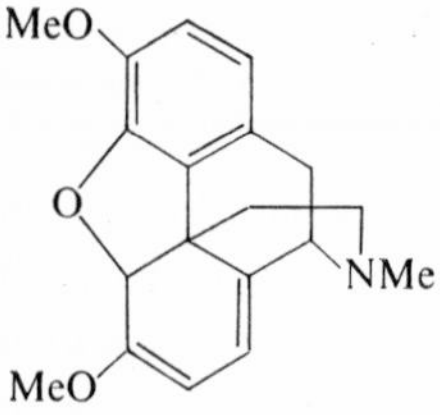

(32)

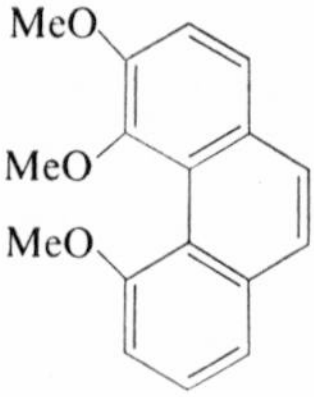

(33)

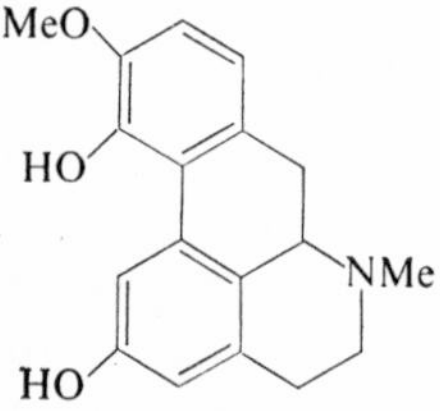

(34)

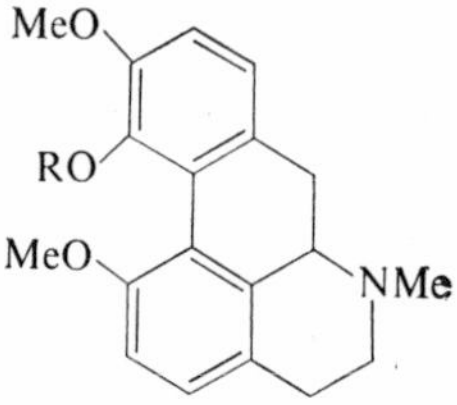

(35)

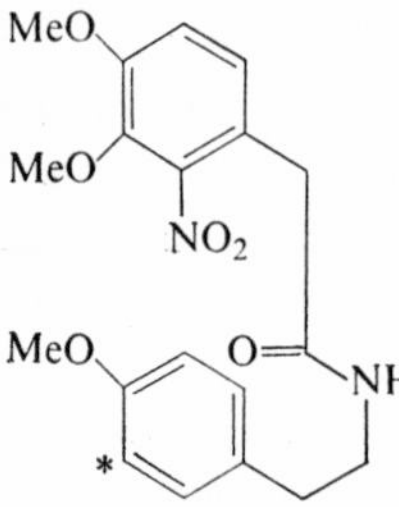

(36)

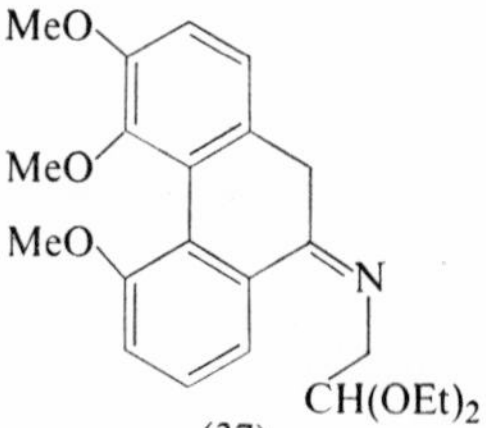

(37)

laboratory into morphothebaine (34), in which the relationship of the guaiacol nucleus and the nitrogen atom are known with certainty, isothebaine methyl ether was assigned the structure (35);

the precise position of the phenolic hydroxyl group was left undecided, though position 4 for this group was regarded as most likely in view of the difficulty experienced in methylating the alkaloid.

On the basis of this work, carried out in 1914 and repeated in 1948, attempts were made to synthesise isothebaine methyl ether, first in 1929 by the conventional route and later in 1948 by the application of the Pomeranz–Fritsch isoquinoline synthesis. The conventional route failed even to yield the intermediate benzyl-isoquinoline since cyclisation of the amide (36) *meta* to the *o,p*-directing methoxyl group could not be achieved even after introduction of the *o,p*-directing acetylamino group at the position marked in (36) with an asterisk. The second attempt at synthesis proceeded satisfactorily as far as the imine (37), but cyclisation of this to the isoquinoline failed.

In 1955, however, a re-examination of the evidence was made, and it was shown that the degradations set out above provide no information whatever about the position of the nitrogen-containing ring in isothebaine, they only fix the positions of the oxygen substituents relative to the dihydrophenanthrene system of the alkaloid, the previously assigned complete structure for the base resting largely on the unproved assumption of the origin of the alkaloid from thebaine. The structure (38, R = Me) for isothebaine methyl ether is equally compatible with the evidence, and is indeed preferable since *all* other naturally occurring aporphine alkaloids have oxygen substituents at positions 5 and 6. The structure (38, R = H) was regarded as most probable for isothebaine itself since the alkaloid fails to couple with diazotised amines in alkaline solution and this is the only phenolic structure derived from either system (35) or (38) that does not have a free nuclear position *ortho* or *para* to hydroxyl available for coupling. The correctness of these deductions was demonstrated by the synthesis of the aporphine (38, R = Et) by the conventional route and the identification of the racemate with (+)-isothebaine ethyl ether by the comparison of their infrared spectra in solution.

Liriodenine

Two interesting bases have been isolated recently from the yellow heart-wood of the tulip tree, *Liriodendron tulipifera.* One of these, liriodenine, has the composition $C_{17}H_9O_3N$, readily gives an oxime

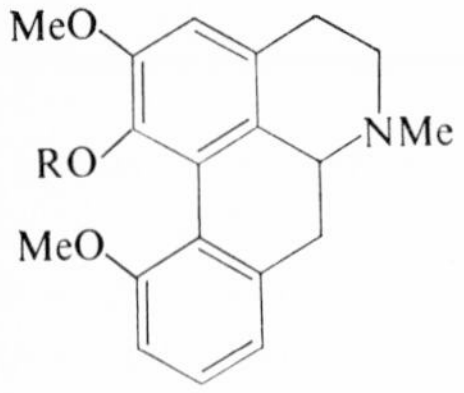

(38)

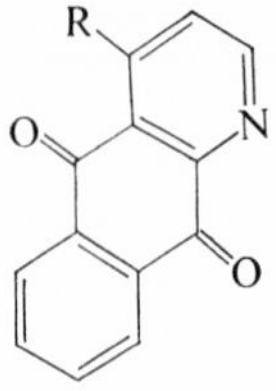

(39)

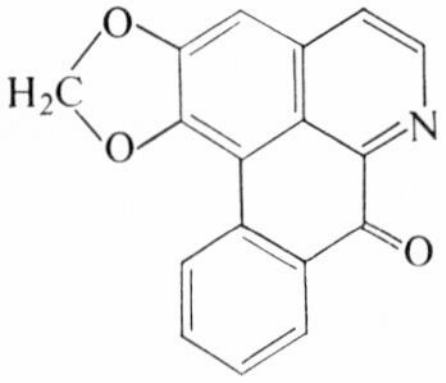

(40)

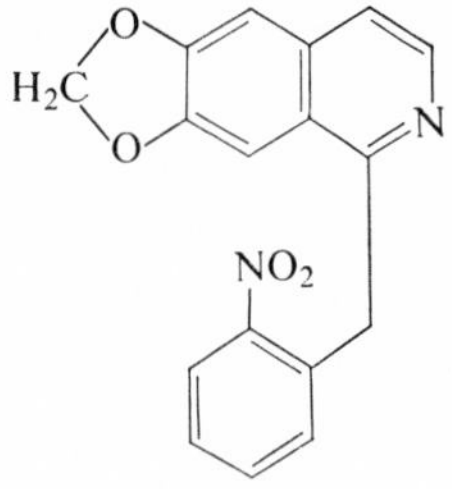

(41)

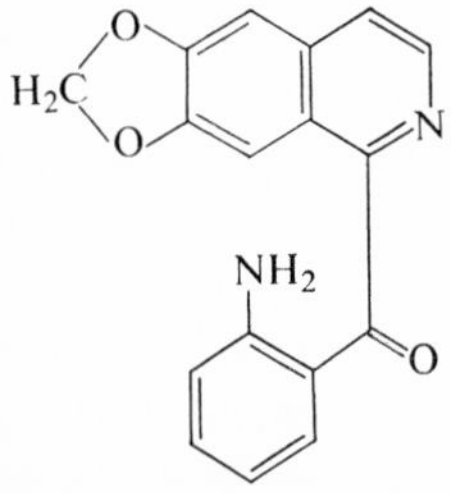

(42)

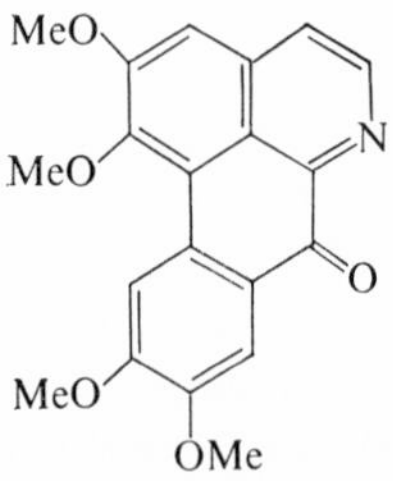

(43)

and is oxidisable to a carboxylic acid $C_{14}H_7O_4N$ (39, R = COOH) that gives 1-azaanthraquinone (39, R = H) on decarboxylation. Infrared studies reveal that the base contains a methylenedioxy group and this, together with the oxime-forming carbonyl group, accounts for all of the oxygen atoms of the alkaloid. On the basis of this limited evidence the occurrence of liriodenine together with bases of the benzylisoquinoline group led to the advancement of the structure (40) for the alkaloid, the methylenedioxy group being placed in the 5,6-position by analogy with all other aporphine alkaloids. The structure was completely confirmed by a synthesis of the alkaloid from the benzylisoquinoline (41), by oxidation to an analogue of papaveraldine, reduction of this to the corresponding amine (42) and closure of the aporphine system by Pschorr's conventional procedure. The co-occurring yellow base of composition $C_{20}H_{17}O_5N$, unnamed, was thought to be the corresponding tetramethoxy-compound (43), and this also was confirmed by an analogous synthesis from 6'-nitropapaveraldine.

Although the syntheses reported above constitute formal conversions of benzylisoquinoline alkaloids into aporphines, the processes occurring in the plants are clearly oxidations involving radical intermediates, as set out in formulae (1)–(4) and (6), and a number of attempts have been made to realise such oxidations in practice in the laboratory. Norlaudanosine (44) on oxidation with chloranil and in a variety of other ways affords, however, not the hoped-for aporphine but the quaternary benzopyrrocolinium salt of structure (45), as a result of the participation of the unshared electron pair on the nitrogen atom in the reaction. It is of interest to note that a trimethyl ether of the related iodide has been isolated recently from the Australian plant *Cryptocaria bowiei* Hook. The required conversion into the aporphine system has, however, recently been accomplished by oxidation in the quaternary salt series, in which the nitrogen no longer possesses an unshared electron pair and can therefore not participate in the reaction. Alkaline potassium ferricyanide oxidation of the methochloride of the base (1, R = Me) gave a salt, presumably of the base (4,

R = Me) that on methylation yielded glaucine methochloride. The reaction has not yet been accomplished in the free base series; presumably in plants the appropriate enzyme system is able to hold the molecules in such a way that C—C rather than C—N coupling occurs or immobilises the electron pair on the nitrogen in some way thus preventing quaternary salt formation.

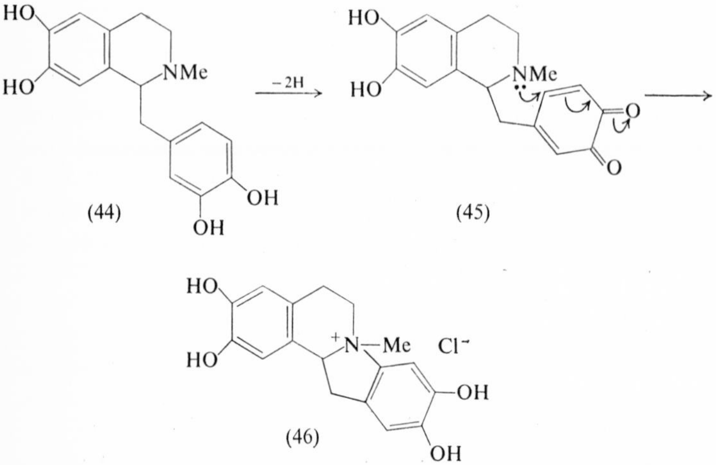

(44) (45)

(46)

The occurrence of and the elucidation of the structure of thalicarpine, a bisbenzylisoquinoline alkaloid one of the units of which is an aporphine, is reported in Chapter 4.

CHAPTER 7

The Morphine Alkaloids

THE alkaloids of the morphine group are formed in Nature by the coupling of the two aromatic nuclei of a benzyltetrahydroisoquinoline in an oxidative process basically identical with that involved in the formation of the aporphines. This may be illustrated essentially as in formulae (1)–(6), in which oxygen substituents not

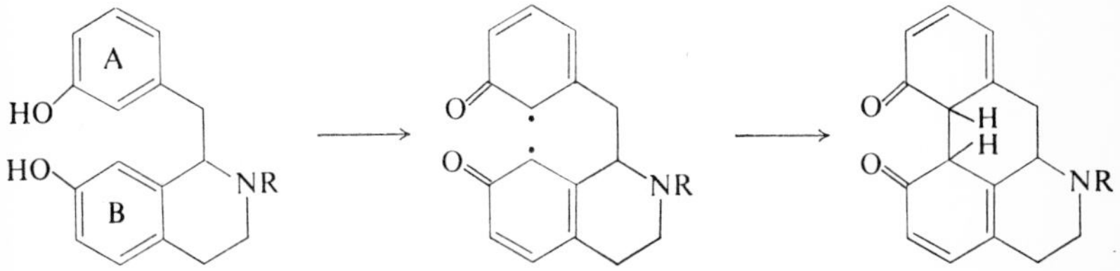

(1)   (2)   (3)

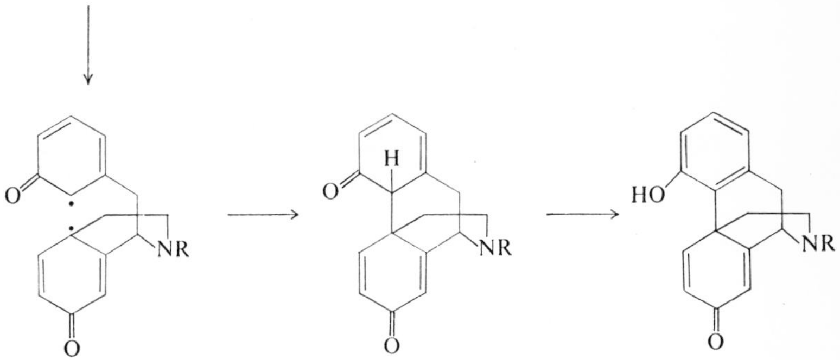

(4)   (5)   (6)

germane to the discussion have been omitted. If the isoquinoline
(1) is oxidised to *ortho* radicals in both aromatic nuclei A and B a

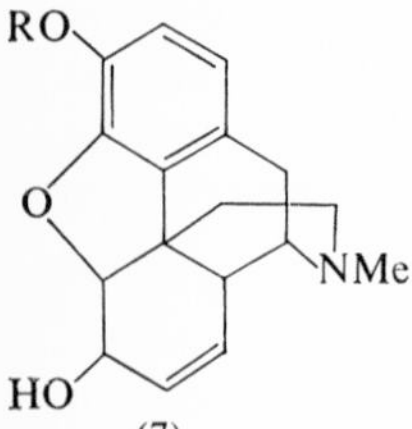

(7)

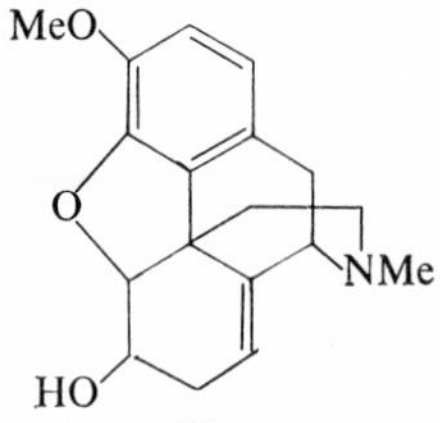

(8)

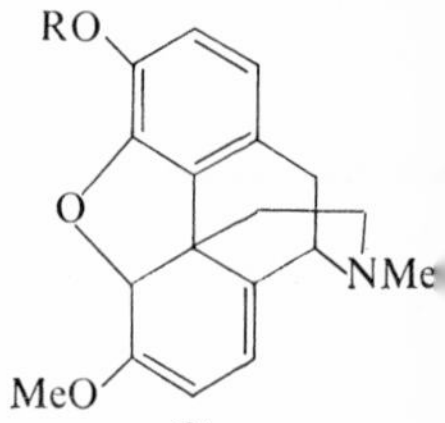

(9)

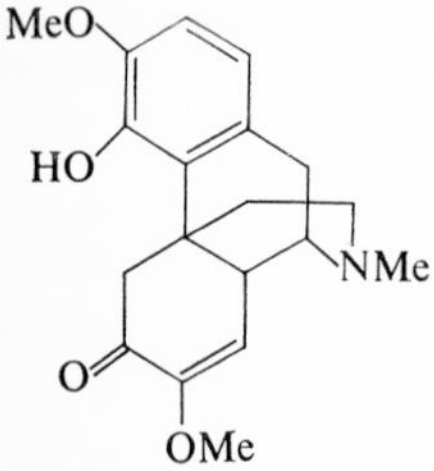

(10)

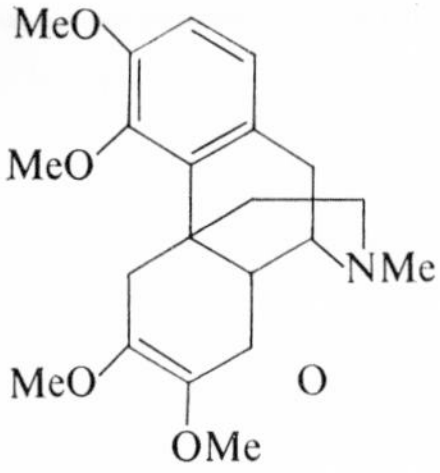

(11)

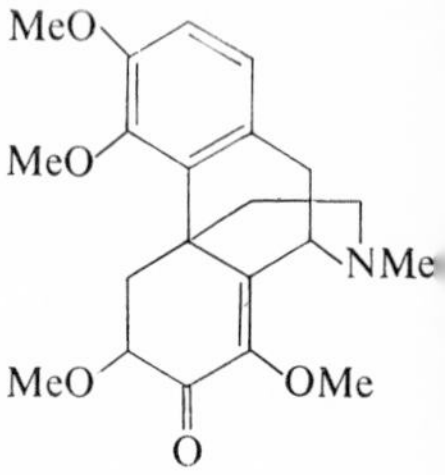

(12)

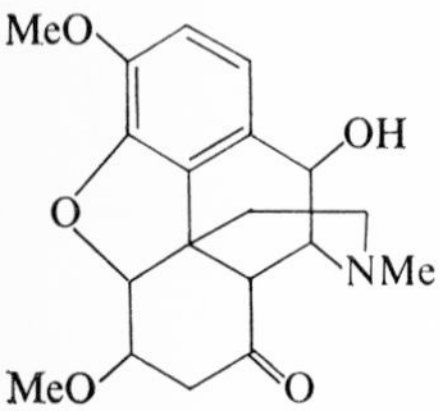

(13)

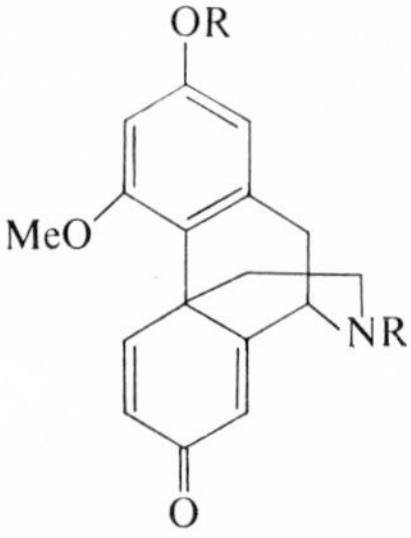

(14)

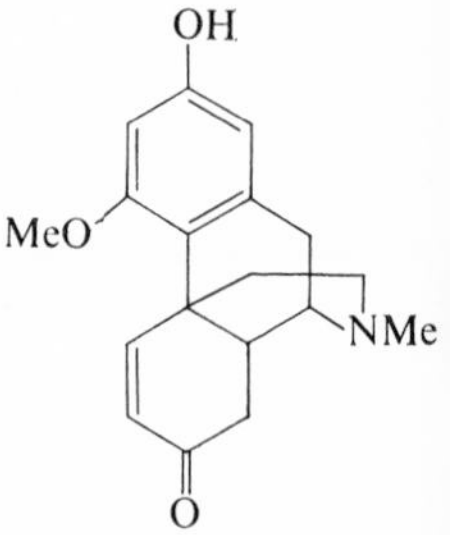

(15)

diradical (2) is formed, and internal radical pairing of this can give
rise to the base (3) in which simple enolisation can result in the
aromatisation of both nuclei with the production of an aporphine.

Oxidation of the base (1) to the diradical (4) followed by internal radical pairing would lead to the bridged structure (5) in which aromatising enolisation is only possible in one nucleus to give the phenol (6), aromatisation of the second ring being prevented by the presence of the angular substituent at position 13 of the reduced phenanthrene system. The formation of *para* radicals from both nuclei of the base (1) followed by coupling and aromatisation would obviously lead to an isomer of the phenol (6) with the hydroxyl group at position 2.

Other changes supervene after the coupling step leading to the phenol (6), and the following bases of the morphine group have been discovered in Nature: morphine (7, R = H), codeine (7, R = Me), neopine (8), thebaine (9, R = Me), oripavine (9, R = H), sinomenine (10), hasubanonine (11) or (12), metaphenine (13), crotonosine (14, R = H), dimethylcrotonosine (14, R = Me) and linearisine (15). As will be seen from the formulae the last three bases are the nearest approaches to the simple oxidative coupling products so far isolated (crotonosine is in fact the simple coupled phenol), though they have a different substitution pattern from the other alkaloids of this group. The bases can be subdivided into two groups namely those with and those without a 4,5-oxygen bridge, and it will be further noted that the alkaloids without such a bridge all have oxygen substituents at position 7, whereas such a substituent is lacking in those bases having the 4,5-oxygen bridge; this coincidence is almost certainly not fortuitous and is doubtless bound up with the subsequent fate of phenols of the type (6) in the plant, which is discussed in Chapter 14.

Morphine, codeine and thebaine

From the chemical standpoint most interest centres on this triad of alkaloids available from opium, since the structures of the less spectacularly reactive bases discovered later were deduced largely by analogy with or reference to work on these three.

The compositions $C_{17}H_{19}O_3N$, $C_{18}H_{21}O_3N$ and $C_{19}H_{21}O_3N$ for morphine, codeine and thebaine had been established by 1852 and the functional groups in the bases were relatively easily established. All three bases contain an *N*-methyl group, thebaine contains two methoxyl groups, codeine one methoxyl and one hydroxyl and morphine two hydroxyl groups; morphine is a phenol and is readily methylated to the non-phenolic codeine, though the reverse demethylation is only accomplished with difficulty. The hydroxyl group in codeine is part of a secondary alcoholic system since the base may be oxidised to a ketone, codeinone, and as this ketone is also obtainable (in very poor yield) by the hydrolysis of thebaine with cold sulphuric acid, thebaine must be the methyl ether of an enolic form of codeinone. The essential relationships of the three bases were thus made clear at an early date and evidence obtained from the degradation of each of them became usable in the structural analysis. The nature of the third oxygen function in the alkaloids was not immediately apparent, but its inactivity led to the belief that it formed part of a cyclic ether system. Both morphine and codeine contain a reducible double bond and, although the reduction of thebaine is complicated, a tetrahydrothebaine can be obtained identical with dihydrocodeine methyl ether.

Exhaustive methylation of codeine proceeds readily with the formation of a base, α-codeimethine, in the first step, indicating that in the alkaloid the nitrogen atom is part of a ring, but the second step is anomalous in that not only the NMe_2 group of the methine but two carbon atoms as well are lost, the product being methylmorphenol $C_{15}H_{10}O_2$, a derivative of phenanthrene. A somewhat similar reaction occurs when α-codeimethine or the methiodides of morphine, codeine or thebaine are heated with acetic anhydride and sodium acetate. This process, generally called acetolysis, results in the formation of β-dimethylaminoethyl acetate together with derivatives of phenanthrene. These results suggest that in the alkaloids the system —CH_2CH_2NMe— is in some way linked to a partially reduced phenanthrene system bearing the oxygen substituents cited above. At this stage there was very little further evidence on which to base any structural hypotheses, but the ready elimination of derivatives of β-dimethylaminoethanol or its equivalent during the degradation of the alkaloids led to the belief that they contain a 1,4-oxazine system. Some support was given to this theory by the discovery that the base (16) can be degraded to naphthalene and β-dimethylamino-ethanol, though the extreme ease of this reaction compared with the more vigorous conditions necessary for the degradation of codeine resulted in the proposal of the structure (17) for this alkaloid in place of the earlier suggestion (18).

(16)   (17)   (18)

The positions of the oxygen functions in all three bases were revealed by the identification of two of the degradation products of codeine and thebaine.

Acetylmethylmorphol and acetylthebaol, the products of aceto-lysis of α-codeimethine and thebaine methiodide respectively, were found to be derivatives of phenanthrene and to give 9,10-phen-anthraquinones on oxidation. No oxygen substituents are lost during the oxidation, however, showing that the acetoxyl and methoxy groups in these two compounds cannot be at positions 9 or 10. Hydrolysis of the two compounds followed by methylation yielded dimethylmorphol and methylthebaol, which were found to be identical with 3,4-dimethoxyphenanthrene (23, R = H) and 3,4,6-trimethoxyphenanthrene (23, R = OMe) respectively, authen-tic specimens of which were prepared by the Pschorr phenanthrene synthesis, developed during the course of this work. Nitroveratric aldehyde (19) was condensed with the appropriate phenylacetic acid (20) to give the stilbene carboxylic acid (21), which on reduc-tion to the amine, followed by diazotisation and cyclisation with copper powder yielded the phenanthrene-9-carboxylic acid (22), and decarboxylation of this furnished the desired phenanthrene (23).

The retention of an oxygen function at position 6 during the degradation of thebaine results from the higher state of oxidation of thebaine (and codeinone of which it is a derivative) compared to codeine, which must lose the hydroxyl group at this position as water as a necessary part of aromatisation.

Morphine, codeine and thebaine were thus shown to be derivatives of a reduced 3,4,6-trioxyphenanthrene, and, since the alcoholic oxygen atom in codeine is presumably at position 6 since it is removed during acetolysis, the oxygen at position 3 or 4 must be involved in the inert ether system of the alkaloids. The aromatic end-product of exhaustive methylation of codeine, however, is not methylmorphol but methylmorphenol, which is non-phenolic and contains two atoms of hydrogen less than methylmorphol. It is clearly a phenanthrene derivative and may be demethylated to the monophenolic morphenol, and the inactivity of the second oxygen atom of this material suggested that it was still present in the ether linkage of the original base. Methylmorphenol was eventually shown to be 3-methoxy-4,5-phenanthrylene oxide (24) by potash fusion to 3,4,5-trihydroxyphenanthrene (25), the trimethyl ether of which was synthesised by the invaluable Pschorr method. This

(24) (25) (26)

synthesis, as will be readily appreciated, also furnished 3,4,7-tri-methoxyphenanthrene and, although a 3,7 or 4,7-ether bridge in methylmorphenol is impossible on steric grounds, the synthesis was repeated via the bromo-acid (26) to provide unambiguous proof of the structure of the phenol (25). Codeine and morphine could thus be assigned the part structure (27, R = Me) and (27, R = H), and the oxazine hypothesis had to be abandoned since the nature of all the oxygen substituents was then clear.

The position of the nitrogen atom

The first indication of the position of the nitrogen atom was obtained by a study of the properties of hydroxycodeine, prepared together with codeinone by the chromic acid oxidation of codeine. This base, as its name implies, contains an additional hydroxyl group, but the methine base obtained by Hofmann degradation contains the new oxygen atom in a keto group, indicating that in the original base the new hydroxyl group and the nitrogen atom must be linked to the same or to adjacent carbon atoms for only in this way can the origin of the carbonyl group be explained, as in formulae (28)–(30). Acetolysis of the methine base gives a di-acetoxymethoxyphenanthrene containing an acetoxy group at the

position occupied by the hydroxyl group in the parent hydroxy-codeine, and oxidation of this to a 9,10-quinone proceeds with the loss of an acetoxy group and the production of acetylmethyl-morphol-9,10-quinone (32). These reactions indicate that the extra acetoxyl group, and therefore the new hydroxyl group of hydroxycodeine, must be at position 9 or 10, and the nitrogen atom in hydroxycodeine and hence in codeine must be located at position 9, 10 or 14. Only recently has the precise position of the new hydroxyl group in hydroxycodeine been shown to be C-10 as in formula (28), showing that the acetolysis product must have structure (31), but this only restricts the position of the nitrogen atom to C-9 or C-10.

Some indication that the nitrogen atom in morphine is linked to C-9 was provided by the researches culminating in the elucidation of the structures of apomorphine and morphothebaine. These bases, obtained by the rearrangement of morphine and thebaine in hot concentrated hydrochloric acid, have the structures (33) and (34), respectively, the proof of which is given in detail in Chapter 6. Consideration of structures for the morphine alkaloids based on a reduced aporphine skeleton was the natural outcome of this work, but Pschorr's original structure (35) for codeine, which would make hydroxycodeine methine (29) a derivative of α or β-naphthol instead of a ketone, was soon modified to give a 5,13 placing of the double bond, even though this represented codeine as an enol ether, though it showed none of the properties of such a compound.

All structures involving attachment of the nitrogen-containing ring at position 8 had to be discarded, however, when the properties of the isomers of codeine and morphine were worked out. Treatment of codeine with phosphorus trichloride or thionyl chloride yields α-chlorocodide by replacement of the alcoholic hydroxyl group by a chlorine atom, and the hydrolysis of this base affords not codeine but a mixture of three isomers of the alkaloid, isocodeine, ψ-codeine and allo-ψ-codeine. The four isomers may be arranged in pairs, codeine and isocodeine being diastereoisomers at the C-6 alcoholic group since they give the same codeinone on oxidation, and ψ-codeine and allo-ψ-codeine being an epimeric pair of structurally isomeric alcohols (36) giving ψ-codeinone on oxidation. Acetolysis of ψ-codeinone methiodide yields 4,8-diacetoxy-3-methoxyphenanthrene (38), identified by hydrolysis and methylation to 3,4,8-trimethoxyphenanthrene identical with material prepared by synthesis, whereas codeinone methiodide under the same conditions yields 4,6-diacetoxy-3-methoxyphenanthrene. ψ-Codeinone must therefore contain a carbonyl group at position 8

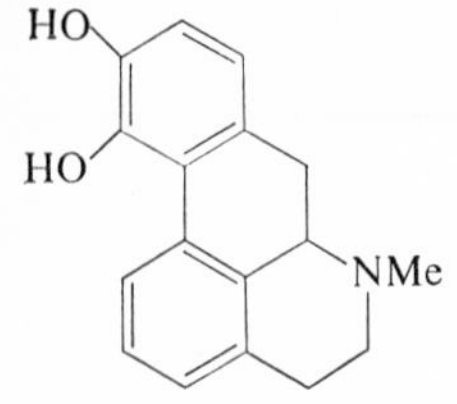

(33)

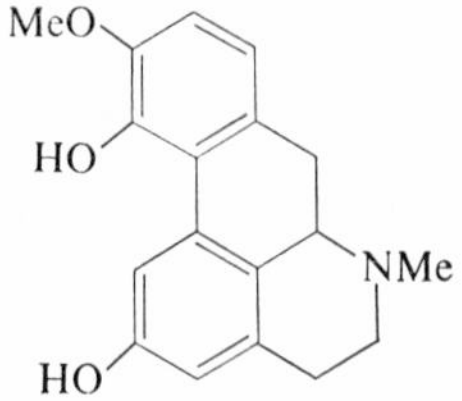

(34)

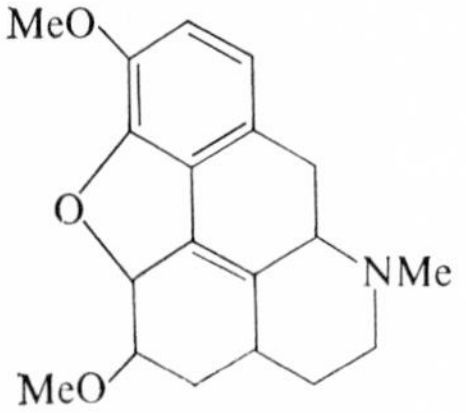

(35)

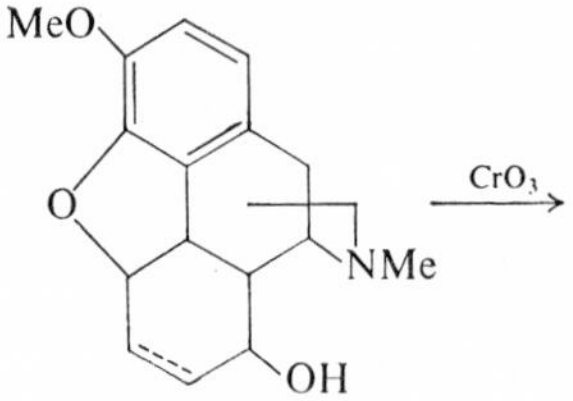

(36)

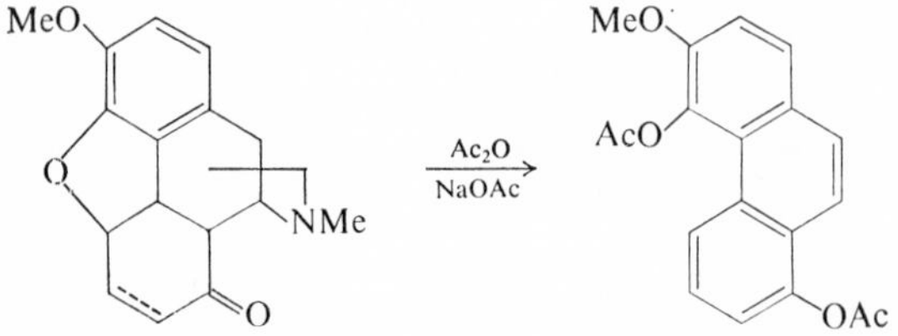

(37)

(38)

(37) and attachment of any other substituent at this position is impossible.

Attachment of the nitrogen-containing ring at position 7 was never seriously considered as for many years ψ-codeinone was believed to contain a reactive methylene group at this point. (Although ψ-codeinone does not contain a methylene group at position 7, the enol form will condense with benzaldehyde at this position, so the reasons for eliminating this as the point of attachment of the nitrogen ring are still valid.) Since the reaction of thebaine with hot dilute hydrochloric acid leads with great rapidity to the secondary base thebenine (39) in which the side-chain was soon proved to be at C-5 (see page 117) the attachment of the carbon end of the nitrogen-containing chain in thebaine at the same point was considered probable by Knorr, who proposed the structure (40) for morphine. This view was maintained for a considerable time during which only minor modifications were made to the formula.

The initial Hofmann degradation product of codeine, α-codeimethine, on heating alone or with bases is converted into the isomeric β-codeimethine, and since both bases yield the same tetrahydro-compound on hydrogenation they can only differ in the position of the double bonds. On the basis of the structure (40) for morphine α-codeimethine must have the structure (41) and the only logical structure for the presumably more stable β-isomer is (42). β-Codeimethine is clearly not a naphthalene derivative, however, and this difficulty led to the modification of structure (40) to (43) for morphine, in which case α-codeimethine becomes (44) and the β-isomer (41). However, it is difficult to reconcile these structures with the failure of β-codeimethine to undergo further isomerisation to the undoubtedly more stable naphthalene structure (42).

A re-examination of all of the degradative data by Robinson in 1923 eventually led to the solution of the structural problem. Realising that the unique and characteristic property of the alkaloids of this group, namely their tendency to lose the whole of the nitrogen-containing side-chain with the formation of fully aromatic phenanthrene derivatives, must result from some peculiarity of the molecule, which any satisfactory formula must be able to explain, he placed the side-chain at an angular position

4

so that its extrusion is an essential part of aromatisation. Of the available positions 13 and 14 the former was selected so as to maintain some structural relationship between the alkaloids of this

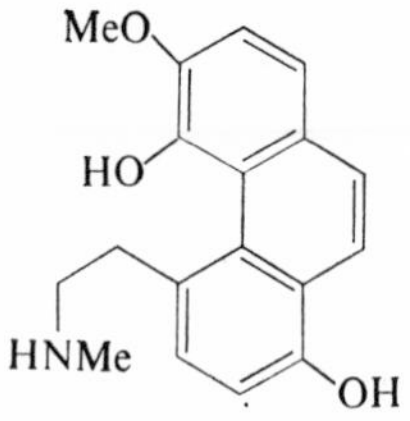

(39)

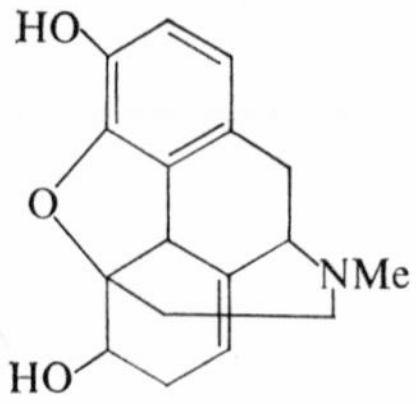

(40)

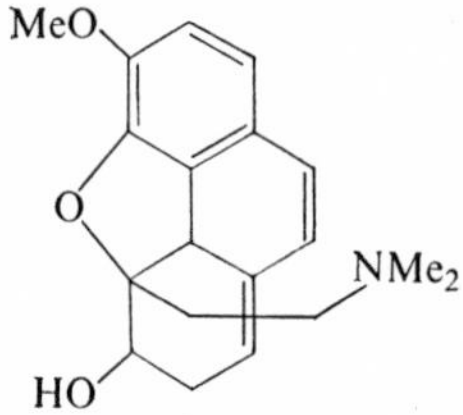

(41)

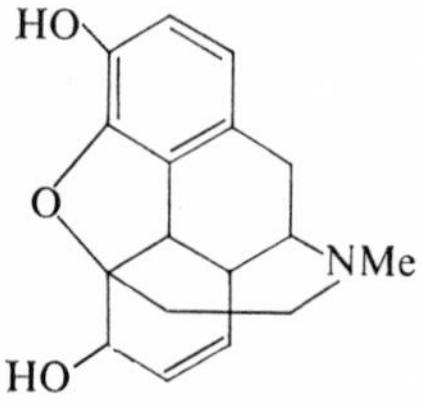

(43)

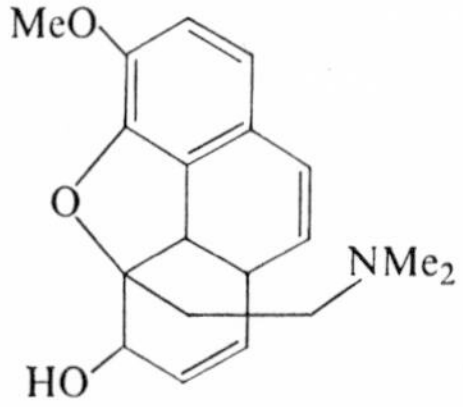

(44)

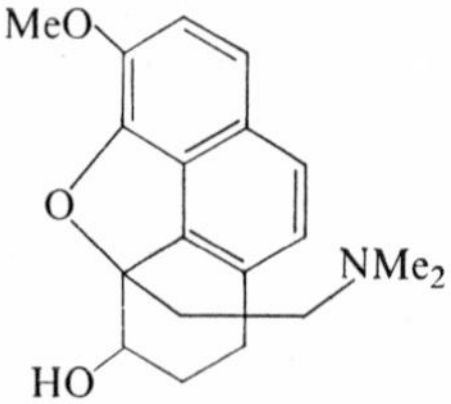

(42)

group and the benzylisoquinolines. The initial proposal on this basis of structure (45a) for morphine was quickly modified to (45, R = H) to account for the undoubted presence of a reducible double bond in the alkaloid. Formulae for codeine (45, R = Me) and thebaine (46) follow logically. On this basis α-codeimethine becomes the styrene (47) and β-codeimethine the conjugated diene

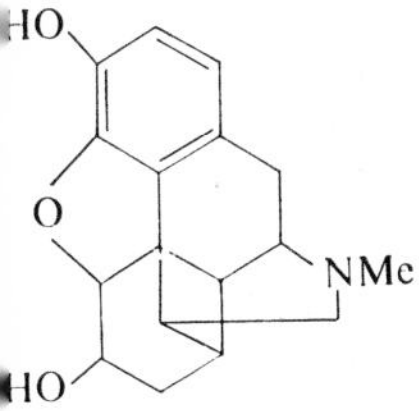

(45*a*) 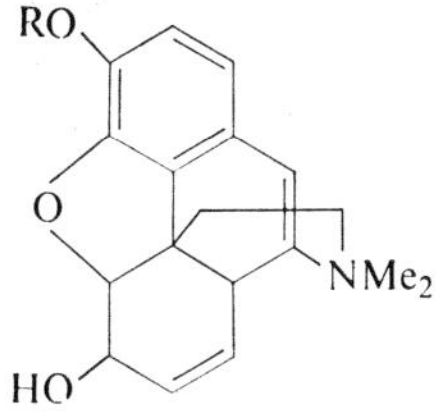   (45) 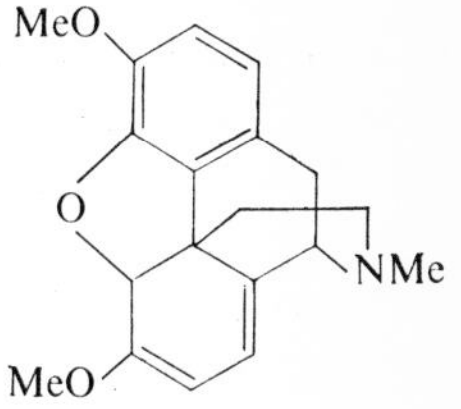   (46)

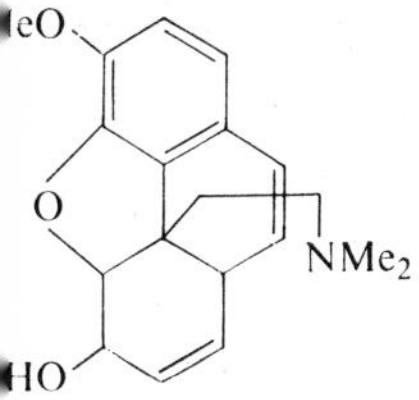

(47) 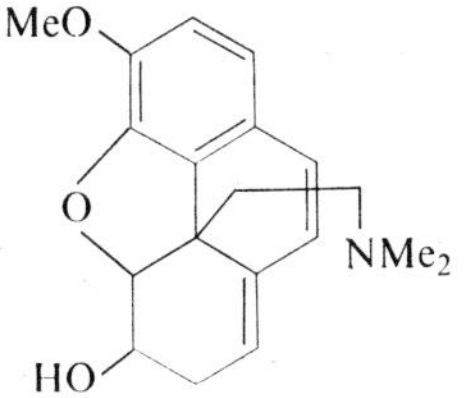   (48) 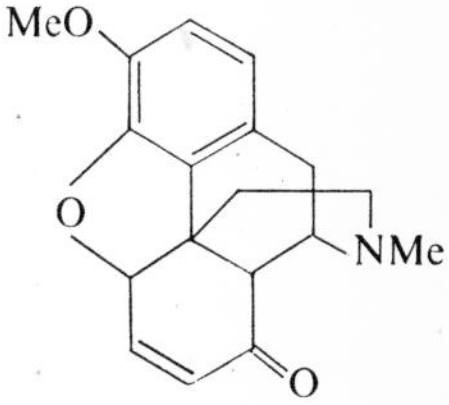   (49)

−H⁺

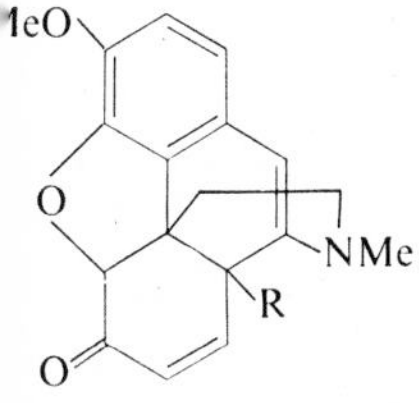

(51) 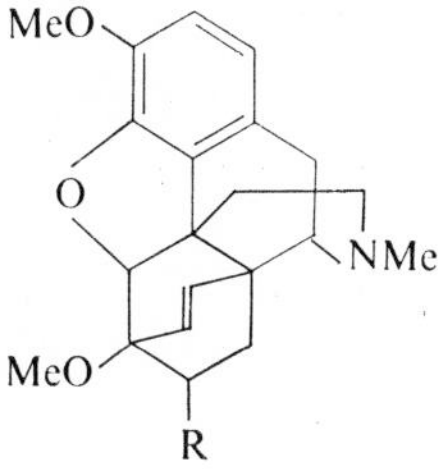   (52) 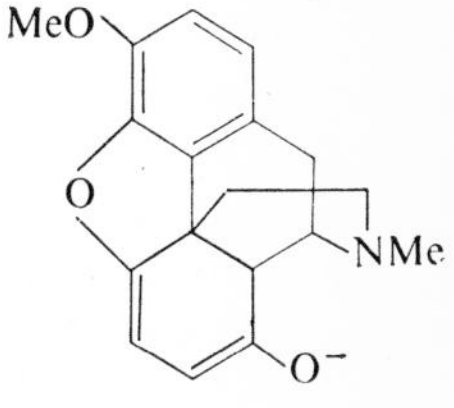   (50)

(48), and the non-conversion of the latter into a naphthalene derivative is a consequence of the presence of the angular substituent. It may be noted that attachment of the side-chain to C-14 would preclude isomerisation of α-codeimethine to the more stable conjugated diene.

The assumed presence of a reactive methylene group in ψ-codeinone, which must be assigned the structure (49), must be due to reaction of the ketone in the enol form (50) in bases, which would be expected to lead to C-7 substituted derivatives. The formulation of thebaine as the conjugated diene (46) rather than as the isomeric 5,7-diene, which is also an enol ether of codeinone, was made on the basis of the conversion of the base into 14-bromo-codeinone (51, R = Br) and 14-hydroxycodeinone (51, R = OH) on treatment with bromine and hydrogen peroxide respectively, reactions that were assumed to involve 1,4-additions of bromine or hydrogen peroxide to the conjugated system. The bromine and hydroxyl groups in the substituted codeinones were placed at C-14 since aromatisation, which now requires the extrusion of *two* angular substituents, can no longer be achieved in the exhaustive methylation or acetolysis of these bases. The structure assigned to thebaine was later confirmed by the Diels–Alder addition of di-enophils to the alkaloid to give bases such as the adducts (52, R = CHO, COMe, COOEt, CN), which are clearly not enol ethers as would be required by the alternative 5,7-diene structure for the alkaloid.

The transformation of codeine (53) into the other isomers of the alkaloid, particularly ψ-codeine (55) through α-chlorocodide (54) may be likened to the conversion of geraniol (56) into linaloöl (58) through geranyl chloride (57), which is a particular case of the general allylic rearrangement familiar in the aliphatic and alicyclic series. The stereochemistry of the process is discussed on page 112.

Until the synthesis of a derivative of codeine by Gates and his co-workers there was no clear chemical proof of the attachment of the nitrogen-containing side-chain at C-13 in the morphine alkaloids. Schöpf carried out a sequence of reactions on dihydro-codeinone designed to distinguish between a C-13 and a C-5 attachment of the chain, but the results were not as clear cut as had been hoped. The Beckmann transformation of ketoximes in general affords amides by a well understood process, but carbon–carbon fission with nitrile formation is sometimes observed in

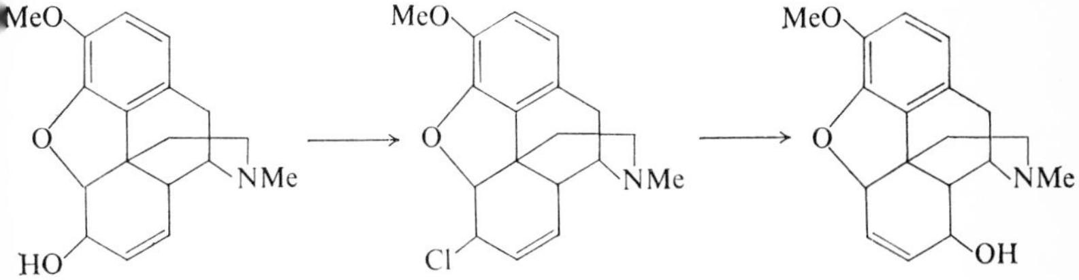

(53)   (54)   (55)

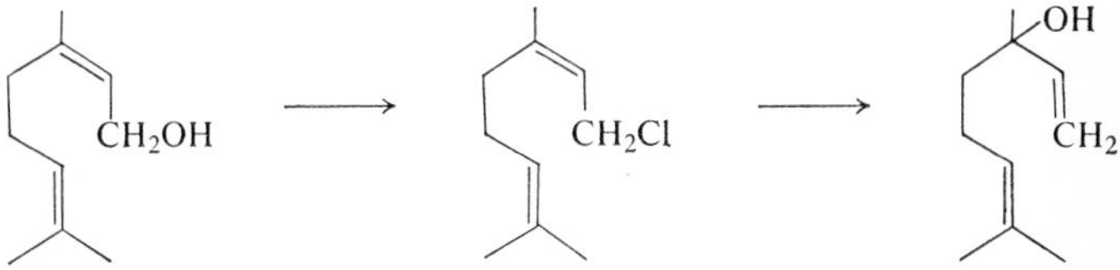

(56)   (57)   (58)

oximes in which the α-carbon atom bears an oxygen substituent, e.g. benzoin oxime in this way affords benzonitrile and benzaldehyde thus:

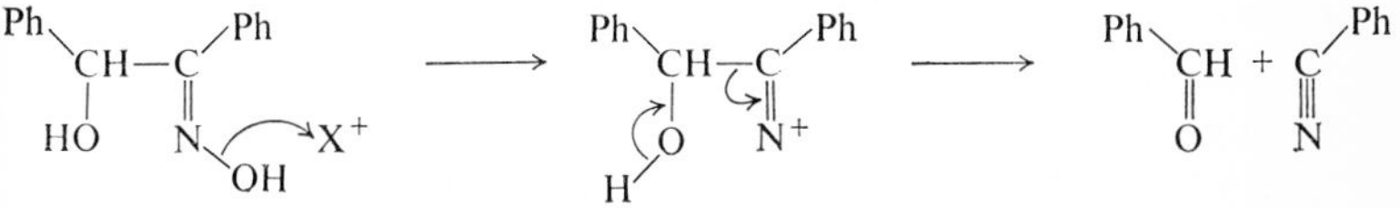

Occurrence of the same process with dihydrocodeinone oxime would be expected to lead to the nitrile-aldehyde (62) on the basis of a C-13 placing of the side-chain (59), but to the ketone (64) if a C-5 placing of the chain (63) is correct. Neither the initial reaction product nor its methyl ether could be identified positively as an aldehyde or a ketone, and a distinction was sought between the two possibilities by further degradation of the methyl ether oxime.

Dehydration of the oxime related to the aldehyde (62) would be expected to give the dinitrile (65) in which the nitrogen-containing ring remains intact, but the oxime related to the ketone (64) under

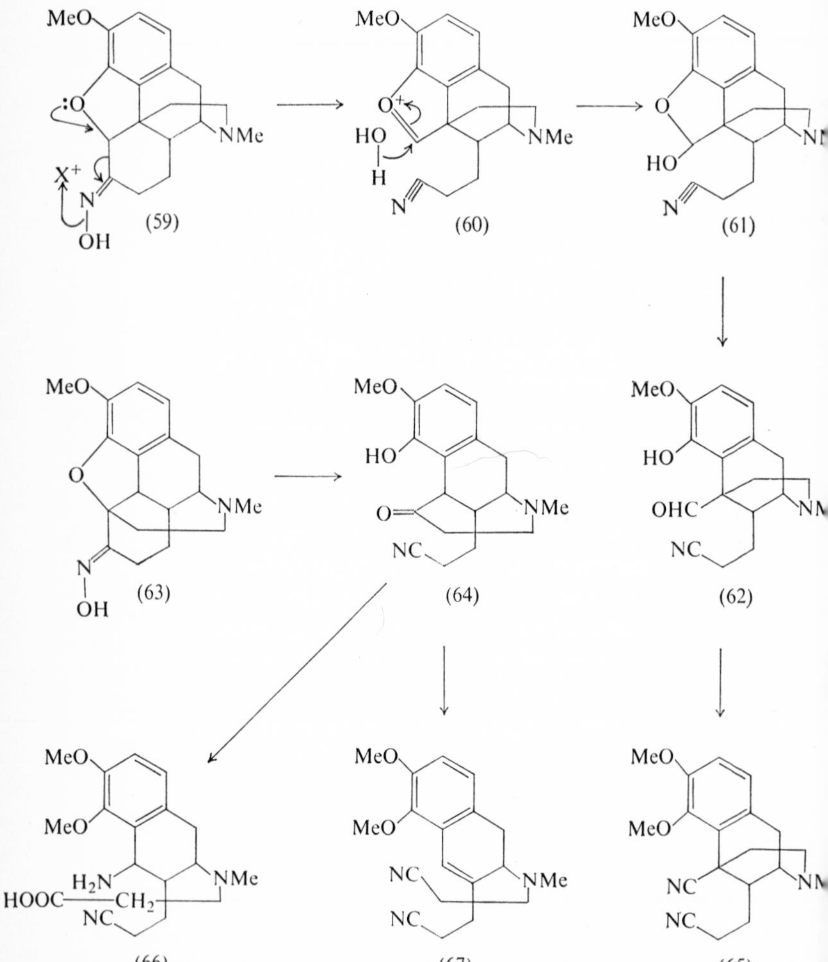

(59)   (60)   (61)

(63)   (64)   (62)

(66)   (67)   (65)

similar conditions would suffer fission of the nitrogen-containing ring to give the amino-acid (66), its lactam, or the nitrile (67), or structures isomeric with these. The actual product of this further transformation was a base that retained all three nitrogen atoms on Hofmann degradation, indicating that the primary Beckmann transformation product from dihydrocodeinone oxime must have been the aldehyde (62), since all bases derived from the ketone (64) would have lost the side-chain completely on Hofmann degradation. These results therefore supported Robinson's formula (45, R = H) for morphine.

(68)   (69)   (70)

Before it was confirmed by synthesis the validity of the Robinson formulae for morphine, codeine and thebaine rested on their ability to account satisfactorily for all of the complex rearrangements of these bases discussed below. It may be noted that the failure of the ketone thebenone (68), a degradation product of thebaine, to undergo condensation with more than one mole of benzaldehyde, which led Knorr to adhere to a C-5 placing of the side-chain, is of no value as evidence, since other cases are known in which only one of two reactive methylene groups adjacent to carbonyl is capable of reacting with aldehydes; in any case a bisisonitroso-derivative of thebenone has been produced recently.

Neopine and oripavine

Neopine, which is a very minor constituent of opium, is isomeric with codeine and gives dihydrocodeine on hydrogenation. It therefore differs from codeine only in the position of the double bond, and since it yields β-codeimethine (48) directly on Hofmann degradation it must have the structure (69). Oripavine, $C_{18}H_{19}O_3N$, isolated from *Papaver orientale* and *P. bracteatum*, is phenolic and gives thebaine on methylation with diazomethane, and must therefore be the phenol (70).

The synthesis of morphine, codeine and thebaine

The first synthesis of the carbon–nitrogen skeleton of the morphine alkaloids was achieved by Grewe and his co-workers, whose method was based on the structural relationship between the alkaloids of this group and the benzylisoquinolines, and on the Bogert–Cook synthesis of hydrogenated phenanthrenes. The essential stage in the Bogert–Cook synthesis is the cyclisation under strongly acid conditions of an olefine such as (71), and for the application of this process to the synthesis of the base (72), containing the carbon–nitrogen skeleton of morphine, the octahydro-isoquinoline (73) was required. Such bases were not known at the commencement of the work and accordingly suitable syntheses had to be devised. Tetrahydroisoquinoline (78) was prepared from carbethoxycyclohexanone (74) by the self-explanatory route shown, and the methiodide of this base was treated with benzylmagnesium bromide when the normal reaction of Grignard reagents with quaternary salts of pyridines occurred, the product being the tertiary base (73*a*), reduction of the exposed double bond of which then gave the desired octahydroisoquinoline (73). This olefine on heating with phosphoric acid was cyclised to a mixture of *N*-methyl-morphinan (72) (mainly) and its C-14 epimer, *N*-methyliso-morphinan. The correct structural assignment was made to these two bases on the assumption of a *trans* addition of the aromatic nucleus to the double bond, but was only later confirmed by comparison with material prepared by Gates and by Ginsburg in their syntheses of the alkaloid.

However, such a synthesis of the requisite octahydroisoquinoline was not applicable to the preparation of the intermediate required for any synthesis of a derivative of codeine or morphine, since Grignard reagents cannot be prepared from veratryl halides, and a new process, set out in formulae (79)–(83), was devised. When the end-product of this reaction sequence was cyclised with concentrated hydrochloric acid at 150° partial demethylation occurred at

(71) (72) (73)

position 4, the product being (±)-tetrahydrodeoxycodeine (84), identical with a 1:1 mixture of the (−) and (+) forms of this base derived respectively from codeine and sinomenine.

 This synthesis, though ingenious, is ill-suited to the task of constructing the somewhat more complex structure of morphine itself, and this end was achieved by a totally different classical synthesis that owes nothing to theories of the biogenesis of morphine.

Gates and his co-workers set out to synthesise the alkaloid by constructing the bridged ring system from a suitable 13-substituted phenanthrene. Dihydrothebainone was a suitable goal for the synthesis since the conversion of this phenol into dihydrocodeinone with closure of the 4,5-oxide bridge had already been accomplished,

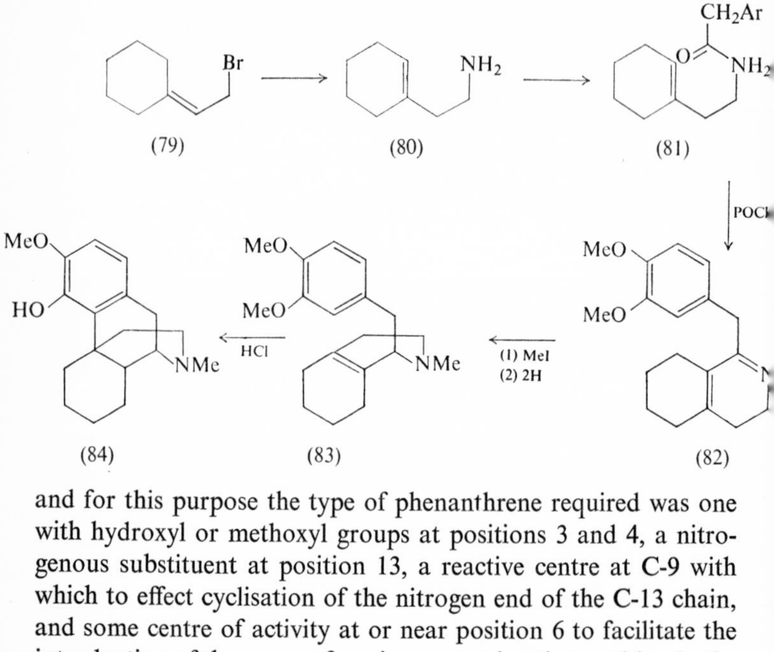

(79) (80) (81)

(84) (83) (82)

and for this purpose the type of phenanthrene required was one with hydroxyl or methoxyl groups at positions 3 and 4, a nitrogenous substituent at position 13, a reactive centre at C-9 with which to effect cyclisation of the nitrogen end of the C-13 chain, and some centre of activity at or near position 6 to facilitate the introduction of the oxygen function occupying that position in the alkaloids. These objectives were achieved by the Diels–Alder addition of butadiene to 4-cyanomethyl-5,6-dimethoxy-1,2-naphthoquinone (94), which was prepared by an ingenious sequence of reactions from 2,6-dihydroxynaphthalene (85) as shown in outline in the formulae (85)–(94), the reaction affording the phenanthrene (95).

It sometimes happens that in spite of the most careful construction of a reactive molecule the desired reactions cannot be effected, but in this case unexpected dividends were reaped from the careful planning, for the desired cyclisation of the nitrogen-containing ring was achieved with exceptional ease during reduction of the nitrile over copper chromite, the product of the reaction being a mixture of the lactam (96) and further reduction products. The lactam (96), when subjected successively to Wolff–Kishner reduction, lithium aluminium hydride reduction and *N*-methylation of the resulting secondary amine, was converted into the tertiary base (97). Earlier work with model compounds lacking the two methoxy groups had led to a base identical with Grewe's *N*-methylisomorphinan in which the stereochemistry at the asymmetric centre C-14 is the reverse of that actually found in the morphine series. Derivatives of codeine in which the isomorphinan stereochemistry holds at C-14 are, however, known, and it was with one of these that correlation was first made.

The base (97) was resolved and the (+)-isomer shown to be identical with *β*-dihydrodeoxycodeine-B, prepared by obvious steps from *β*-dihydrothebainone (98), the C-14-epimer- of dihydrothebainone. (Dihydrothebainone may be obtained directly from the reduction of thebaine, see page 114, and the *β*-isomer is obtained by the reduction of *β*-thebainone, which is the hydrolysis product of dihydrothebaine-*φ* (155), page 115.) *β*-Dihydrothebainone itself was then prepared from the base (97) by hydration of the double bond with sulphuric acid, which gave a mixture of the 6 and 7-hydroxydihydro-compounds and the first of these was then partially demethylated (at C-4) by heating with potassium hydroxide in diethylene glycol and the product submitted to Oppenauer oxidation. The problem was then reduced to the inversion of the asymmetric centre at C-14 in order to obtain entry into the normal morphine series, and this was achieved as follows.

Bromination of *β*-dihydrothebainone (98) afforded a dibromo-compound (100) which on treatment with 2,4-dinitrophenyl-hydrazine underwent hydrazone formation with dehydrobromina-tion; the product of the reaction was not, however, the hydrazone

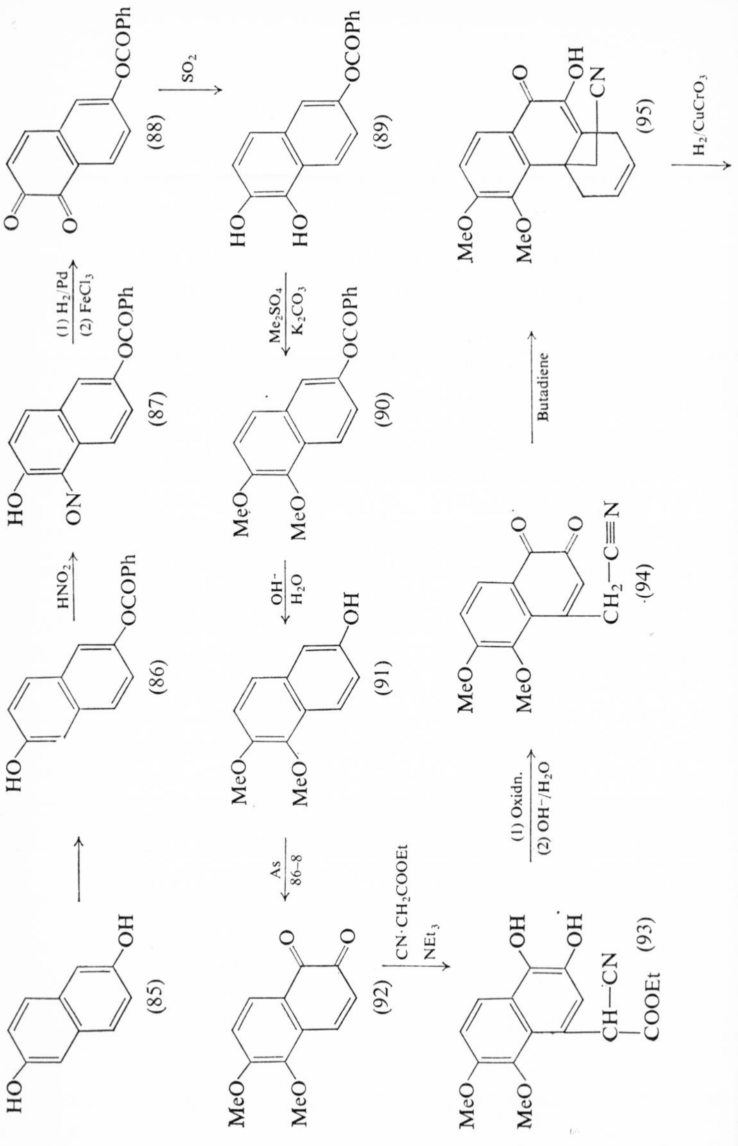
(85)
(86)
HNO_2
(87)
(1) H_2/Pd (2) $FeCl_3$
(88)
SO_2
(89)
Me_2SO_4 K_2CO_3
(90)
OH^- H_2O
(91)
As 86–8
(92)
$CN\cdot CH_2COOEt$ NEt_3
(93)
(1) Oxidn. (2) OH^-/H_2O
(94)
Butadiene
(95)
$H_2/CuCrO_3$

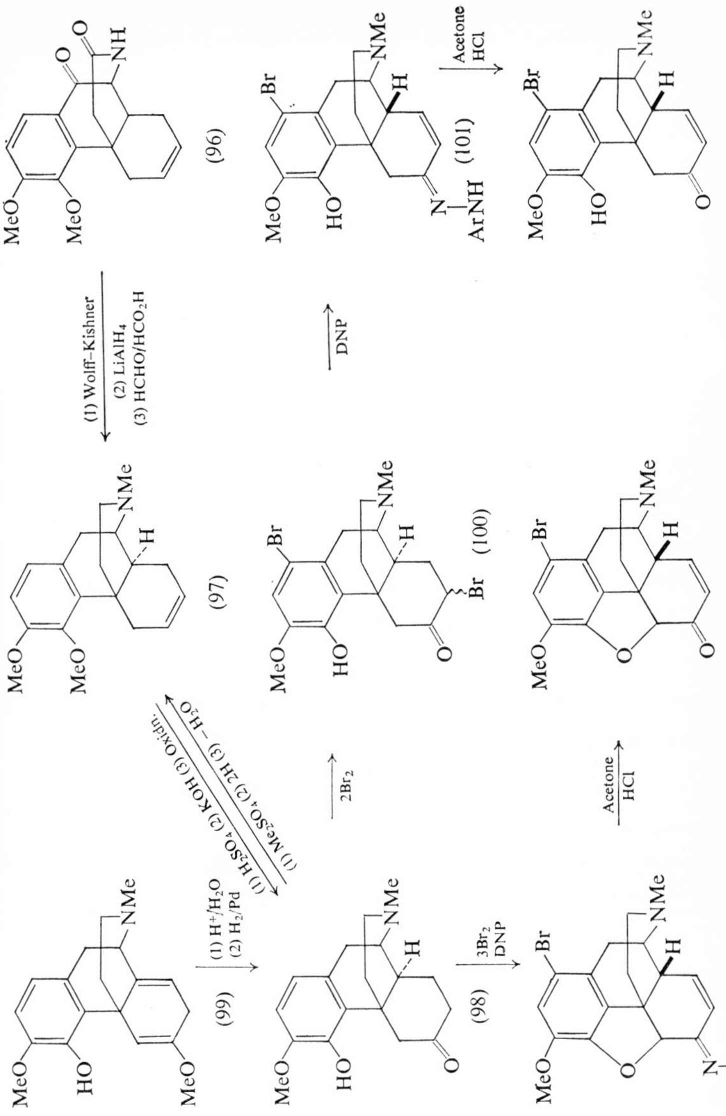
(96)
(1) Wolff–Kishner
(2) LiAlH₄
(3) HCHO/HCO₂H
(97)
(1) Me₂SO₄ (2) H₂ (3) – H₂O
(1) H₂SO₄ (2) KOH (3) Oxidn.
(99)
(1) H⁺/H₂O
(2) H₂/Pd
(98)
2Br₂
(100)
DNP
(101)
Acetone
HCl
(102)
3Br₂
DNP
(103)
Acetone
HCl
(104)
MeO
HO
NMe
NH
Br
ArNH

of 1-bromo-β-thebainone but of 1-bromothebainone, inversion at C-14 having occurred during the process. The very rapid inversion at this centre, which results from the lability of the γ-hydrogen atom in the αβ-unsaturated ketone derivative, was verified with the dinitrophenylhydrazone of β-thebainone itself. Fission of the dinitrophenylhydrazone (101) with acetone and hydrochloric acid gave 1-bromothebainone (102). As Schöpf had earlier shown that closure of the 4,5-oxygen bridge in dihydrothebainone can be achieved through the bromo-compound, β-dihydrothebainone (98) was then treated with three moles of bromine and then with dinitrophenylhydrazine as before. The product of these reactions was the hydrazone of the 4,5-bridged analogue of 1-bromo-thebainone, namely 1-bromcodeinone (103). Fission of the hydrazone with acetone and acid yielded 1-bromocodeinone itself (104), though the yield was poor owing to the ease with which derivatives of codeinone undergo rearrangement in acid. 1-Bromo-codeinone was then reduced directly to codeine by lithium aluminium hydride, and demethylation of the codeine with pyridine hydrochloride yielded morphine, identical with the natural alkaloid. 1-Bromothebainone (102) can be reduced to dihydrothebainone which, like the β-isomer, can be converted into morphine.

A second synthesis of dihydrothebainone, and hence of morphine, has been accomplished by Ginsburg and his co-workers by the preparation of a suitably substituted 9-aminohydrophen-anthrene and closure of the nitrogen bridge with an activated C-13. For this purpose a suitable substituent at C-5 was required for the activation of C-13, and this same substituent also served to activate C-6 for the introduction of the necessary oxygen atom at that point. The intermediate required for this synthesis was the diketone (108), and this was prepared by the Michael addition of ethyl malonate to the substituted cyclohexenone (105), a process shown to give the *trans* adduct (106), which was converted via the acid (107) into the diketone (108). The carbonyl groups of this diketone differ in reactivity, one being isolated and the other adjacent to an aromatic

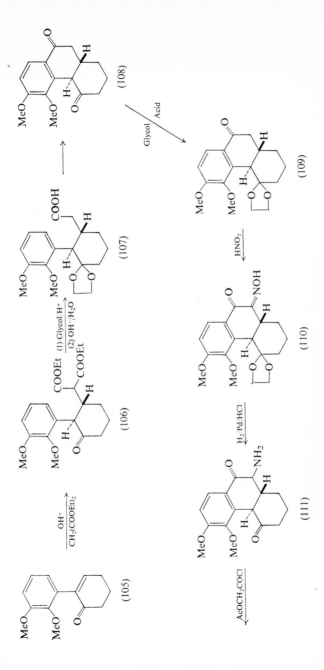

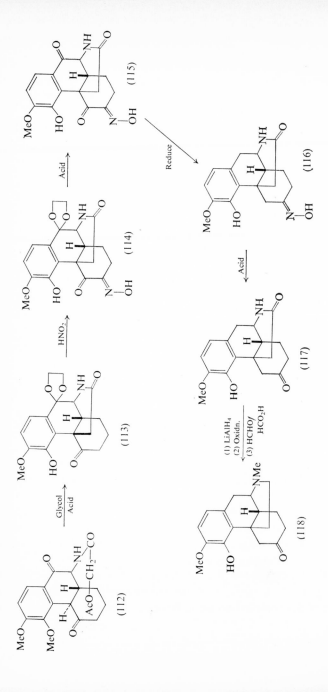

nucleus, and the most active one was protected and deactivated by selective ketalisation with ethylene glycol, leaving the aromatic carbonyl in the ketal (109) to activate C-9 for nitrosation. The isonitroso-compound (110) resulting from this reaction was reduced and hydrolysed to the keto-amine (111), the acetoxyacetyl amide of which (112) underwent an unusual cyclisation with the activated C-13 on heating with *p*-toluenesulphonic acid in ethylene

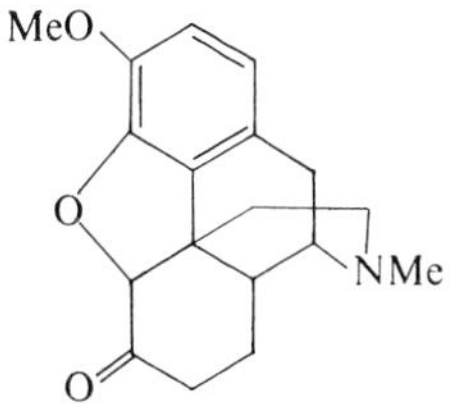

(119)

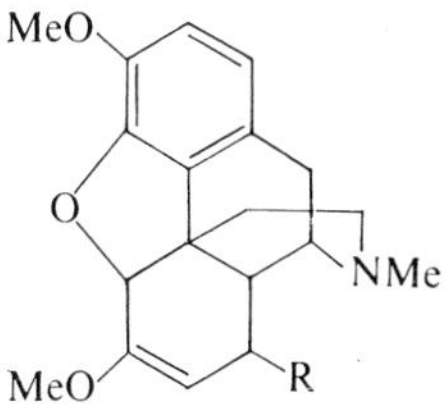

(120)

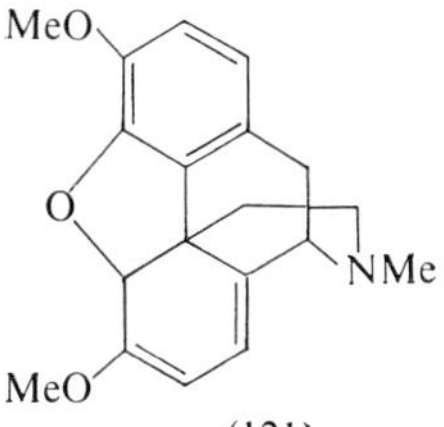

(121)

glycol, during which two other useful processes occurred, namely ketalisation of the carbonyl group at position 10 and demethylation of the C-4 methoxy group. The final product of these reactions was the lactam (113) in which the stereochemistry at C-14 is the correct one for the morphine series. It will be noted that cyclisation of the nitrogen-containing ring can only occur so as to give a *cis* arrangement of substituents at positions 9 and 13. The C-5 carbonyl group is not affected during this process, which results in ketalisa-tion of the carbonyl group at position 10, probably because it is deactivated by hydrogen bonding with the newly produced hydroxyl group at C-4. The free keto group at C-5 then activates position 6 and nitrosation at that point resulted in the oxime (114), which was hydrolysed to the diketo-oxime (115). Modified Wolff–Kishner reduction of this diketone in the absence of alkali so as to avoid hydrolysis of the oxime then gave the reduced oxime (116), which was hydrolysed to the keto-lactam (117) and this yielded dihydrothebainone on reduction with lithium aluminium hydride, Oppenauer oxidation and *N*-methylation.

The formal synthesis of thebaine was completed by the conversion of dihydrocodeinone (119) into the enol ether (120, R = H), which is dihydrothebaine, the bromination of this with *N*-bromosuccinimide to the allylic bromide (120, R = Br) and the dehydrobromination of this to thebaine (121).

The stereochemistry of the morphine alkaloids

Morphine contains five asymmetric carbon atoms, but since the 9–13 nitrogen–carbon bridge must of necessity be linked *cis* to the hydrogenated phenanthrene nucleus the possible stereoisomers are only 16 in number, divided into eight pairs of enantiomorphs. A number of attempts have been made to deduce the stereochemistry of the alkaloid on purely chemical grounds, but ambiguities are inherent in all of the arguments as will be shown here, though it must be admitted that the conclusions reached in this way have been confirmed by the unambiguous X-ray diffraction studies.

It has been argued that since dihydrocodeinone (119) is not epimerised by alkalis it must have the *cis* arrangement of hydrogen and side-chain at C-5 and C-13 as *cis* fused hydrindanones are more stable than the *trans* fused isomers, and the oxide ring and carbons 5, 6, 7, 8, 14 and 13 resemble the hydrindanone system. This argument is valueless, however, since the stereochemistry of the whole molecule should be considered in deciding the relative stabilities of different arrangements at any point, and the examination of structural models shows that either structure (122) or (123) is reasonably strain free, and that epimerisation at C-5 (or C-14) in each case would be impossible as this would lead to a highly strained structure. The failure of dihydrocodeinone to be epimerised in alkali thus only establishes the relative stereochemistry at C-5 and C-14. (See also page 111.)

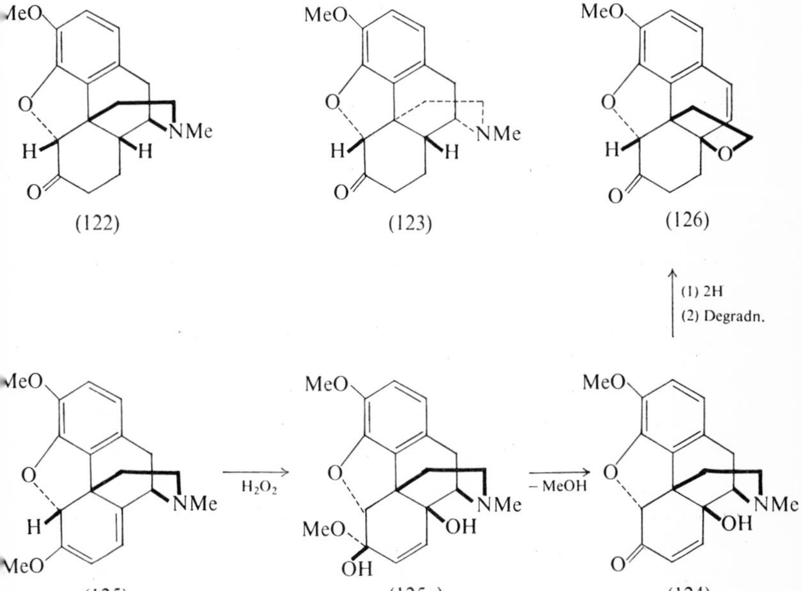

(122)   (123)   (126)

(1) 2H
(2) Degradn.

(125)   (125a)   (124)

14-Hydroxycodeinone (124), prepared from thebaine by the action of hydrogen peroxide, presumably by way of the intermediate (125a), on catalytic reduction and exhaustive methylation affords as nitrogen-free product a 13–14 cyclic ether in which the ether ring must of necessity be *cis* linked to the phenanthrene system and which must therefore have the structure (126) or its mirror image. (Throughout this discussion unless otherwise stated no distinction should be made between any structure given and its mirror image.) Assuming that no epimerisation at C-5 occurs during the alkaline degradation leading to the ether (126), structure (124) may be assigned to 14-hydroxycodeinone. This base is formed by the addition of hydrogen peroxide to thebaine, which yields dihydrocodeine methyl ether on catalytic hydrogenation, and on the reasonable assumption that these two processes yield products with the same stereochemistry at C-14, structure (125) for thebaine and structure (122) for dihydrocodeinone follow. However, although this assumption is reasonable it is not conclusive, since addition of hydrogen peroxide could occur on the opposite side to the addition of hydrogen and still give rise to a stable structure if epimerisation at C-5 occurred under the acid conditions of the reaction. Accordingly in the absence of definite evidence correlating the positions of hydrogen and hydroxyl at C-14 there are no *a priori* grounds for preferring structure (122) to (123).

Further chemical evidence has been sought by Rapoport more recently. Ozonolysis of dihydrocodeine (127) gives the lactone-ester (128), which on catalytic and lithium aluminium hydride reduction affords the tetrol (129); similar reactions with dihydro-isocodeine yield the C-6 epimeric tetrol. Of these two tetrols the one derived from dihydrocodeine is oxidised by lead tetra-acetate three times faster than its epimer, from which it follows that the C-5 and C-6 oxygen atoms in codeine have the *cis* relationship. Determination of the steric relationship of the C-6 hydroxyl group and the carbon chain at C-13 in codeine or isocodeine is now sufficient to settle the whole stereochemical problem, and evidence on this point was claimed as a result of the Hofmann degradation of γ-tetrahydrocodeimethine (130), prepared from isocodeine. This reaction provides, together with other *N*-free products described in Chapter 1, a small quantity of the cyclic ether codiran, containing a 6–13 bridge. Since in this compound the bridge must be *cis* fused to the phenanthrene system it was concluded that the C-6 hydroxyl group and the C-13 side-chain of the methine base and hence of isocodeine are also *cis* and that codiran and isocodeine have the structures (131) and (132) respectively. However, models of the structure (131) reveal considerable strain in the 4–5 oxide bridge and in fact the structure (131*a*) for codiran is less strained, and this could arise from an alternative structure for *γ*-tetrahydrocodeimethine (still retaining a *trans* disposition of oxygen substituents at C-5 and C-6) by an abnormal reaction involving replacement of —NMe$_3$+ by hydroxyl in the quaternary salt, followed by substitution with inversion at C-6 by the resulting *β*-hydroxyethyl side-chain. Once again, therefore, the argument is not entirely conclusive.

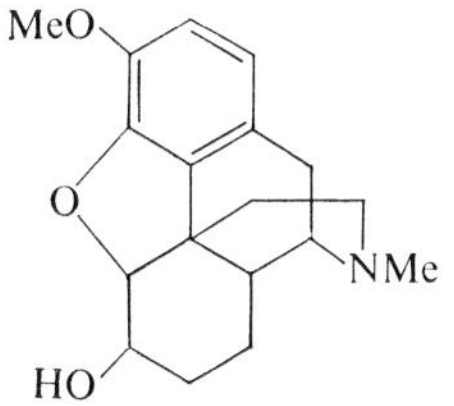

(127) 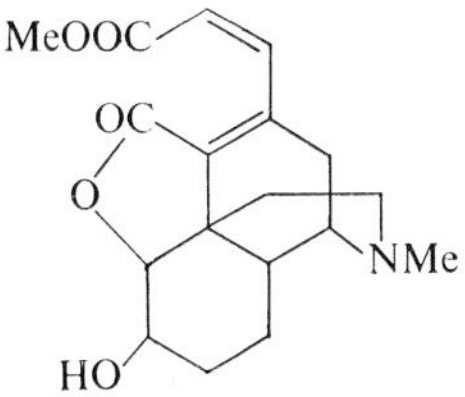   (128) 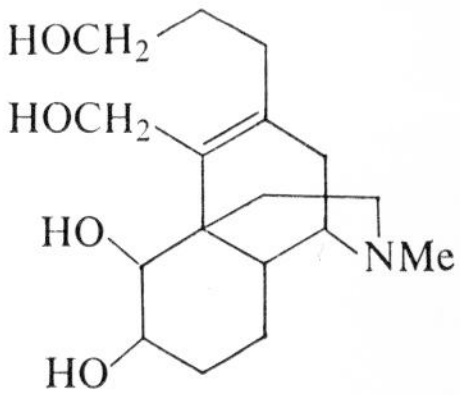   (129)

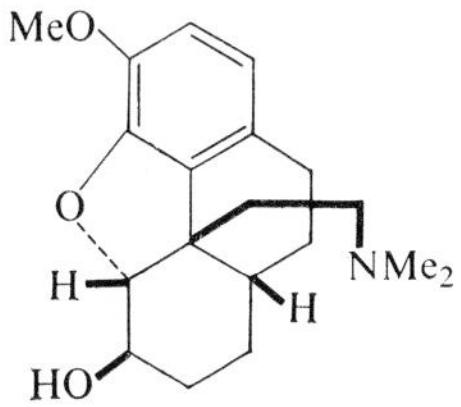

(130) 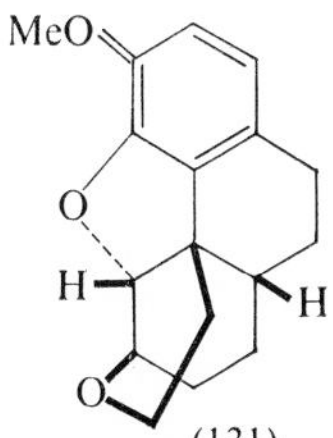   (131) 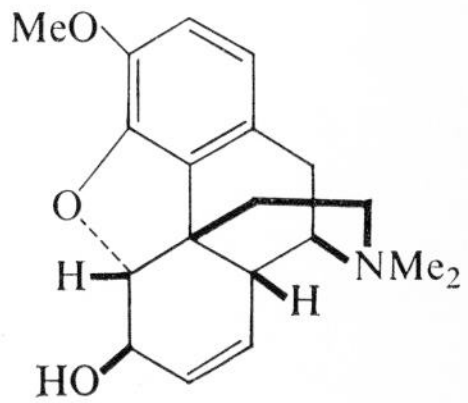   (132)

As the relative stereochemistry at C-5 and C-14 is the same in both structures (122) and (123) determination of the relative arrangement at C-13 and C-14 would also settle the whole problem, and evidence on this point was sought in the following way. Thebenone (133), the *N*-free product of exhaustive methylation of dihydrothebainone (118) was converted via the bisisonitroso-compound (134), the dinitrile (135) and the amido-acid (136) into the imide (137), whereas the same sequence of reactions with β-thebenone, the C-14-epimer of thebenone, could be accomplished only as far as the amido-acid corresponding to (136). It was assumed that imide formation would be favoured by a *cis* arrangement of —CO·NH$_2$ and —CH$_2$COOH substituents at C-13 and

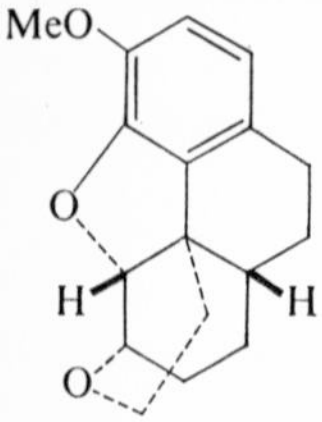

(131*a*)

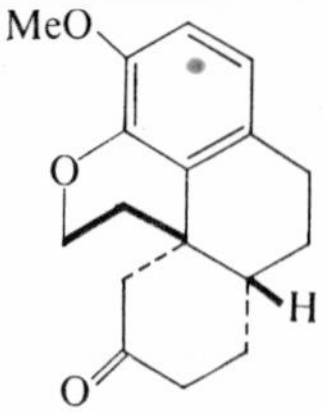

(133)

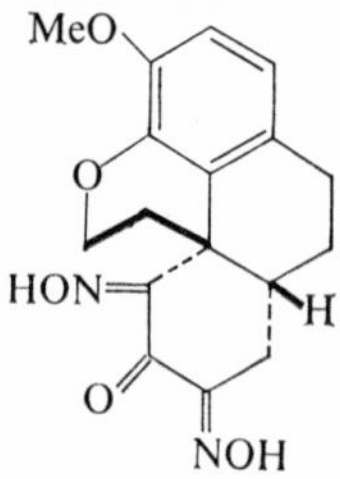

(134)

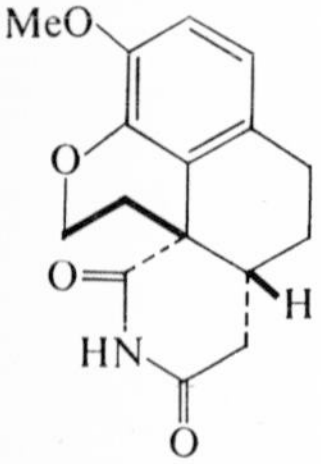

(137)

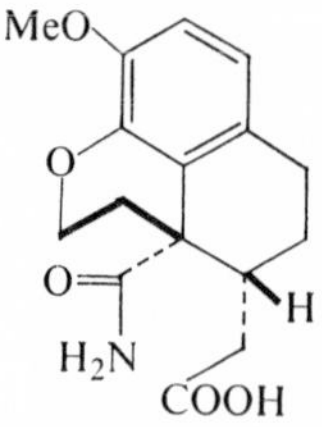

(136)

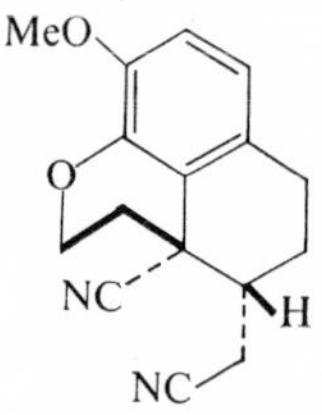

(135)

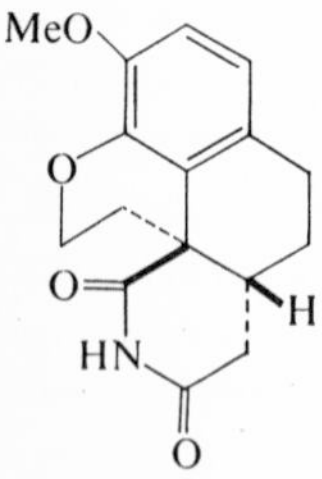

(137*a*)

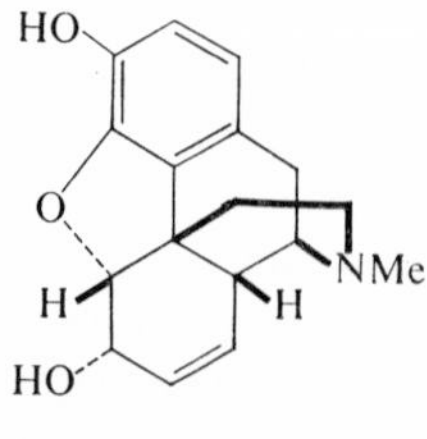

(138)

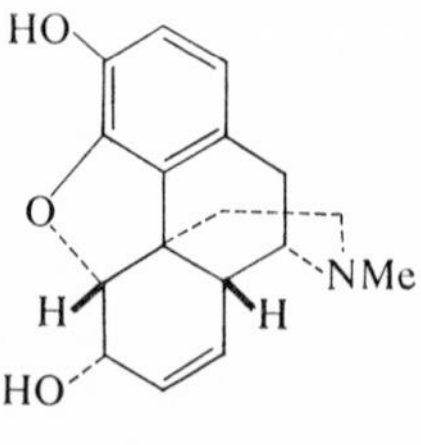

(139)

C-14 in the amido-acid and that thebenone must accordingly have the stereochemistry shown in (133). However, a strain-free model of the imide (137a) can be constructed and so the ambiguity remains.

The chemical evidence, therefore, favours the structure (138), or its mirror image, for morphine, but does not exclude the structure (139). X-ray studies have indeed proved that morphine is correctly represented by (138), but the validity of the criticism given

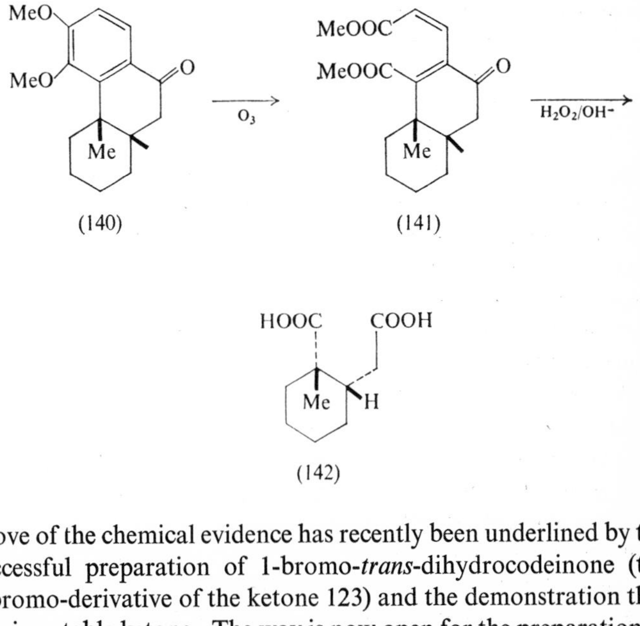

(140)

(141)

(142)

above of the chemical evidence has recently been underlined by the successful preparation of 1-bromo-*trans*-dihydrocodeinone (the 1-bromo-derivative of the ketone 123) and the demonstration that this is a stable ketone. The way is now open for the preparation of other 13,14-*trans* derivatives, including possibly *trans*-morphine itself. That morphine is in fact represented completely by (138) and not its mirror image has been proved recently by the oxidation of the ketone (140), prepared by a ten-stage degradation of dihydro-codeinone (132), to an optically active dicarboxylic acid (142), identified as (−)-*cis*-2-methyl-2-carboxylcyclohexylacetic acid.

This degradation, which was accomplished after completion of the X-ray studies, provides satisfactory chemical evidence of the relative arrangement of groups at C-13 and C-14.

The reactions of the halogenocodides

The assignment of the correct stereochemistry to codeine made possible rationalisation of the formation and reactions of the halogenocodides. The treatment of codeine with thionyl chloride, phosphorus trichloride or concentrated hydrochloric acid results in replacement of the hydroxyl group at C-6 by a chlorine atom to give α-chlorocodide, which on hydrolysis affords a mixture of isocodeine, ψ-codeine and allo-ψ-codeine. Of these isomers ψ-codeine with thionyl chloride gives α-chlorocodide, but iso- and allo-ψ-codeine give a different base, β-chlorocodide, also accessible by the isomerisation of α-chlorocodide. α-Chlorocodide must have the chlorine atom at C-6 since on reduction it yields 6-chloro-dihydrocodide, obtainable also from dihydrocodeine. Dihydro-isocodeine, however, fails to give any halide and these facts are explained by assuming S_N2 displacement of hydroxyl by a chloride ion from the unhindered rear in codeine and dihydrocodeine as shown in (143). Such displacement is greatly hindered by the rest of the molecule in the C-6 epimeric structures isocodeine and dihydroisocodeine, but in the former the presence of the 6,7-double bond facilitates an S_N2' replacement as shown in (144) to give the 8-halogenated β-chlorocodide (146), whereas even this process cannot occur with the dihydro-compound.

Of the remaining isomers of codeine allo-ψ-codeine gives β-chlorocodide by S_N2 displacement and must therefore have the hydroxyl group on the same side of the ring as does codeine, whereas ψ-codeine reacts by the S_N2' process to give α-chlorodide and must thus have the hydroxyl group on the same side as iso-codeine. α-Chlorocodide, being formed by a process that involves inversion at C-6, has the same stereochemistry as isocodeine, and resists S_N2 displacement during hydrolysis, which therefore proceeds by the S_N2' mechanism with the formation of ψ-codeine together with a small amount of allo-ψ-codeine and isocodeine, the last of these being formed by S_N2' hydrolysis of β-chlorocodide resulting from isomerisation of the α-compound.

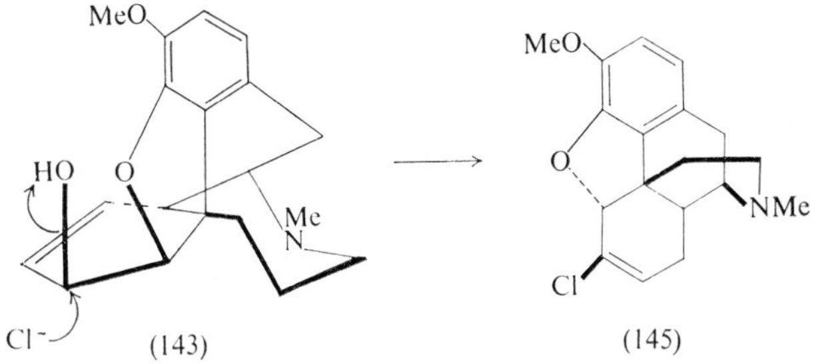

(143)

(145)

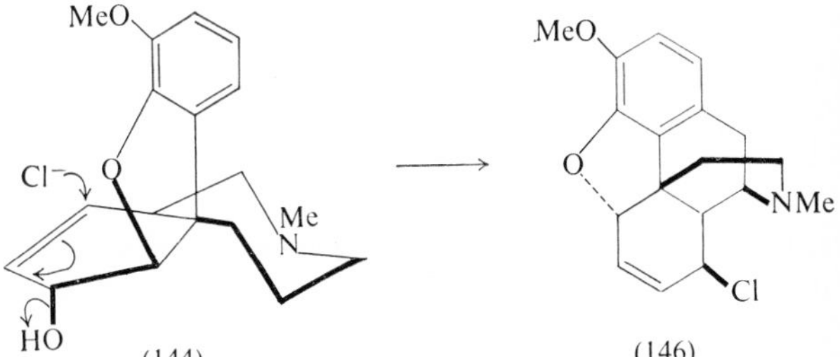

(144)

(146)

The reduction of thebaine

Thebaine contains a most interesting unsaturated ether system, the behaviour of which on reduction is most versatile. The system

$$\overset{6}{Ar}-\overset{}{O}-\overset{5}{CH}-\overset{4}{C}=\overset{3}{CH}-\overset{2}{CH}=\overset{1}{C}$$ can suffer 1,2; 1,4; 1,6; 3,4; 3,6 or 5,6 reduction according to the conditions employed. The compounds obtainable are those named in formulae (147)–(158); those not isolated are (150), (153) and (157), which are at least as easily hydrogenated as their immediate progenitors. These bases can, however, be obtained in other ways; (153) is codeine methyl ether and this on heating with sodium ethoxide is isomerised to the phenolic enol ether (150), and the base (157) may be obtained in stages from thebainone (159). Thebainone is the hydrolysis

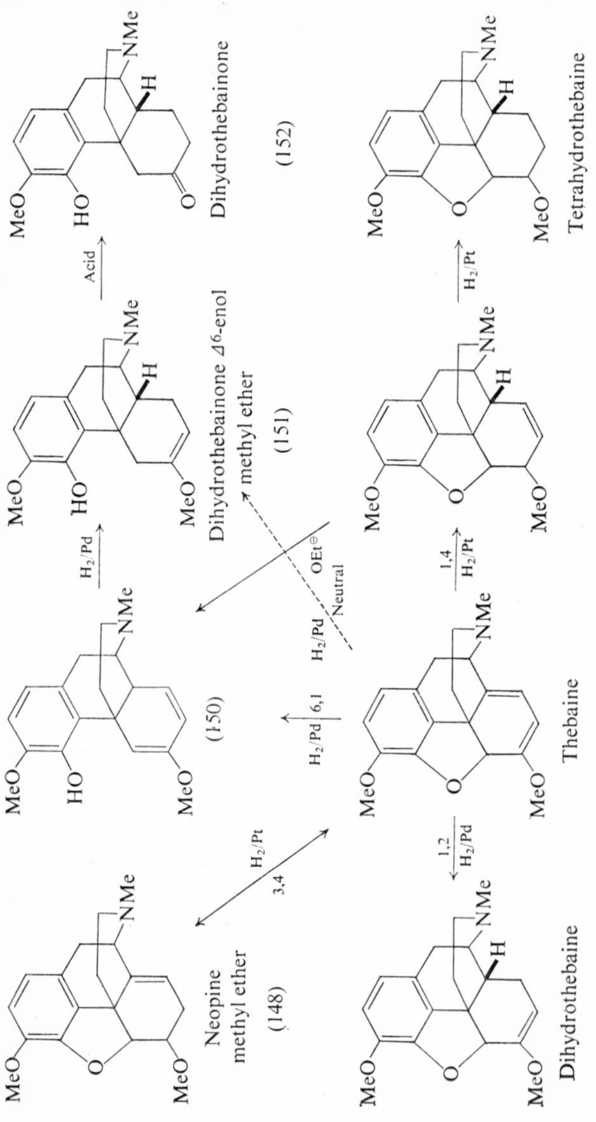

Dihydrothebainone (152)

Dihydrothebainone Δ^6-enol methyl ether (151)

(150)

Neopine methyl ether (148)

Tetrahydrothebaine (154)

(153)

Thebaine (147)

Dihydrothebaine (149)

Acid

H_2/Pd

H_2/Pd Neutral OEt$^\ominus$

H_2/Pd 6,1

H_2/Pt 3.4

H_2/Pt

1,4 H_2/Pt

1,2 H_2/Pd

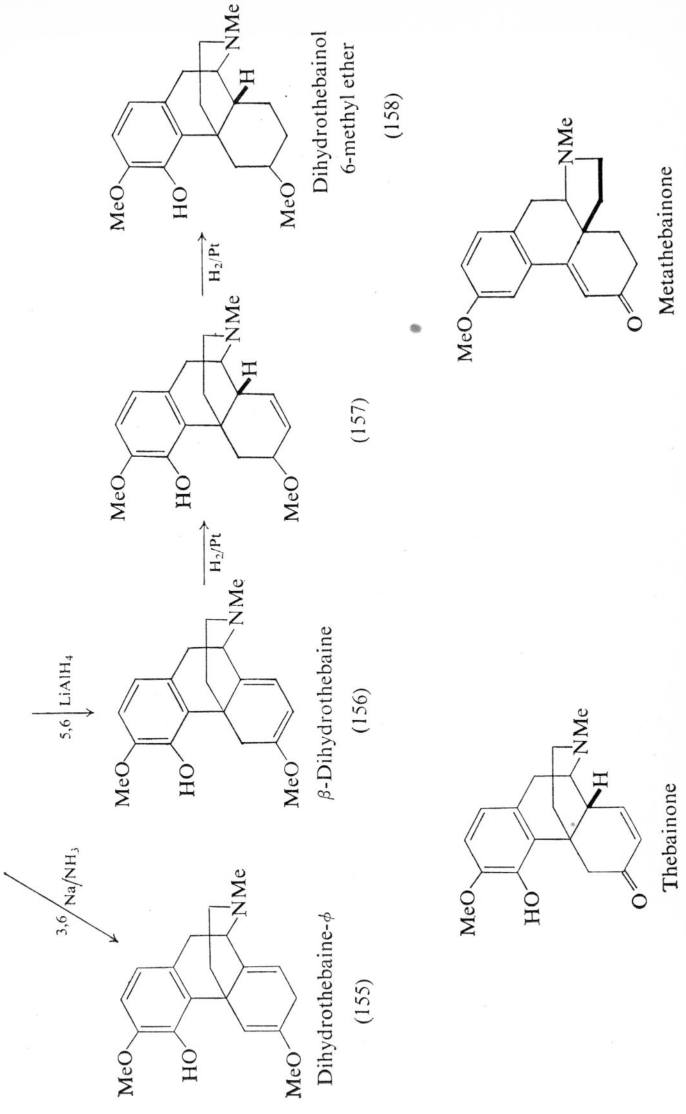

Dihydrothebaine-φ (155)

β-Dihydrothebaine (156)

(157)

Dihydrothebainol 6-methyl ether (158)

Thebainone (159)

Metathebainone (160)

product of the enol ether (150), and is obtainable also by the reduction of thebaine with stannous chloride and hydrochloric acid under carefully controlled conditions. If the conditions of the stannous chloride reduction are modified the rearranged ketone metathebainone (160) is obtained, and this also results from the hydrogenation of thebaine in concentrated hydrochloric acid.

The addition of hydrogen at C-14 always occurs in the same way in these reductions, though it may be noted that the hydrolysis of the enol ethers (155) and (156) during which an asymmetric centre is generated at C-14, affords β-thebainone, the C-14 epimer of thebainone (159), but this appears to be governed by reaction rates and not by the stabilities of the ketones, since thebainone is more stable than β-thebainone.

MOLECULAR REARRANGEMENTS IN THE MORPHINE–THEBAINE GROUP

The alkaloids of the morphine–thebaine group have attracted much attention from organic chemists on account of the wide variety of molecular rearrangements that they undergo under suitable conditions, indeed the alkaloids, especially thebaine, have been called by Robinson "the star performers in the field of molecular acrobats" which is indeed an apt description. Almost all of the rearrangements take place under acid conditions and they are initiated by the attack of the cyclic ether oxygen atom by an acidic atom or group. As thebaine is an enol ether of codeinone this base also undergoes the same acid-catalysed rearrangements as thebaine.

A. The apomorphine, morphothebaine and thebenine rearrangements

When morphine is heated with concentrated hydrochloric acid at 150° dehydration and rearrangement to apomorphine (161) occurs; similarly thebaine and codeinone are rearranged by hot concentrated hydrochloric acid to morphothebaine (162), though as these bases are in a higher state of oxidation than morphine loss of the oxygen function at C-6 is not a necessary part of aromatisation. The structures of these two rearrangement products are discussed in detail in Chapter 6. When thebaine or codeinone is heated in dilute hydrochloric acid a different rearrangement takes

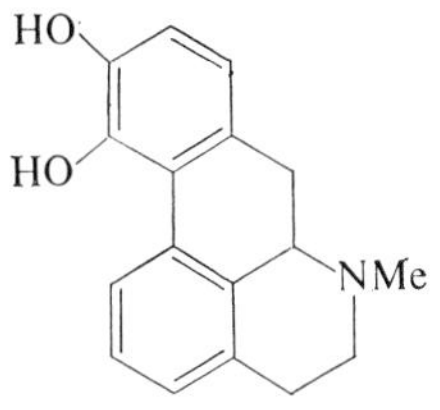

(161)

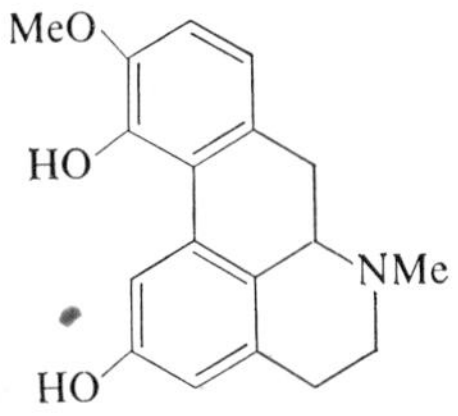

(162)

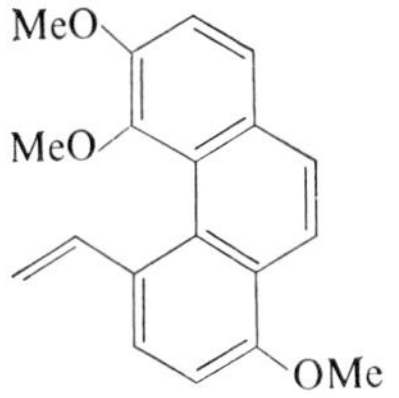

(164)

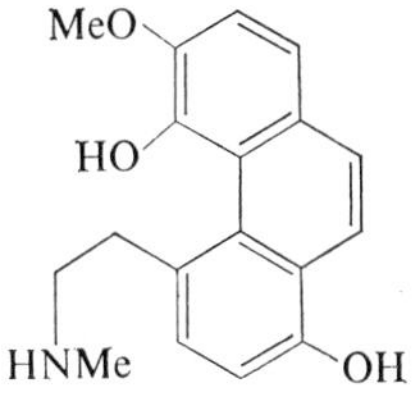

(163)

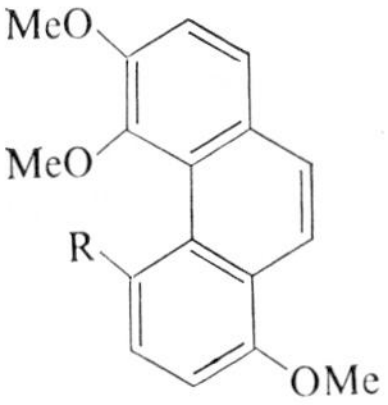

(165)

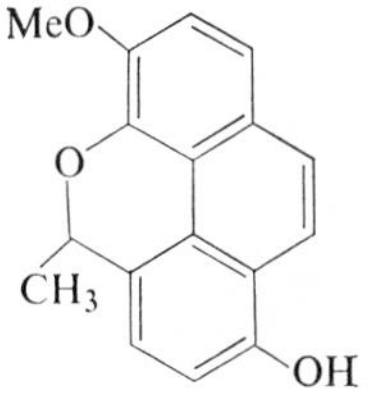

(166)

place very rapidly, the product being the secondary base thebenine (163), the 8-alkyl ethers of which may be obtained by carrying out the reaction in alcohols. The structure of this phenolic base follows from the Hofmann degradation of *O,O,N*-trimethyl-thebenine methiodide to 3,4,8-trimethoxy-5-vinylphenanthrene

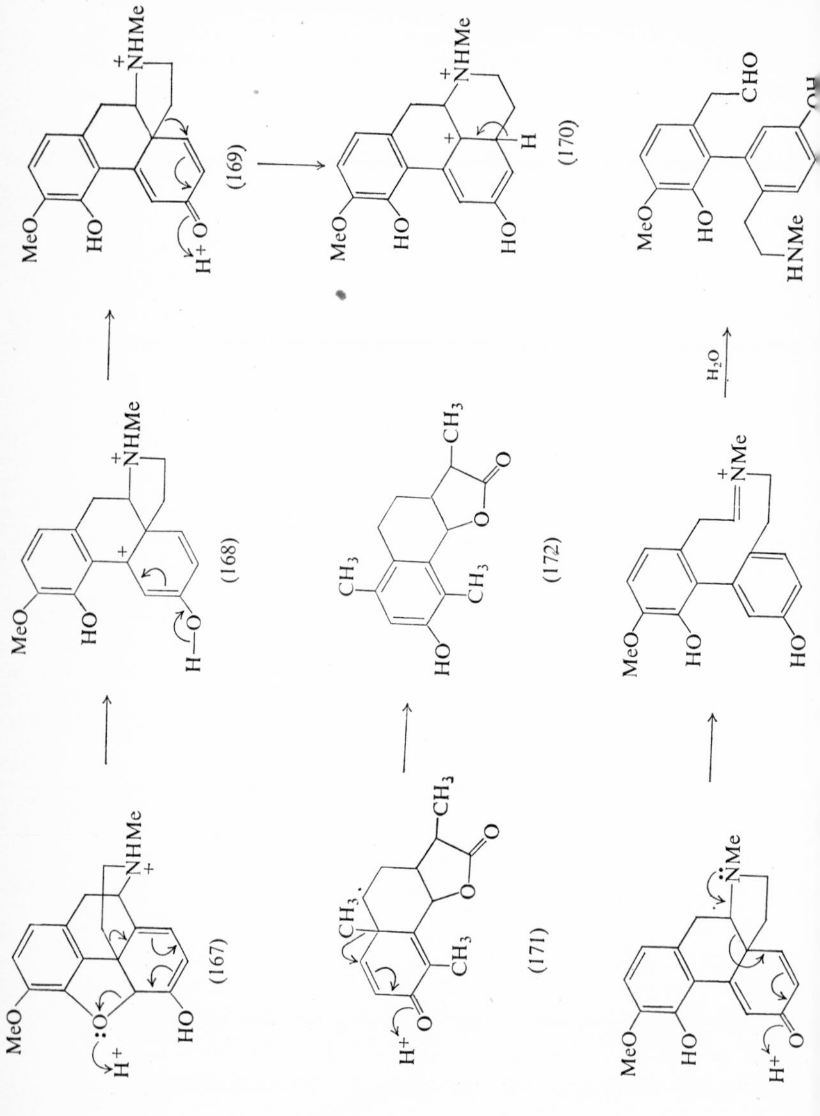

(167)

(168)

(169) → (170)

(171)

(172)

CHO

H₂O

(164), the reduction of this to the 5-ethyl-compound (165, R = Et) identical with material of this structure prepared by synthesis, and oxidation to the 5-carboxylic acid (165, R = COOH), which yields 3,4,8-trimethoxyphenanthrene (165, R = H) on decarboxylation. The Hofmann degradation of the phenolic *N*-methylthebenine methiodide yields the cyclic ether thebenol (166) which contains one C-methyl group and thus does not have the same type of ether ring as is present in thebenone (133).

The mechanisms of these transformations may be represented as follows. When thebaine is dissolved in cold concentrated hydro-chloric acid an orange-red solution is obtained from which no trace of thebaine may be recovered. The colour is due to halochromism and is discharged on dilution, but heating of the orange solution gives morphothebaine and catalytic reduction of it affords meta-thebainone (160), while dilution and heating leads to thebenine. The rearrangements undoubtedly begin by attack of the cyclic ether oxygen atom by a proton in the enol form of codeinone (167), which would be the immediate hydrolysis product of thebaine. The subsequent electron shifts could lead through the carbonium ion (168) to the dienone (169), which could be responsible for the orange-red colour of thebaine in concentrated acid. Dienone–phenol rearrangement of (169), similar to the rearrangement of santonin (171) to desmotroposantonin (172), could then lead simply through the carbonium ion (170) to morphothebaine (162).

An alternative fate for the dienone when the acid is sufficiently dilute to allow the presence of some molecules as the free base rather than as the salt involves fission of the C-14,C-9 bond, with participation of the now unshared pair of electrons on the nitrogen atom as in (173), to give the Schiff base quaternary salt (174), hydrolysis of which would proceed with great rapidity in the acid solution yielding the aldehyde (175), and cyclisation of this with the reactive position *ortho* to the phenolic hydroxyl group would then give thebenine (163). Reduction of the exposed double bond of the dienone (169) would afford metathebainone (160).

The apomorphine rearrangement doubtless proceeds in a

similar way, though in this case dehydration is a necessary part of aromatisation, and the initial product of loss of water from morphine (176) may be converted into apomorphine (161) via the carbonium ions (177) and (178).

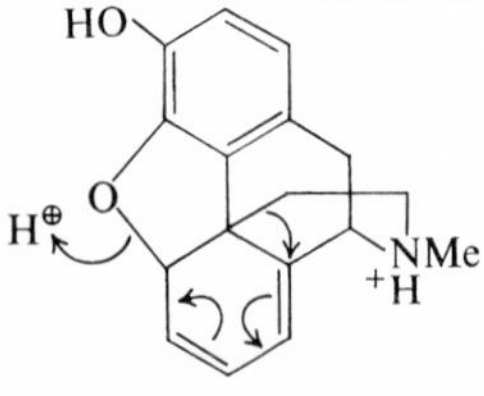

(176) 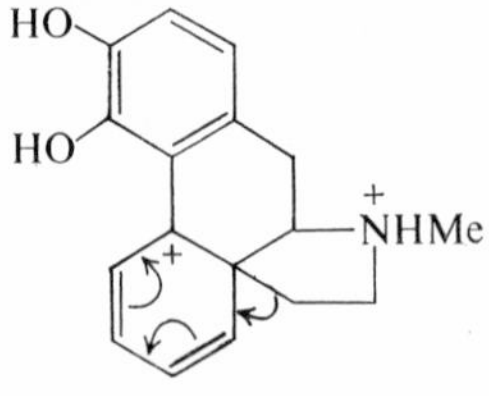   (177)

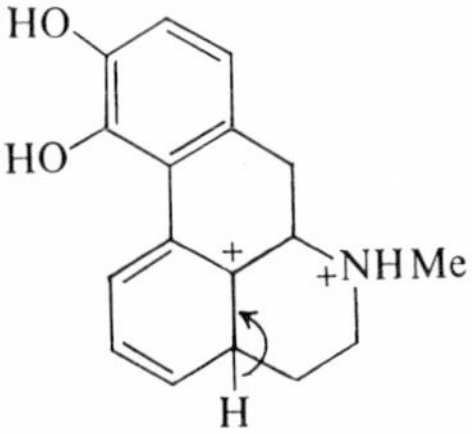

(178)

B. Metathebainone

This base, produced by the reduction of thebaine under strongly acid conditions, is a phenolic $\alpha\beta$-unsaturated ketone, and was for many years thought to be the true thebainone (159). Unlike thebainone, however, metathebainone exhibits halochromism in strongly acid solution and dissolves in alkalis to give a deep yellow solution, suggesting that the unsaturated ketone system is conjugated with the aromatic nucleus, and indeed the colour reactions of the base are reproduced very closely by salicylideneacetone (179, R = Me) and salicylideneacetophenone (179, R = Ph). If such an extended conjugated system is present in the molecule the

C-13 side-chain must have migrated to make way for the necessary 5,13-double bond, and of the two possible points of attachment of the chain C-14 (180) and C-8 (181) the former is chosen to account for the extrusion of the side-chain during the acetolysis of meta-thebainone methyl ether methine, which results in 3,4-dimethoxy-phenanthrene. This degradation is unusual, however, since

(179)   (180)   (181)

acetolysis of thebainone (159) and sinomenine ((+)-7-methoxy-thebainone) methiodides, which are in the same state of oxidation as the metathebainone methine, does not involve loss of the C-6 oxygen substituent. No positive evidence of the attachment of the nitrogen-containing ring in the base has yet been obtained, but it should be possible to degrade it to 14-ethyl-3,4-dimethoxy-6-keto-6,7,8,14,9,10-hexahydrophenanthrene, the synthesis of which is in progress.

C. Phenyldihydrothebaine

Grignard reagents RMgX react with derivatives of thebaine and codeine containing a 4,5-oxygen bridge and 6,7-double bond to give phenolic bases, the composition of which corresponds to the addition of RH to the starting material. The nature of the bases derived in this way from dihydrothebaine, dihydrocodeinone enol acetate and deoxycodeine-C is easily deduced (see page 141), but the bases derived in this way from thebaine and from ψ-codeinone are unusual in a number of respects. Phenyldihydrothebaine $C_{25}H_{27}O_3N$ is derived from thebaine $C_{19}H_{21}O_3N$ by the action of

5

phenylmagnesium bromide and all attempts to assign a structure to this base on the basis of a simple addition of a hydrogen atom and a phenyl group lead to formulae incapable of explaining the following properties of the compound.

(a) Unlike thebaine and any of its dihydro-derivatives it is remarkably resistant to hydrogenation, and forced hydrogenation simply results in reductive scission of the nitrogen containing ring, with the production of a secondary amine phenyltetrahydrothebaimine, a reaction without parallel in the whole morphine group.

(b) Unlike thebaine and its dihydro-derivatives (149), (150), (155) and (156) it is extremely stable to acid hydrolysis; under vigorous conditions it can be demethylated to a trihydric phenol which may be remethylated to phenyldihydrothebaine methyl ether.

(c) Exhaustive methylation proceeds with retention of the residue of the nitrogen-containing side-chain as a vinyl group, instead of extrusion as ethylene as observed with codeine, which is in the same oxidation state.

(d) Four stereoisomers of the base exist, two of which, the $(+)$-α and $(+)$-δ forms, being produced during the entry of the phenyl group; these two forms are partially isomerised by heat to $(-)$-δ and $(-)$-α respectively. The choice of these designations is unfortunate since the optical antipode of $(+)$-α is called $(-)$-α, whereas since two centres of dissymmetry are involved, it would be preferable to refer to it as $(-)$-δ, using the symbols α, δ, $(+)$ and $(-)$ to represent d and l at each of the two centres. One of these centres of dissymmetry, that responsible for the $\alpha : \delta$ isomerism, is an asymmetric carbon atom attached directly to nitrogen since fission of the nitrogen ring by reduction or Hofmann degradation results in its disappearance. As thebaine is a pure optical isomer the asymmetric carbon atom attached to nitrogen is configured in one sense only and is immune to inversion in other reactions in the morphine group. The second centre of dissymmetry, responsible for the $(+):(-)$ isomerism persists throughout exhaustive methylation, with or without reduction of the generated double bonds, right through to the nitrogen-free product.

This fascinating structural puzzle was ingeniously solved by Robinson in 1947, 42 years after the first preparation of the base, and since the deductive processes leading to the correct structure have been largely misrepresented in a recent book their reproduction here is timely.

The resistance of phenyldihydrothebaine to hydrogenation and acid hydrolysis, and the production from it on demethylation of a trihydric phenol, indicate that the near-aromatic ring of thebaine, which bears the hydrolysable methoxyl group, has become fully aromatic in phenyldihydrothebaine. Other conclusions follow logically from this primary one. Exhaustive methylation of phenyldihydrothebaine $C_{25}H_{27}O_3N$ leads to an optically active nitrogen-free product $C_{24}H_{22}O_3$ with loss of one carbon atom (in trimethylamine). Of the 24 carbon atoms of this compound two are present in methoxy groups, 18 must be present in three benzene rings (one present in thebaine, one generated and one introduced during the Grignard reaction) and the remaining four are present in two reducible double bonds, and so no asymmetric carbon atom can be present. The optical activity of the N-free product must therefore be a consequence of dissymmetry resulting from restricted rotation about a carbon–carbon bond, presumably, since thebaine may be regarded as being derived from diphenyl, in a diphenyl system. With this knowledge consideration of the probable mode of attack of the Grignard reagent led to a wholly satisfactory structure (185) for phenyldihydrothebaine.

The mechanism may be represented as in formulae (182)–(185) by a process similar in essentials to the thebenine transformation. As the reaction is carried out in neutral solution the unshared electron pair on the nitrogen atom is available as in the thebenine transformation, but hydrolysis of the methoxyl group at C-6 does not occur. Obviously the whole process is a concerted one, but inclusion of the intermediate carbonium ions simplifies the pictorial representation. The intermediate quaternary ion (184) has probably been isolated as its iodide from the reaction between thebaine and anhydrous magnesium iodide; it gives phenyldihydro-thebaine with phenylmagnesium bromide, but does not give thebenine 8-methyl ether with hot dilute hydrochloric acid, probably because cyclisation of the phenanthrene system *ortho* to methoxyl is more sluggish than cyclisation *ortho* to hydroxyl. The reaction results in configuration of the 2,2'-bridged diphenyl system in one way only, but the asymmetric carbon atom bearing the phenyl group is configured in both senses though steric factors result in predominant attack by the phenyl anion from one side, and the presence of only two isomers, in different amounts, in the initial reaction mixture is logically explained.

Hofmann degradation of phenyldihydrothebaine yields two isomeric methine bases, (186) and (187), which give the same optically active N-free product (188) on further degradation. This N-free product may be cyclised by hot hydrochloric acid to the ether (189) which, as it is virtually planar, is optically inactive since the new asymmetric centre (marked with an asterisk) is generated equally in both forms and free or restricted rotation in the diphenyl system is no longer possible. The same ether may be prepared from the methine (187) via the cyclised product (190), but is then found to have a small residual activity, presumably as a result of the production of a slight excess of one isomer at the new asymmetric centre in the base (190) during its formation under the influence of the existing asymmetric carbon atom in the methine (187).

As will be seen from the foregoing discussion the deductions, contrary to a recent statement by Ginsburg, owed nothing to spectroscopy and were made entirely on the basis of existing data. Indeed the ultraviolet spectroscopic evidence seemed at first to be at variance with the deduced structures since the spectra of phenyl-dihydrothebaine and its derivatives gave no indication of the appearance in these compounds of a second aromatic nucleus linked directly to that present in thebaine, but the chemical evidence was

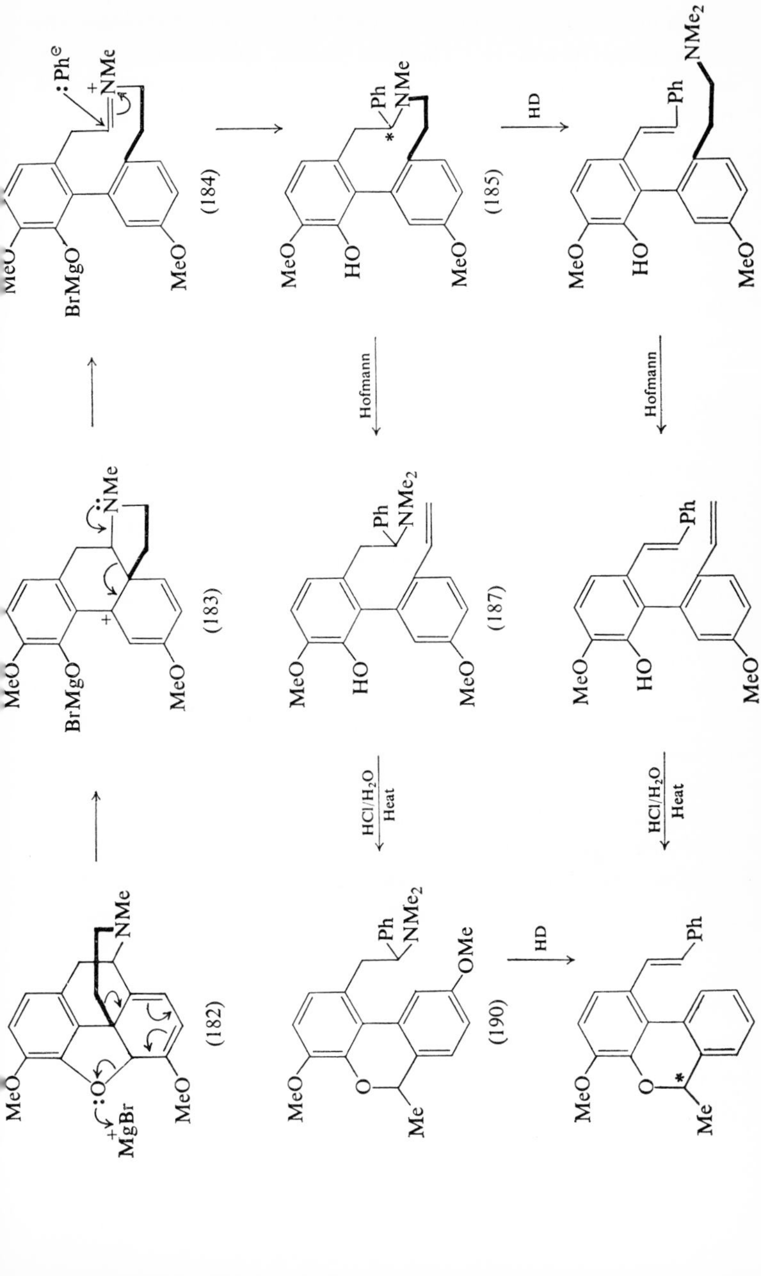

(182)
(183)
(184)
(185)
(186)
(187)
(188)
(189)
(190)
Hofmann
HD
HCl/H$_2$O
Heat

so strong that it was concluded that the ultraviolet spectra were misleading. It was subsequently found that evidence already existed at that time showing that non-coplanar diphenyls show ultraviolet absorption only of the isolated aromatic nuclei, since the planar requirements for conjugation are not met.

The structure (185) for phenyldihydrothebaine was proved correct by oxidation of the base to 4-methoxyphthalic acid (191) and of the methyl ether of the *N*-free product (188) to 5,6,5'-trimethoxydiphenic acid (192, R = Me), which was also prepared via the acetoxy-compound (192, R = Ac) by the oxidation of acetylthebaol quinone (193).

(191)   (192)   (193)

(194)   (195)

Methyldihydro-ψ-codeinone, prepared by the action of methyl-magnesium iodide on ψ-codeinone (194), is also strongly resistant to hydrogenation, and resembles phenyldihydrothebaine in many of its reactions, and doubtless has the structure (195).

D. Flavothebaone

The rearrangements of thebaine to morphothebaine, thebenine and phenyldihydrothebaine, all initiated by attack of the cyclic ether oxygen by a positive ion, involve the neutralisation of the electron deficit at C-5 resulting from opening of the ether bridge by migration of the C-13 side-chain. It is, however, possible, by introducing other substituents into the molecule, to provide a pathway for the neutralisation of this deficit without migration of the C-13 side-chain, though suitable compounds were not deliberately prepared for this purpose, and indeed the rearrangements made possible in this way were not correctly formulated until almost twenty years after they were first encountered. Compounds suitably configured for this purpose are accessible by the Diels–Alder addition of dienophils to thebaine, and in particular the *p*-benzoquinone adduct (196) has been subjected to the most detailed study.

The double bond remaining as a 6,14-bridge in the adduct (196) is so sheltered by the rest of the molecule that adsorption on a catalyst surface is very difficult, and hydrogenation of the adduct at that bridge cannot be effected. Irreversible enolisation of the adduct, however, gives the hydroquinone (197), in which reduction of the ethylenic bridge can be accomplished.

When the hydroquinone (197) is heated with concentrated hydrochloric acid it is converted in good yield into a yellow base, flavothebaone, with the loss of CH_2 only. Flavothebaone contains three phenolic hydroxyl groups, one methoxy group and a readily reduced $\alpha\beta$-unsaturated ketone system. It dissolves in alkalis to give an intense orange solution, whereas its colourless dihydro-compound gives no colour in alkalis, and these facts led initially to the supposition that the base contained the system (198). By analogy with the morphothebaine rearrangement the structure (201), produced via the intermediates (199) and (200), was advanced for flavothebaone. This structure, though differing in composition from $C_{24}H_{23}O_5N$ previously accepted for flavothebaone, could nevertheless be harmonised with existing analytical data and was

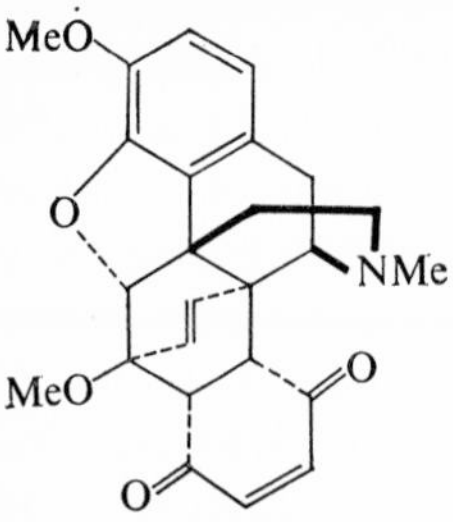

(196)

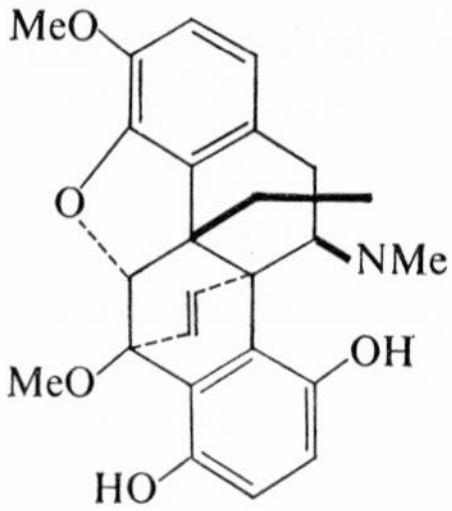

(197)

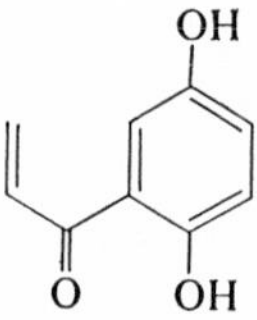

(198)

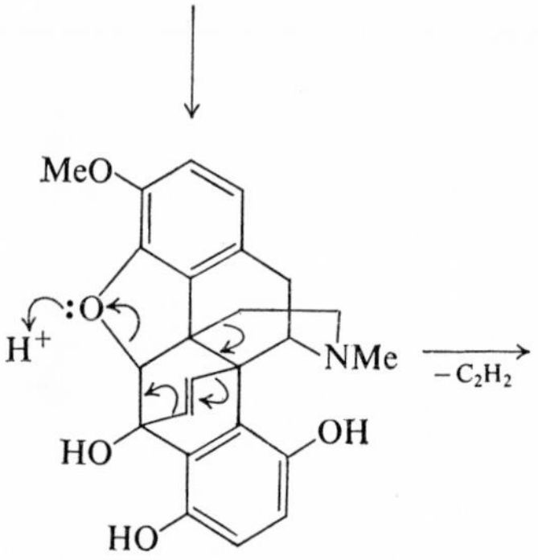

(199)

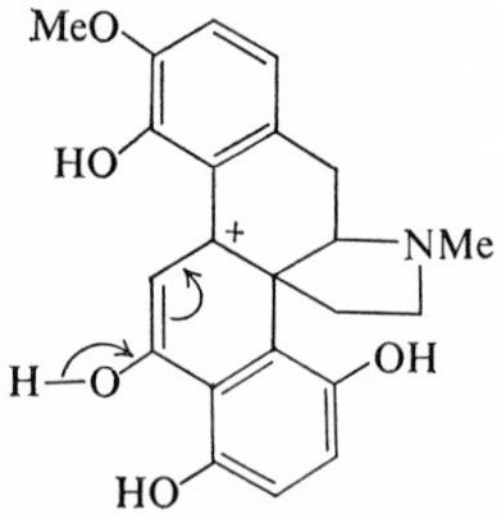

$-C_2H_2$

(200)

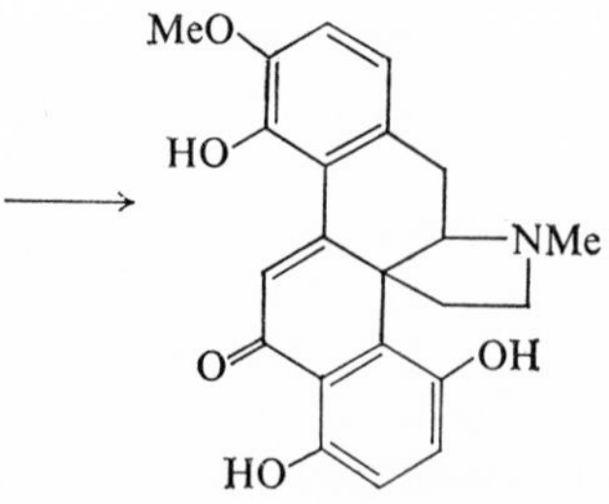

(201)

not ruled out by careful crystallographic molecular weight determinations. However no C_2 fragment could be detected by the most careful examination of the reaction mixture, and since dihydroflavothebaone trimethyl ether shows infrared absorption at 1710 cm^{-1}, and thus cannot be an aromatic ketone, the structure is clearly incorrect.

Hofmann degradation of flavothebaone trimethyl ether methiodide affords a methine base $C_{28}H_{31}O_5N$, the ultraviolet absorption of which is very nearly the sum of the absorptions of flavothebaone and α-codeimethine (47), and, since the aromatisation of this base cannot be effected under the most vigorous treatment with acetic anhydride, it was concluded that the hydrophenanthrene skeleton of thebaine and the hydroquinone (197) contains a second aromatisation-blocking group, as does 14-hydroxycodeinone (51, R = OH). The same conclusion follows from the failure of the methine base to isomerise to an analogue of β-codeimethine (48) when heated with alkalis, the reaction leading to a ψ-methine $C_{27}H_{33}O_5N$ with the loss of one carbon atom. Such a second angular substituent can only be at C-14 and must be the quinol nucleus, which is already linked at this point in the quinol (197). Since the ultraviolet spectrum of flavothebaone in no way resembles that of metathebainone (160), the double bond must be placed at C-7:8 (assuming that the carbonyl group arises from the unmigrated methoxyl group at C-6) and the part-structure (202) emerges for flavothebaone, in which the nitrogen-containing sidechain and the quinol nucleus must both be linked further to the phenanthrene system.

Flavothebaone trimethyl ether cannot be condensed with piperonal, whereas its dihydro-derivative condenses with this aldehyde with ease, indicating that flavothebaone must contain the system —CHR—CO—CH=C— and in this the group R must be the quinol nucleus, since the further degradations of the ψ-methine can only be explained if the C-13 side-chain occupies its original position in thebaine; these degradations (see below) also provide independent confirmation of the linkage of the quinol nucleus to

C-5.   Flavothebaone may thus be assigned the structure (204), and its production from thebaine-quinol (197) may be represented by the combined ether bridge fission and 1,2-shift of the quinol nucleus as in (203). This process, which is essentially similar to the pinacol–pinacolone transformation, is particularly favoured by the geometry of the molecule, which holds the four participating centres in one plane, with the ether oxygen at C-5 and the quinol nucleus at C-6 180° *trans* about the C-5:C-6 bond. The resulting deficiency of electrons at C-6 is made up by the oxygen atom of the methoxyl group, which finally loses CH_3 to become carbonyl. The double bond takes no part in this process, and in accordance with this dihydrothebainequinol may be rearranged directly to dihydro-flavothebaone.

(202)   (203)   (204)

The rearrangement of flavothebaone trimethyl ether methine to the ψ-methine and the further degradation of this base provides a complex series of further transformations easily interpreted on the basis of the structure (204) for flavothebaone. It has been implied by Ginsburg in a recent book that the writer was only able to explain these transformations after the (independent) deduction of the correct structure for flavothebaone by Meinwald. This is not so; in fact the whole of the problem of flavothebaone and its further transformation products was elucidated by the writer and his co-workers over a year before Meinwald's publication, and in this work the solution of some of the secondary rearrangements preceded that of the basic transformation.

The trimethyl ether methine (205) is rearranged by boiling alcoholic potassium hydroxide to the ψ-methine, $C_{27}H_{33}O_5N$, which contains a C-methyl group and a *saturated* carbonyl group, which must be present as an acetyl group since the piperonylidene derivative of the ψ-methine contains no C-methyl. Unlike the methine the ψ-methine methiodide can be aromatised by acetolysis or by Hofmann degradation to an optically inactive ketone $C_{23}H_{22}O_5$, which may be hydrolysed to a non-ketonic substance $C_{21}H_{20}O_4$, and in the Hofmann degradation these two compounds are accompanied by a third, non-ketonic, substance $C_{22}H_{22}O_4$. All of these compounds have the same characteristic ultraviolet spectrum, which closely resembles those of β but not α-phenyl-naphthalenes, and all three give complexes with 1,3,5-trinitro-benzene and with picric acid. The simplest of these compounds has a composition differing by only one carbon atom from that of a tetramethoxy-β-phenylnaphthalene $C_{20}H_{20}O_4$ and the only logical structure is that of a tetramethoxybenzofluorene, and, assuming that the C-14 linkage of the quinol nucleus is retained throughout the degradations, only the structures (206, R = H) and (207, R = H) suffice for the C_{21} compound. In either case the C_{23} compound, which loses acetic acid on hydrolysis, must be the corresponding *C*-acetyl-derivative (R = Ac), and it was shown that the C_{22} compound is the *C*-methyl-derivative by methylation of the simple fluorene with methyl alcohol and sodium methoxide.

On the basis of these findings the ψ-methine may be represented by the structure (208), since the extrusion of the side-chain during aromatisation indicates its presence at an angular position, and the alternative structures (209) and (210), based on the structure (207) for the fluorene, are incompatible with the ultraviolet spectrum of the ψ-methine, which indicates the conjugation of the double bond only with the *quinol* nucleus. These last two structures have been recently ruled out of consideration also by the identification of the

C_{21} degradation product with authentic material of structure (206, R = H) prepared by unambiguous synthesis. The elimination of the side-chain and aromatisation of the methine doubtless

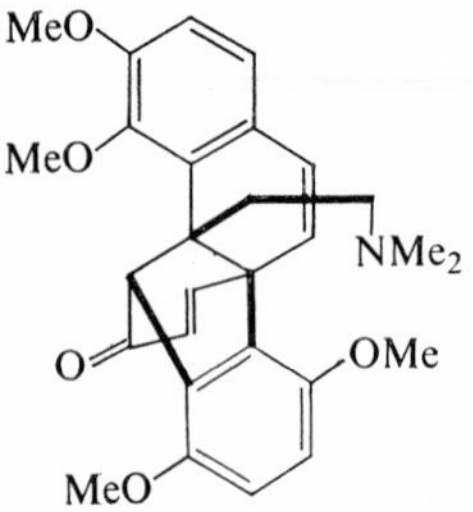

(205)

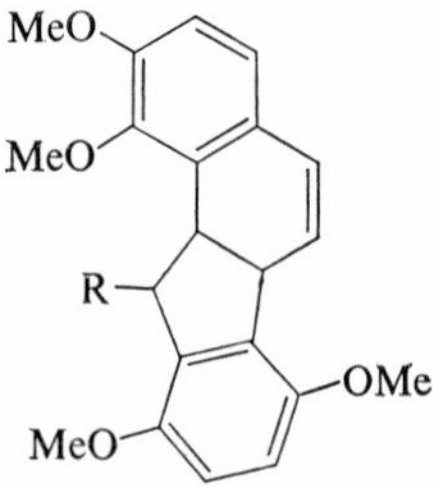

(206)

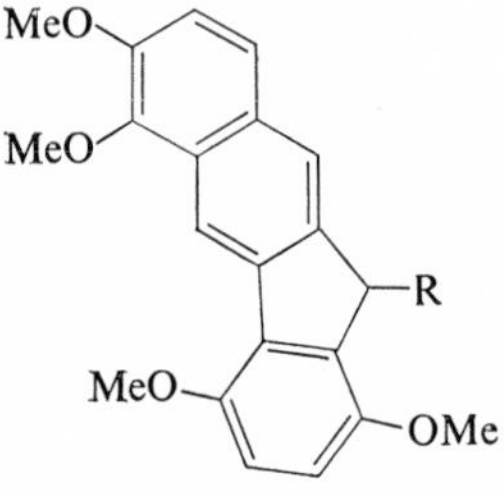

(207)

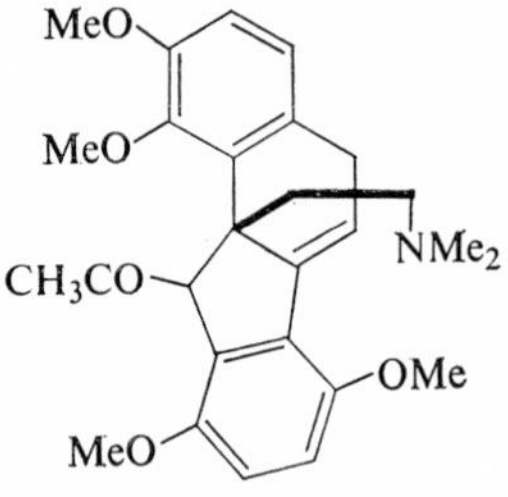

(208)

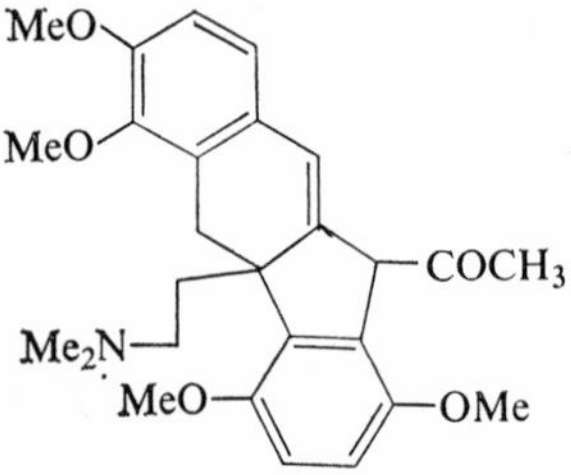

(209)

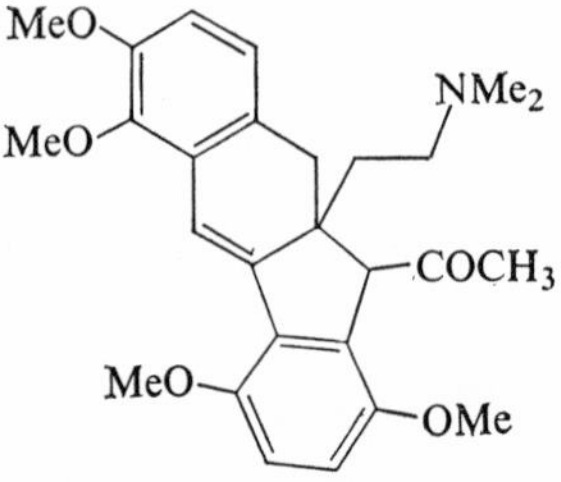

(210)

MeO
MeO
HO⊖ H
CH$_3$CO
NMe$_3$
MeO
OMe
OH$^-$
(211)
MeO
MeO
HO⊖
H
CH$_3$—C
O
MeO
OMe.
(212)
OH$^-$
MeO
MeO
CH$_3$CO
MeO
OMe
(213)
OH$^-$/H$_2$O
MeO
MeO
MeO
OMe
(214)
C-methylation
MeO
MeO
Me
Ac
MeO
OMe
(215)
OH$^-$/H$_2$O
MeO
MeO
Me
MeO
OMe
(216)

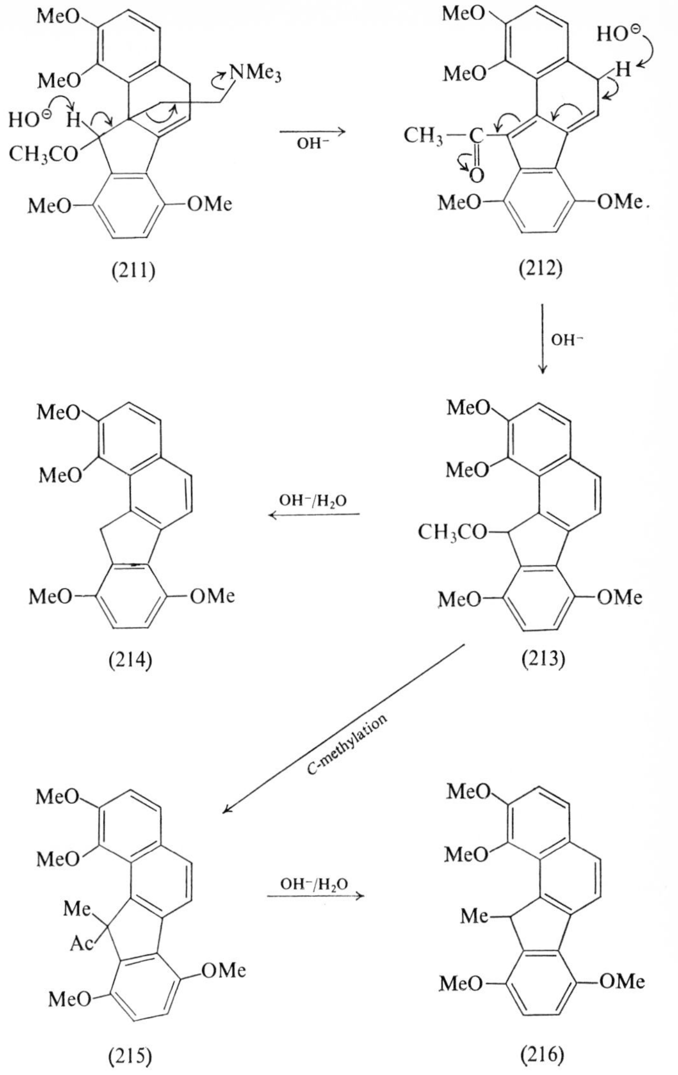

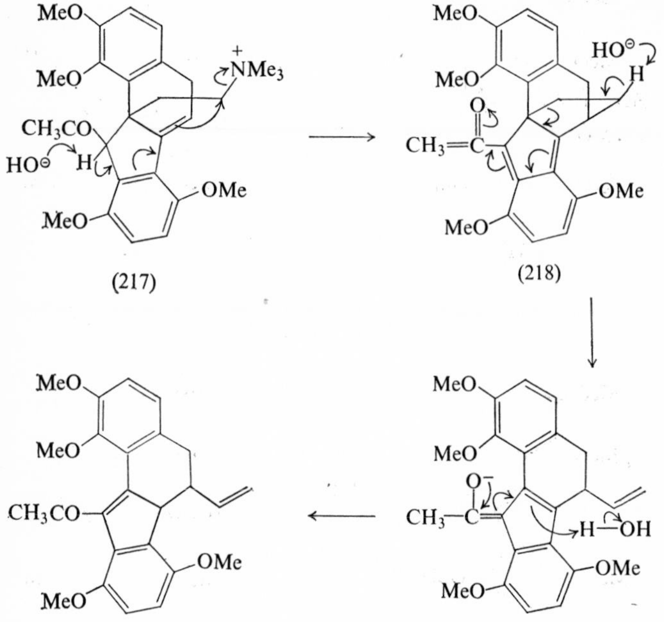

(217)

(218)

(220)

(219)

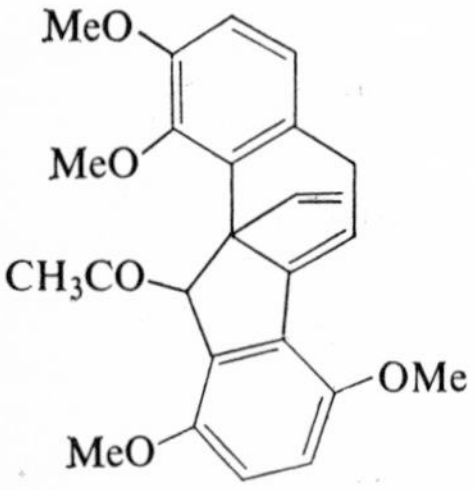

(221)

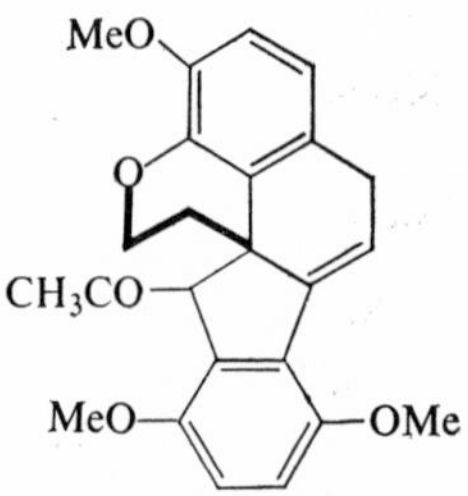

(221*a*)

proceeds as shown in (211), via (212) giving the acetyl compound (213), which on hydrolysis affords the benzofluorene (214). The C_{22} compound (216) could arise by methylation of the anion of (213) by the quaternary salt (211) (which is thus converted into ψ-methine base) to give (215), followed by hydrolysis.

Under certain conditions the Hofmann degradation of the ψ-methine affords also a fourth N-free substance, an optically active ketone $C_{25}H_{26}O_5$, containing one reducible double bond and an unreducible $\alpha\beta$-unsaturated ketone system, the double bond of which is conjugated with both aromatic nuclei. This compound is clearly not the normal Hofmann elimination product (221) (which may be prepared by pyrolysis of the ψ-methine N-oxide) and the change in optical rotation from $+185°$ to $-293°$ occurring during its preparation suggests that at least one asymmetric centre has been modified. Only the structure (220) appears to fit the facts, and this could arise from the ψ-methine quaternary salt as shown in formulae (217)–(220). A fifth N-free product from the methine has all the properties that would be expected of the thebenone analogue (221a), and it is known from work in the dihydrothebainone series that the tendency to form the thebenone system is sufficiently great to cause demethylation of a methoxyl group at C-4.

The rearrangement of the trimethyl ether methine (205) to the ψ-methine (208) occurs by hydration of the $\alpha\beta$-unsaturated ketone, dealdolisation of the product (222) and elimination of formic acid from the resulting aldehyde (223).

Beckmann transformation of the ψ-methine oxime (224) takes an interesting course, leading as shown to the base (225), which may be stereospecifically dehydrated with migration of the side-chain to give the optically active basic benzofluorene (226), which may be degraded by N-oxide pyrolysis to the optically active vinyl compound (227) and this may be racemised by alkalis. Pyrolysis of the ψ-methine N-oxide gives the N-free product (221) and the oxime of this on Beckmann transformation gives the vinyl compound (227) directly, presumably because the vinyl group migrates more readily than the β-dimethylaminoethyl group of the ψ-methine oxime.

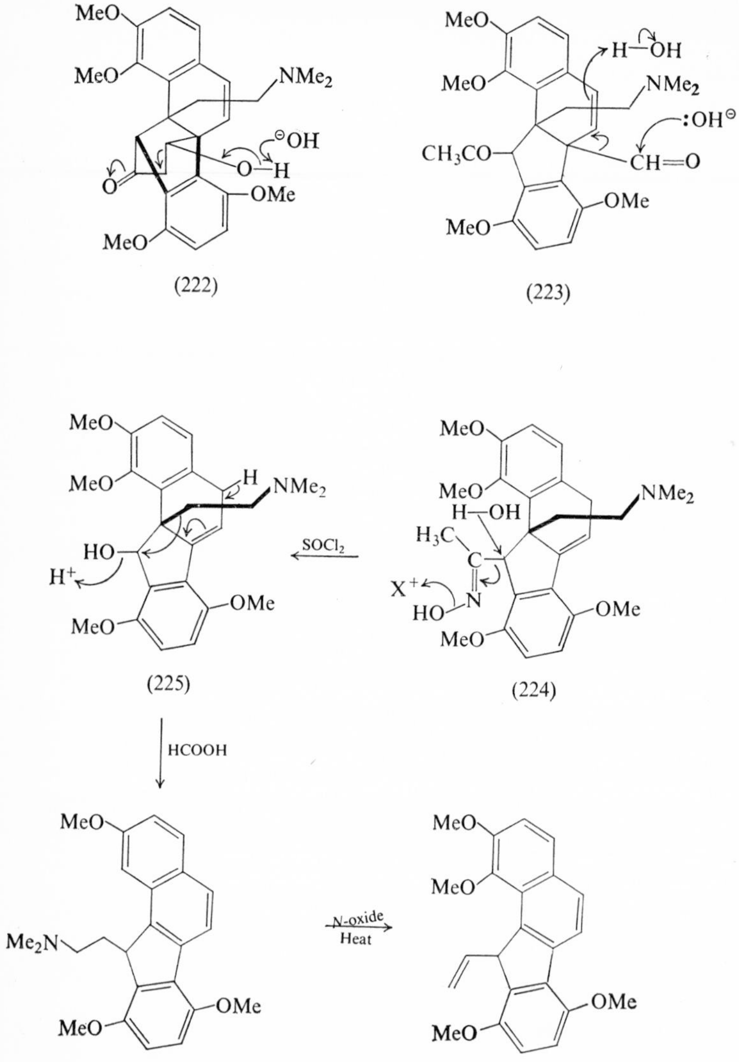

(222)

(223)

(225)

(224)

(226)

(227)

The pyrolysis of *N*-oxides is particularly useful for the preparation of unrearranged *N*-free products in the flavothebaone series, and in this way even the simple 13-vinyl compound related to the methine (205) can be prepared.

The ultraviolet spectrum of flavothebaone shows a long wavelength absorption band, λ_{max} 3450, ϵ_{max} 2200, the appearance of which is very difficult to explain in terms of the structure (204), which contains no highly conjugated chromophore. An attempt has been made to explain this on the basis of homoconjugation of the type shown in (228), but this is at variance with the finding that benzflavothebaone (229), and particularly flavonepenthone (230), which contains no oxygen substituents from which the necessary electrons can be made available, also show the same absorption band at the same position with the same intensity. It may be noted that the closest approach of the quinol nucleus of flavothebaone (204) and benzflavothebaone (229) and of the styrenoid double bond of flavonepenthone (230) to the $\alpha\beta$-unsaturated ketone system is about 3 Å, and probably the enone system (which normally shows weak absorption at about 3450 Å) is perturbed by this close approach of the π-orbitals of another unsaturated system to about the same extent, giving rise to greatly intensified absorption at this point in all three compounds. The colour of flavothebaone in alkaline solution is due to the anion, which is then affected by the close enone system, and when that system is not present, as in the dihydro-base, the alkaline solution is colourless. It may be noted that benzflavothebaone, in which a different anion is involved, is violet in alkaline solution, and flavonepenthone is almost colourless.

E. *Nepenthone, flavonepenthone and isonepenthone*

The addition of phenyl vinyl ketone to thebaine affords the adduct (231), which was given the trivial name nepenthone. This base can be reduced by the Meerwein–Ponndorf method to the alcohol (232), nepenthol, which can be dehydrated with ring fission to the 14-substituted codeinone nepenthene (233), and both this

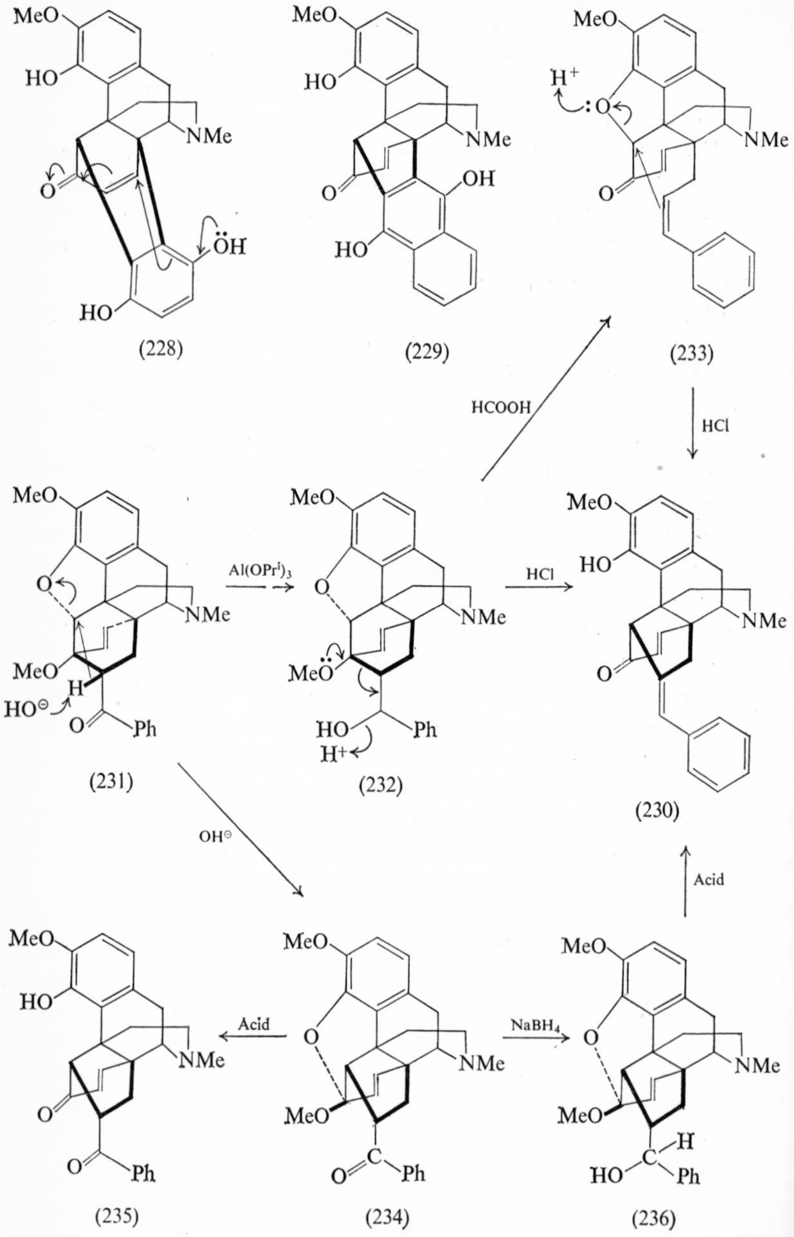

(228)

(229)

(233)

HCOOH

HCl

Al(OPr^i)$_3$

HCl

(231)

(232)

(230)

OH$^\ominus$

Acid

OH$^\ominus$

Acid

NaBH$_4$

(235)

(234)

(236)

and the parent alcohol can be converted into flavonepenthone (230) by heating with concentrated acid. When, however, nepenthone is heated with alkalis, instead of being epimerised to the more stable (?) ketone, it is rearranged with displacement of the phenate ion from the 4,5-oxygen bridge and the establishment of a new carbon–oxygen bond to give isonepenthone (234), in which the ketal system is sufficiently unstable to allow rapid hydrolysis of the base in cold dilute acid to the diketone ψ-nepenthone (235). Sodium borohydride reduction of isonepenthone yields isonepenthol (236), acid hydrolysis of which affords the secondary alcohol analogous to the ketone (235), together with some flavonepenthone (230) resulting from dehydration. Unfortunately none of these bases form quaternary salts, so potentially interesting degradations cannot be effected; only flavothebaone and benzflavothebaone of the derivatives of the Diels–Alder adducts of thebaine form quaternary salts, and evidently the steric factors governing the ease of quaternisation are very finely balanced in compounds of this type.

F. Thermal rearrangement of Diels–Alder adducts of thebaine

Coincident with the completion of the manuscript for this book a further piece was added to the jig-saw puzzle of the rearrangement of thebaine and its derivatives. The addition of the acetylenic dienophils ethyl propiolate and dimethyl acetylenedicarboxylate to thebaine affords the adducts (I) and (II), which are more unsaturated than those of type (231), and the disposition of the added unit makes reduction of the olefinic bridge possible in these bases. Thermal rearrangement of the adducts proceeds with the loss of ethylene and the production of the benzazocine derivatives (III, R = Et, R' = H) and (III, R = Me, R' = COOMe) and this rearrangement may be compared with the aromatisation of the adduct of cyclohexadiene and dimethyl acetylenedicarboxylate (VI) to dimethyl phthalate (VII) with the extrusion of ethylene.

The reduction of the diester (III, R = Me, R' = COOMe) with lithium aluminium hydride affords the diol (IV), which readily

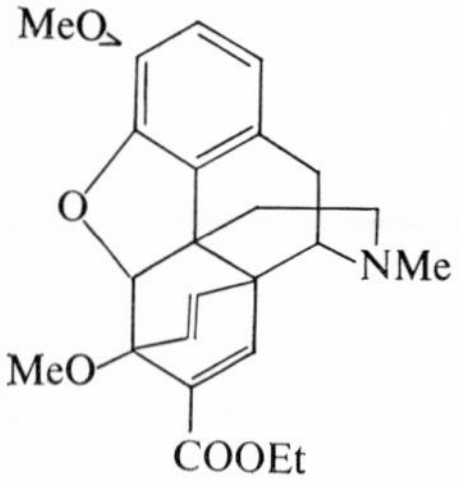

(I)

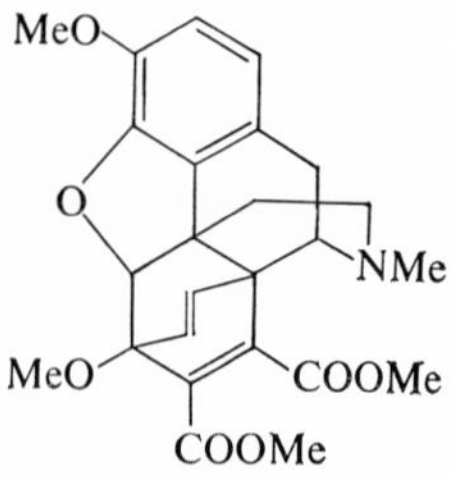

(II)

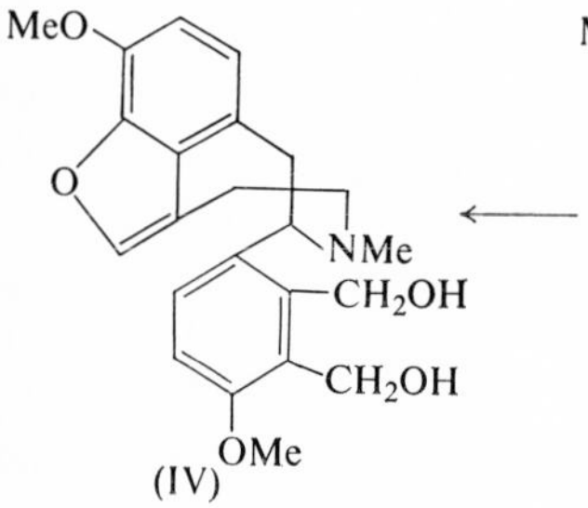

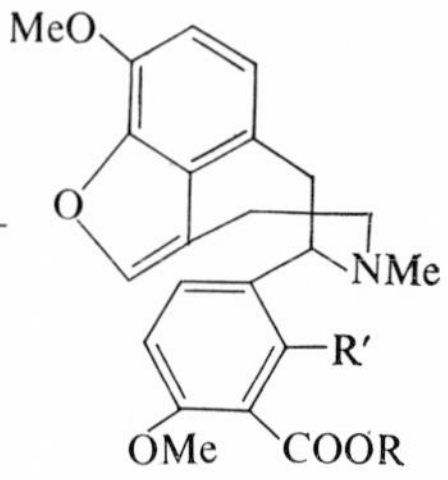

(III)

(IV)

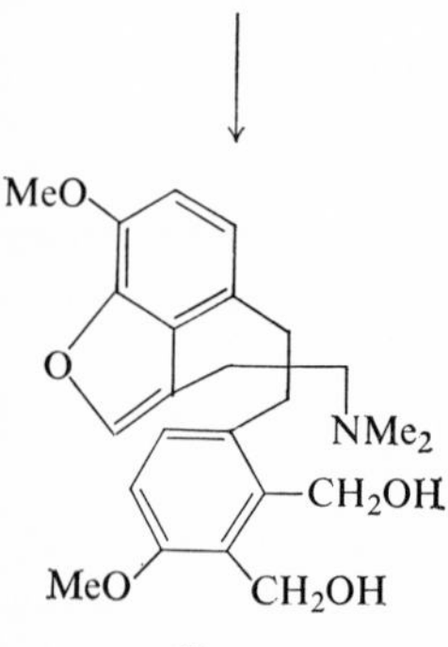

(V)

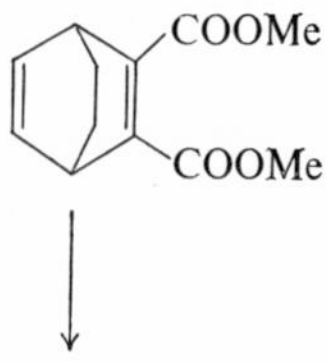

(VI)

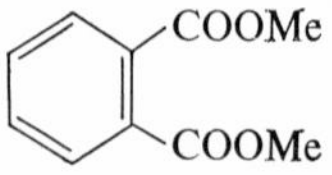

(VII)

forms a methiodide and may be degraded to the methine base (V), the ultraviolet spectrum of which provides clear evidence of the conjugation of the two aromatic nuclei. Attempts to effect a similar thermal rearrangement of thebainequinol (197) failed, and possibly an electron-withdrawing group at position 7 in the adduct is necessary for easy transformation.

G. *The reaction of dihydrothebaine and related bases with Grignard reagents*

It has been shown that the rearrangements of thebaine have a key move, namely the attack of the 4,5-ether bridge by a proton or other positive ion, but the process can only go to completion if there is some way of neutralising the electron deficit at C-5 resulting from fission of the ether link. In the rearrangements the deficit is made up by migration of the side-chain (morphothebaine, thebenine, phenyldihydrothebaine) or of the quinol nucleus of thebainequinol (flavothebaone). Dihydrothebaine (237, B = OMe), dihydro-codeinone enol acetate (237, B = OAc) and deoxycodeine-C (237, B = H) all contain a 4,5-oxygen bridge activated by a 6,7-double bond, but these compounds do not suffer ether bridge fission when heated with acids, as no stabilisation of the carbonium ion can occur by rearrangement, since the driving force of aromatisation is absent. However, when the electron deficit at C-5 can be made up by the supply of an electron pair from the reagent, ether bridge fission does occur. Grignard reagents can supply such an electron pair and the necessary positive ion to attack the ether bridge, and all three bases are attacked by such reagents with the production of phenolic bases. Neutralisation of the initially-formed carbonium ion can occur by attack by the alkyl anion directly at C-5 (238) or by attack at C-7 and migration of the double bond (238a). In the cases of dihydrothebaine and dihydrocodeinone enol acetate the initial products are sensitive enol ethers or acetates and these are readily hydrolysed during isolation of the products, which are 5- and 7-alkyldihydrothebainones (239) and (239a). Deoxycodeine-C also adds ethyl mercaptan with ether bridge opening presumably by a similar process, to give ethylthiodihydrodeoxycodeine. Dihydrocodeinone undergoes ether bridge opening on reduction by Clemmensen's method, the necessary electron pair being

(237)   (238)   (239)

(237a)   (238a)   (239a)

(240)   (241)   (242)

supplied by the zinc, the product being dihydrothebainone, which is also obtained from the same starting material by the action of concentrated hydrochloric acid and ethyl mercaptan; the electron pair in this case comes from the sulphur atom (240) and the initial product (241) then loses the added group to give dihydrothebainone (242).

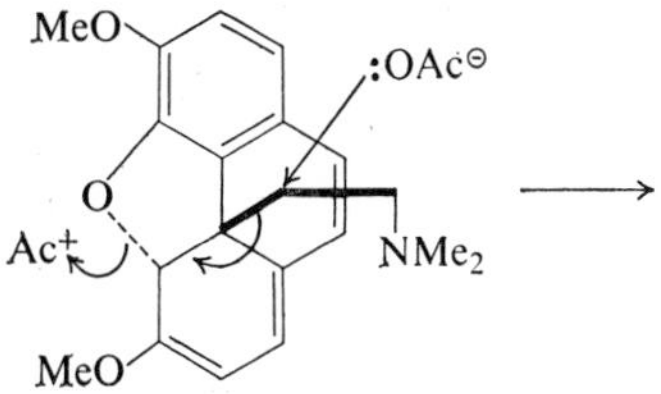

(243)

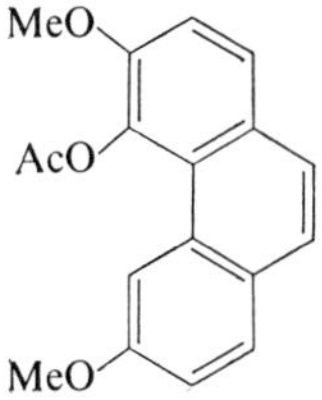

(244)

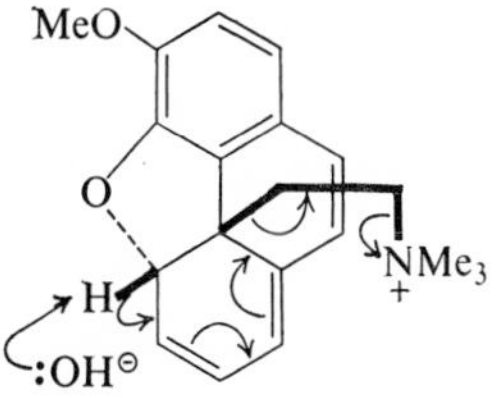

(246)

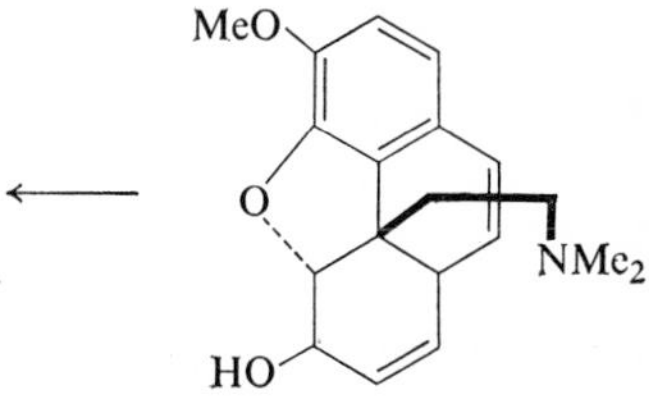

(245)

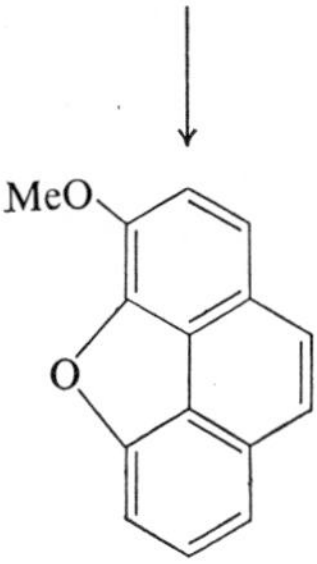

(247)

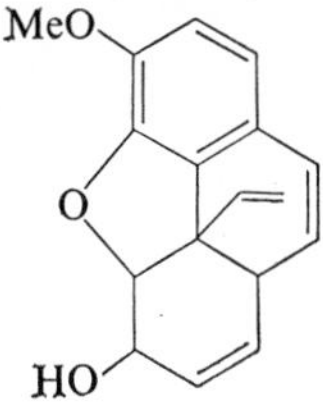

(248)

H. Other aromatisations

The acetolysis of thebaine methiodide to acetylthebaol (244) presumably proceeds by initial fission of the nitrogen containing ring and subsequent opening of the ether bridge with *trans* elimination of the side-chain as β-acetoxydimethylamino-ethane, as shown in formula (243). α-Codeimethine (245) can achieve the same state of oxidation as the base (243) by dehydration, and the subsequent course of the acetolysis of this base is clear. The elimination of the side-chain from α-codeimethine on Hofmann degradation proceeds by dehydration and non-stereospecific elimination of the C-5 hydrogen and the C-13 substituent (246) to give methyl morphenol (247). It may be noted that pyrolysis of the *N*-oxide of the methine base gives the 13-vinyl compound (248), which is then stable to attack by alkali.

Potent analgesics derived from the morphine alkaloids

An extensive study has been made of the effects of modification of the morphine molecule on analgesic power, and the following generalisations may be made.

(a) Methylation of the phenolic hydroxyl group decreases the activity by about 80–90 per cent.
(b) Methylation of the alcoholic hydroxyl group almost doubles the activity.
(c) Reduction of the double bond results in an approximately three-fold increase in activity.
(d) Oxidation of the alcoholic group to a C-6 carbonyl group increases the activity 2–6-fold.
(e) Removal of the C-6 hydroxyl group and replacement of this by hydrogen increases the activity about three times.
(f) Quaternisation of the nitrogen atom, fission of the nitrogen ring and opening of the oxide bridge generally involve complete loss of activity.

(g) Replacement of the *N*-methyl group by *N*-β-phenylethyl brings about a 10–15-fold increase in activity, but replacement by *N*-allyl results in the production of a compound capable of antagonising the analgesic and respiratory depressant effects of morphine, although alone the compound appears to be an effective analgesic in man with a potency about equal to that of morphine.

(h) The introduction of a C-14 hydroxyl or acetoxyl group and of a C-5 methyl group in certain cases brings about a considerable increase in activity.

The most active analgesics obtained in this way are methyldihydromorphinone (249), derived from the base (239), 14-acetoxydihydrocodeinone (250) and *N*-β-phenylethylnormorphine (251).

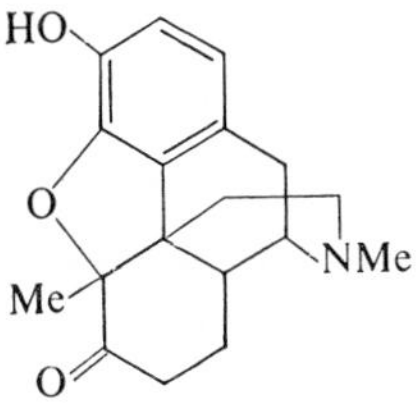

(249)

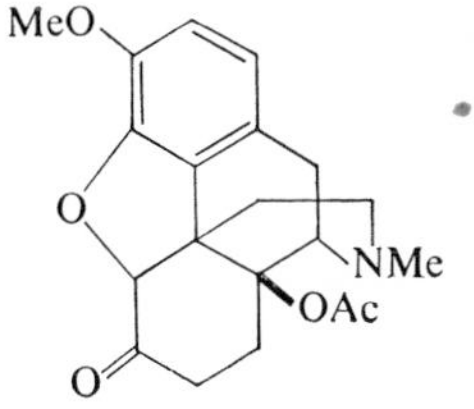

(250)

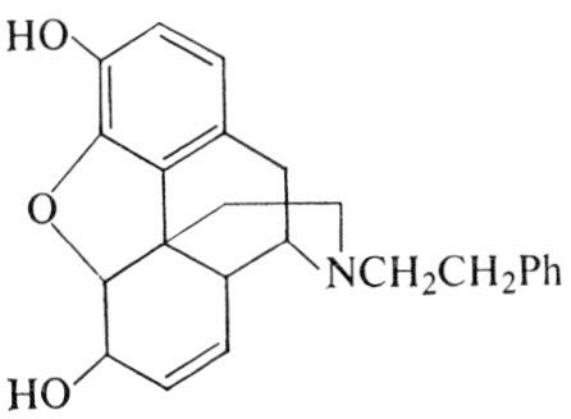

(251)

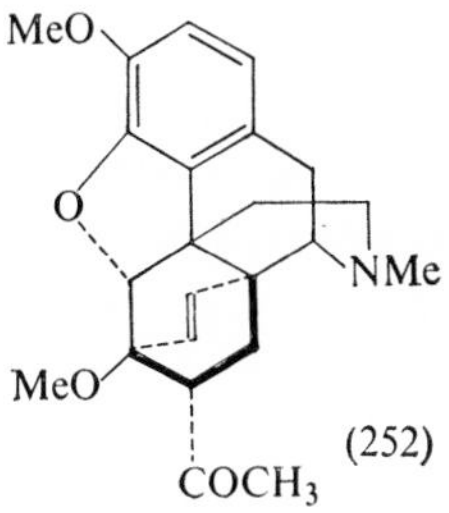

(252)

However, the writer has recently discovered a series of bases derived from the Diels–Alder adduct (252) of thebaine and methyl vinyl ketone (this adduct itself is about as potent an analgesic as morphine) having activities never previously approached in the whole morphine series. Treatment of this adduct with Grignard reagents affords a series of alcohols (253) one of which (253,

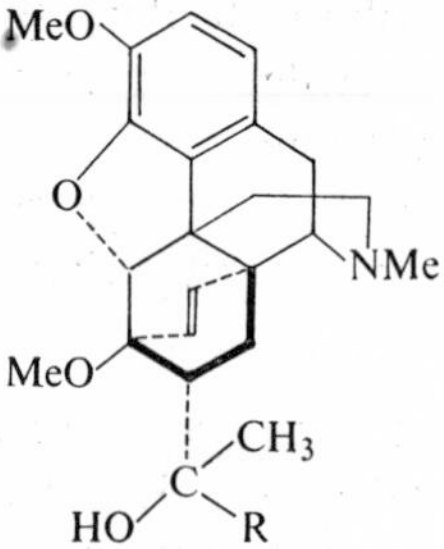

(253)

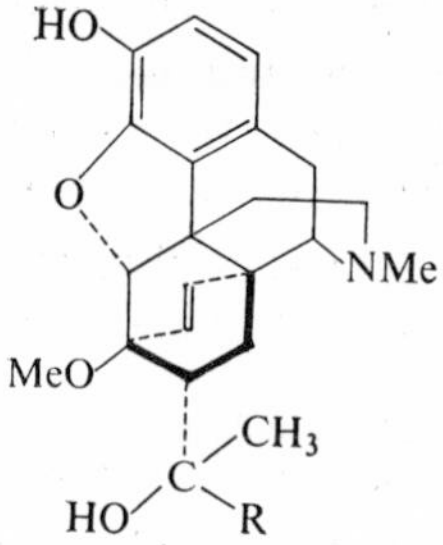

(254)

R = CH_2CH_2Ph) is 555 times as potent as morphine, and de-methylation of these alcohols yields a series of even more potent phenols (254) several of which are more than 1,000 times as active as morphine and one (254, R = isoamyl) is almost 10,000 times as potent as the alkaloid, and is the most potent analgesic so far discovered.

OTHER ALKALOIDS OF THE MORPHINE GROUP

A. Sinomenine

This alkaloid, from the Japanese plant *Sinomenium acutum* is a phenolic base of composition $C_{19}H_{23}O_4N$ containing two methoxyl groups and a reducible $\alpha\beta$-unsaturated ketone system. Like thebaine it is very easily degraded to fully-aromatic phenanthrene derivatives with the loss of the *N*-methyl group and two other carbon atoms, and the ready occurrence of this characteristic reaction quickly led to the assignment of the alkaloid to the morphine group. Sinomenine methiodide when heated with benzoic anhydride is degraded in this way to dibenzoylsinomenol (255, R = COPh), which may be hydrolysed to sinomenol (255,

R = H), the structure of which was revealed by methylation to 3,4,6,7-tetramethoxyphenanthrene (255, R = Me) and ethylation to 4,6-diethoxy-3,7-dimethoxyphenanthrene (255, R = Et), both of which were identical with material prepared by the Pschorr phenanthrene synthesis.

(255)   (256)   (257)

These reactions clearly indicated the substitution pattern of the phenanthrene nucleus and suggested a possible relationship of sinomenine to thebainone (159), which gives 4,6-diacetoxy-3-methoxyphenanthrene on acetolysis, and this was quickly confirmed by reduction of the base with sodium amalgam, which results in double bond reduction and removal of the methoxyl group from the α-methoxyketone so produced, to yield demethoxydihydrosinomenine (257), which is the *antipode* of dihydrothebainone (152). Sinomenine may thus be assigned the structure (256), with which all of its reactions are compatible. From demethoxydihydrosinomenine (257), using Gates's procedure (+)-morphine, the enantiomorph of the natural alkaloid, has been prepared. The oxide bridge between positions 4 and 5 may be closed in sinomenine itself by bromination, giving 1-bromo-sinomeneine (258), which may be hydrolysed to the α-diketone (259), and this may be converted through the benzilic acid (260) into the ketone (261). Sinomenine itself may also be hydrolysed to an α-diketone, sinomeninone (262), which on oxidation with

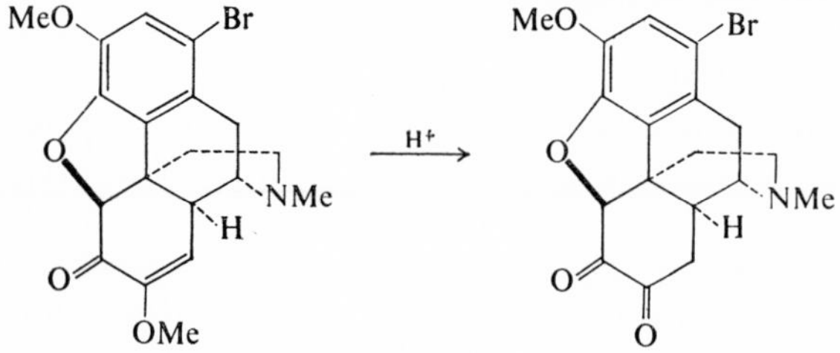

(258)

(259)

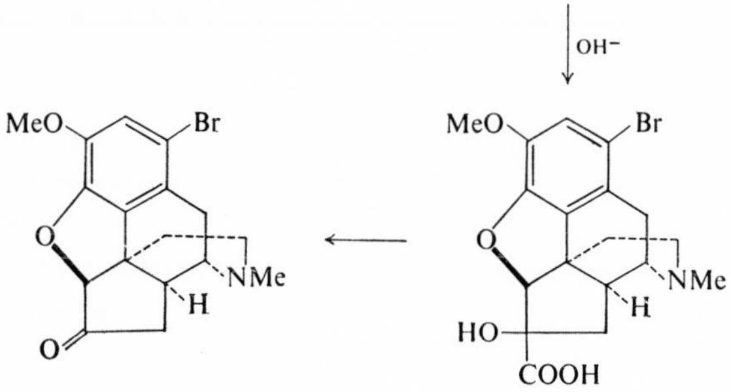

(261)

(260)

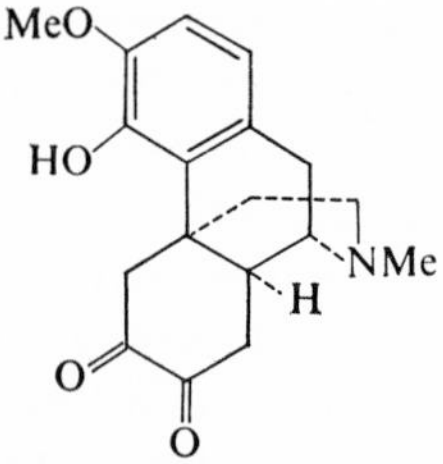

(262)

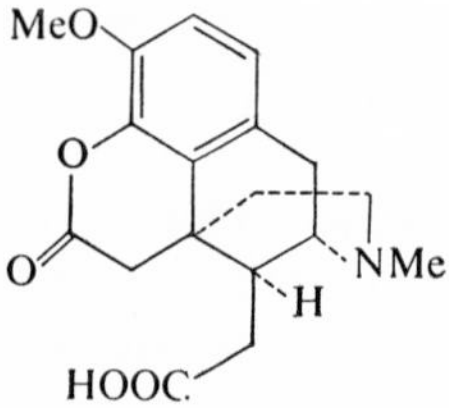

(263)

hydrogen peroxide suffers ring fission to give the lactone-acid (263), sinomeninic acid.

B. Hasubanonine

Hasubanonine is an alkaloid isolated from the Japanese plant *Stephania japonica* Miers. It has the composition $C_{21}H_{27}O_5N$, is non-phenolic and contains four methoxyl groups, one *N*-methyl and a carbonyl group which is shown spectroscopically to be part of an $\alpha\beta$-unsaturated ketone system. Hofmann degradation of the alkaloid proceeds with the formation of an alkali-soluble methine base isomeric with the original alkaloid but containing only three methoxyl groups. When this methine base is heated with acetic anhydride and sodium acetate it suffers aromatisation and loss of the nitrogen-containing side-chain, indicating that hasubanonine belongs to the morphine group. The product of this acetolysis, acetylhasubanol, may be hydrolysed and methylated to methyl-hasubanol, which is 3,4,6,8-tetramethoxyphenanthrene identical with material prepared by the Pschorr phenanthrene synthesis.

Since the colour reactions of hasubanol indicate that it contains a free position *para* to the hydroxyl group this phenol must have the structure (264) or (265), and of these the former is ruled out since hasubanonine itself may be oxidised to hemipinic acid (266). The Hofmann degradation of hasubanonine to the methine base $C_{21}H_{27}O_5N$ clearly involves *O*-demethylation and this base must owe its alkali solubility to the presence of an enolised α- or β-diketone system in the molecule, because it is inconceivable that a *phenolic* hydroxyl group would be lost during acetolysis. The only α- or β-diketone system degradable to hasubanol that can be constructed is that of (268). The original workers in this field assumed that the hydroxyl group of hasubanol is derived from the carbonyl group of hasubanonine and assigned the structure (267) to the alkaloid, but, as the writer has pointed out elsewhere, this assumption is unwarranted, and the methine base (268) could equally well arise from the structure (269), which is equally compatible with all the recorded reactions of the alkaloid. Hasu-

banonine resists hydrogenation and in both structures (267) and
(269) the double bond is fully substituted, and would accordingly
be expected to be difficult to reduce. There is little to choose between
the two possibilities on biogenetic grounds, as is revealed in
Chapter 14.

(264)   (265)   (266)

(267)   (268)   (269)

C. Metaphenine

The structure of this alkaloid, which occurs alongside hasubanonine, has not yet been determined with certainty. It has the
composition $C_{19}H_{23}O_5N$ and contains two methoxyl groups, one
alcoholic hydroxyl group and a carbonyl series. It appears to
belong to the morphine series since alkaline degradation of its
methiodide gives a phenanthrene derivative (the structure of which

has not been determined) with the loss of the nitrogen-containing side-chain. Hydrogenation of the base proceeds with elimination of the hydroxyl group, which is therefore placed in the benzylic position 10; the carbonyl group is unaffected during this reaction and since the C-6 carbonyl group of dihydrocodeinone is reducible the placement of this group at the more hindered position 8 is plausible. Assuming that the base contains a C-3 methoxyl group

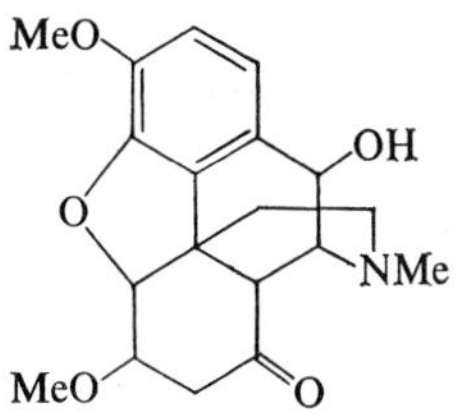

(270)

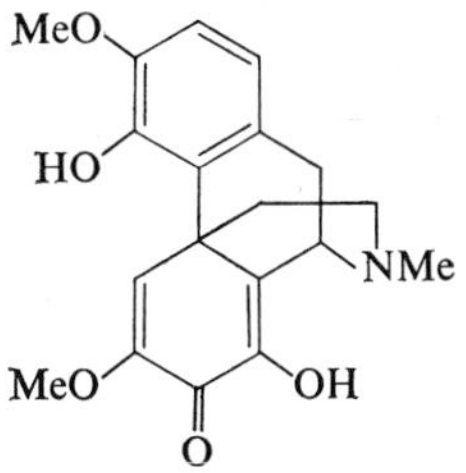

(271)

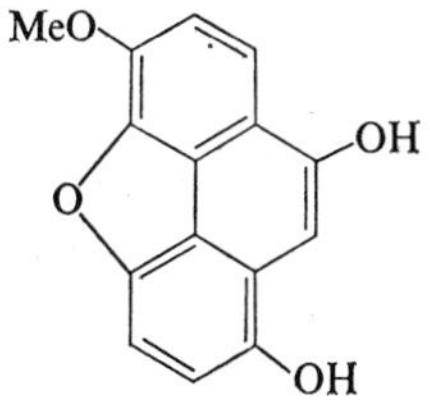

(272)

and that the fifth oxygen atom, which is inactive, is present in a 4,5-ether bridge, the further finding that metaphenine contains a reactive methylene group leads to the formula (270) for the base, and the derivation of both this and hasubanonine (either possible structure) from the precursor (271) presents no difficulties (see Chapter 14). If the structure (270) for metaphenine is correct the most likely structure for the phenanthrene degradation product is (272).

D. *Alkaloids from* Croton *species*

The Jamaican plant *Croton linearis* Jacq. (Spanish rosemary) contains, among other alkaloids, three bases that may be assigned to the morphine group, although the substitution pattern, particularly in the aromatic nucleus, is different from that encountered

(273)   (274)   (275)

(276)   (277)   (278)

in the other alkaloids of the group. Of these bases crotonosine, $C_{17}H_{17}O_3N$, contains one phenolic hydroxyl, one methoxyl, one secondary amino and one carbonyl group, and the last of these, together with two reducible double bonds, forms an isolated cross-conjugated dienone chromophore. Allowing for the presence of these groups the composition of the alkaloid indicates that it must be tetracyclic. The first indication that crotonosine might belong to the morphine group was provided by the acid-catalysed re-arrangement of the alkaloid to a non-ketonic phenol having the u.v. absorption of an aporphine. Such a structure could only arise from a dienone of the type (273) or (274) and crotonosine cannot contain the system of (274) in which the dienone system is conjugated with the aromatic nucleus. This assignment to the morphine group was supported by the acetolysis of *O,N*-dimethylcrotonosine methioide, which proceeds with the extrusion of the nitrogen-containing side-chain and the formation of a nitrogen-free product having the ultraviolet absorption of a phenanthrene. The position of the two remaining oxygen atoms on the skeleton of (273) in crotonosine could most convincingly be determined by the synthesis of either this phenanthrene or the aporphine mentioned above, but this has not been done. Instead the assignment was made on the basis of the nuclear magnetic resonance spectra of the aporphine *O,O*-dimethyl-*N*-acetylapocrotonosine, *N,N*-diacetylcrotonosine and *N,N*-diacetyltetrahydrocrotonosine, which, together with the failure of the Gibbs colour test with crotonosine (this when positive indicates the presence of a free position *para* to a phenolic hydroxyl), led to the structure (276) for the alkaloid, and (275) for the related aporphine.

The other two alkaloids from the same source are closely related to crotonosine. "Base-A" is identical with *O,N*-dimethyl-crotonosine, while linearisine, $C_{18}H_{21}O_3N$, which contains a simple $\alpha\beta$-unsaturated ketone chromophore, is phenolic, gives a negative Gibbs colour test and on *O*-methylation and hydro-genation yields *O,N*-dimethyltetrahydrocrotonosine, must be *N*-methyldihydrocrotonosine. That this is the 8,14-dihydro-compound (277) and not the 5,6-dihydroisomer was shown by the fact that the ultraviolet absorption of the methine base (278) is very similar to that of α-codeimethine (47) and quite different from that of β-codeimethine (48).

The biogenesis of these alkaloids is discussed in Chapter 14.

Since completion of the manuscript of this book the necessity for revision of the structures in the foregoing section has been

6

indicated. Careful study of the nuclear magnetic resonance spectra of crotonosine and its derivatives has shown that the alkaloid has the structure (279), the corresponding apo-compound being (280), the precise orientation of hydroxyl and methoxyl groups being undefined. Another alkaloid, pronuciferine, is the *O,N*-dimethyl ether of crotonosine and sodium borohydride reduction of this

R/R' = H/Me or Me/H

gives the dienol (281) which with acid yields the aporphine alkaloid nuciferine (282). It is probable that the dioxy-substituted aporphine alkaloids are formed in Nature by such a route, through bases of the crotonosine-pronuciferine group. The precise structure of linearisine remains to be determined since the ultraviolet absorption spectrum of the methine base is no longer definitive.

CHAPTER 8

The Berberine and Tetrahydroberberine Alkaloids

THE bases of this group are either the quaternary hydroxides of structure (1), the corresponding pseudo-bases (2) or the tetrahydro-bases (3). They all, with one exception, have the substitution pattern of the bases (1)–(3), and they are believed to arise naturally by the condensation of secondary bases of the benzylisoquinoline series (4) with formaldehyde or its equivalent, the condensation

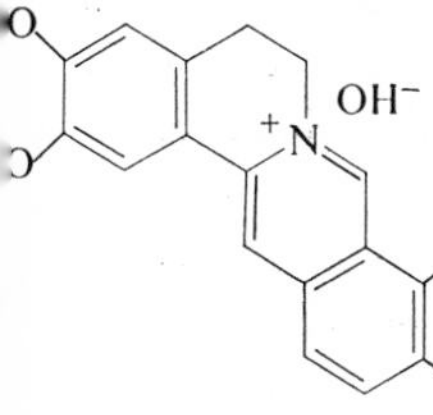

(1) 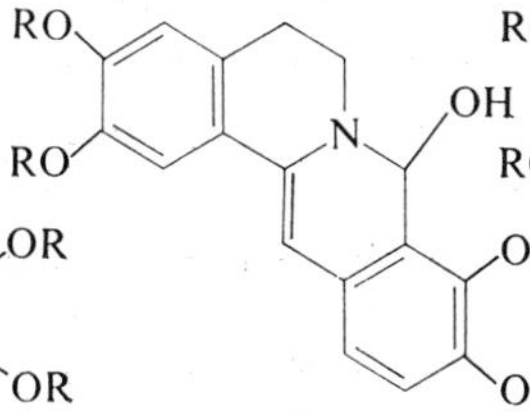   (2) 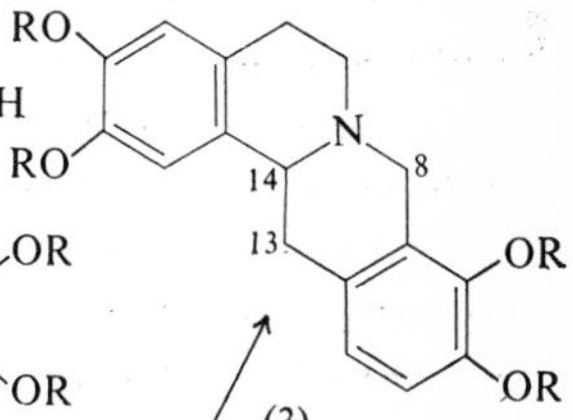   (3)

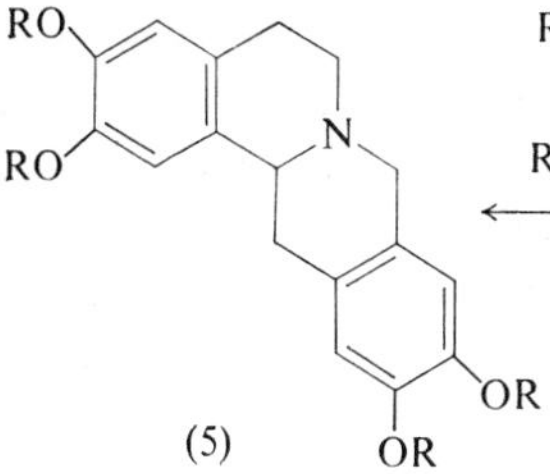

(5) 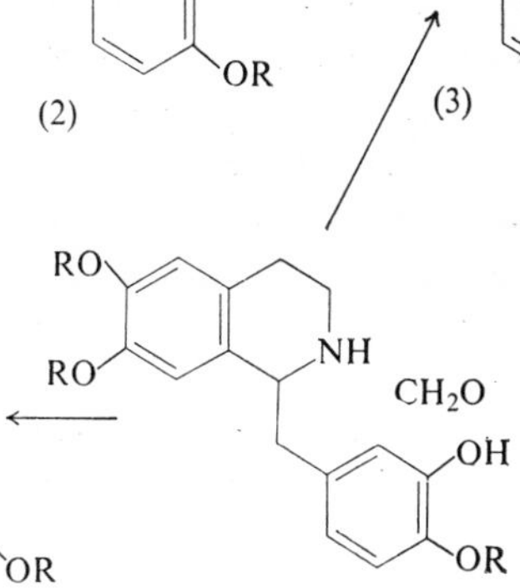   (4)

probably occurring *ortho* to a phenolic hydroxyl group in the precursor. Attempts to realise this condensation in the laboratory have led to a mixture of bases of types (3) and (5) when both substituents in the benzyl nucleus are hydroxyl groups, but only to bases of type (5) in the fully methylated series; only one alkaloid has so far been found with the substitution pattern (5).

Berberine

This widely distributed alkaloid, which has the composition $C_{20}H_{19}O_5N$ and contains one methylenedioxy and two methoxyl groups, when carefully generated from its salts by barium hydroxide is obtained as a strong base in the form of a quaternary hydroxide having the same ultraviolet absorption as the salts, but this is converted by an excess of alkali into an isomeric weaker base showing different ultraviolet absorption, which, however, still gives the same salts with acids. This second base behaves in some reactions as if it were an aldehyde, condensing with acetone and hydroxylamine, and undergoing the Cannizzaro reaction. These reactions indicate that berberine is a quaternary hydroxide (6) readily converted by an excess of alkali into the related pseudo-base (7), which is in equilibrium with the secondary-amino aldehyde (8); both the quaternary hydroxide and the pseudo-base give the same salt with mineral acids. In this respect the pseudo-base form of berberine and similar bases in this series resemble cotarnine (9, R = OMe) and hydrastinine (9, R = H) which are in equilibrium with the corresponding aldehyde forms (9*a*) and readily form quaternary salts (10) with mineral acids. These bases, obtainable from the alkaloids narcotine and hydrastine, are discussed in detail in Chapter 11.

The oxidation of berberine with an excess of permanganate affords hemipinic acid (11), but the use of a restricted amount of the oxidising agent results in less drastic fission of the alkaloid, and five compounds still containing all the original 20 carbon atoms of berberine but with increasing oxygen content can be obtained in this way, namely oxyberberine $C_{20}H_{17}O_5N$, dioxyberberine

$C_{20}H_{17}O_6N$, berberal $C_{20}H_{17}O_7N$, anhydroberberilic $C_{20}H_{17}O_8N$ and berberilic acid $C_{20}H_{19}O_9N$. The elucidation of the structures of these degradation products enabled a structure to be assigned to the parent alkaloid.

Berberilic acid contains two carboxyl groups and is readily converted with loss of water into anhydroberberilic acid which

only contains one. Both acids on hydrolysis with sulphuric acid yield hemipinic acid (11) and a primary amino-acid $C_{10}H_{11}O_4N$ which is very readily dehydrated to a lactam $C_{10}H_9O_3N$ containing an imino group. The easy closure of the lactam ring indicates that the amino-bearing chain and the carboxyl group must be *ortho* substituents on the oxidation-stable aromatic nucleus. As the lactam can be converted into oxyhydrastinine (12, R = Me) by a process involving the replacement of —NH— by —NMe— it must itself have the structure (12, R = H) and the amino-acid from which it is derived must be (13). Since this acid can be converted back into anhydroberberilic acid by heating with hemipinic acid, anhydroberberilic acid must have the structure (14) and berberilic acid, two forms of which have been isolated both giving the anhydro-acid on dehydration, may be assigned the structures (15) and (16).

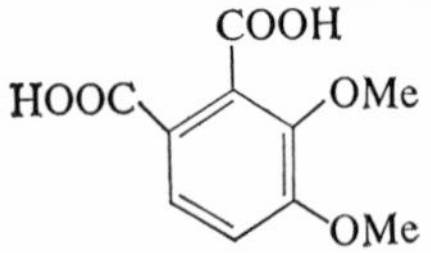

(11)

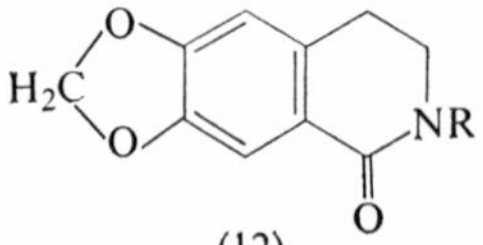

(12)

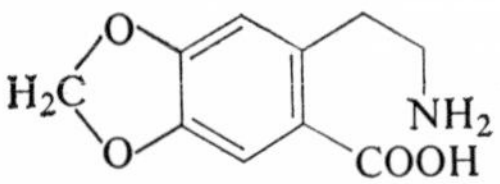

(13)

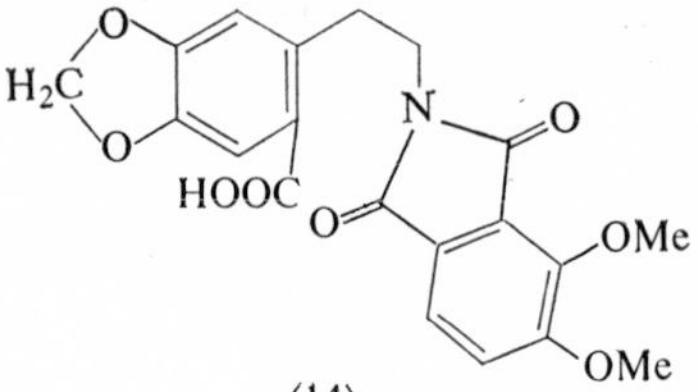

(14)

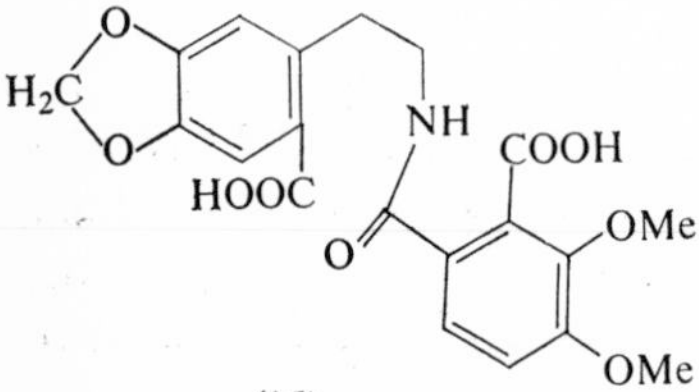

(15)

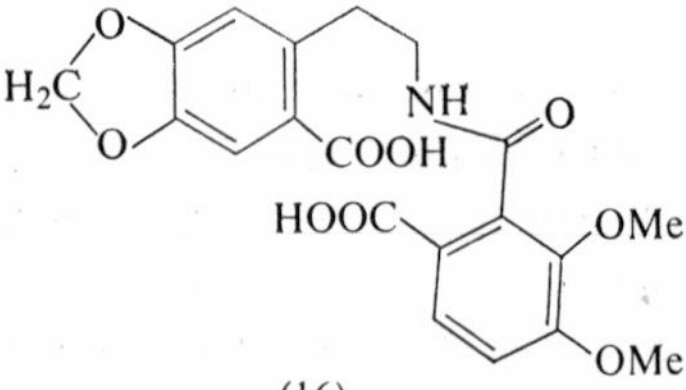

(16)

Berberal, which is in a lower state of oxidation than berberilic acid, on hydrolysis with sulphuric acid yields the same amino-acid (13) as the latter, together with ψ-opianic acid $C_{10}H_{10}O_5$. ψ-Opianic acid is isomeric with and bears a strong resemblance to opianic acid, obtainable by the hydrolysis or oxidative hydrolysis of narcotine and hydrastine (see Chapter 11). Both are mono-basic aldehydic acids giving hemipinic acid on further oxidation, and both give lactones, ψ-meconine and meconine, on reduction. Meconine must have the structure (18) since it can be synthesised from 2,3-dimethoxybenzoic acid (17) by the action of formaldehyde and hydrochloric acid and accordingly ψ-meconine must have the isomeric structure (19) since both are related to hemipinic acid (11), and opianic acid and ψ-opianic acid may be formulated as (20)

and (21) respectively. It has been conclusively proved that opianic acid reacts in the hydroxymeconine form (22, R = OH) and that in its reaction with aniline the nitrogen atom of the base becomes attached to the aldehydic carbon atom, the product being the lactonised aldehyde–ammonia (22, R = PhNH), and assuming that ψ-opianic acid behaves in the same way, berberal, which may be obtained from the amino-acid (13) and ψ-opianic acid, may be assigned the structure (23), from which the structures (24) and (25) for the pseudo-base and quaternary hydroxide forms of berberine may be deduced.

The first product of oxidation of berberine is the amide oxyberberine (29) and electrolytic reduction of this affords tetrahydroberberine (30), which is the alkaloid canadine. As oxidation of
canadine yields berberine a synthesis of oxyberberine can be
regarded as a total synthesis of berberine. Such a synthesis has been
achieved by the Bischler–Napieralsky cyclisation of the imide (28)

(23)   (24)

(25)

prepared from homopiperonylamine (26) and homohemipinic
anhydride (27), and also by zinc–acetic acid reduction of the
product (32) of cyclisation of the amide (31) obtained from homopiperonylamine (26) and meconine carboxylic acid. Oxyberberine
(29) is also one of the products of Cannizzaro reaction on berberine,
the second product being the non-hydroxylic dihydroberberine.

Bases of both the berberine and tetrahydroberberine type occur
naturally, and the former are believed to arise from the latter by
oxidation in the plant, and as a result of the ease with which this

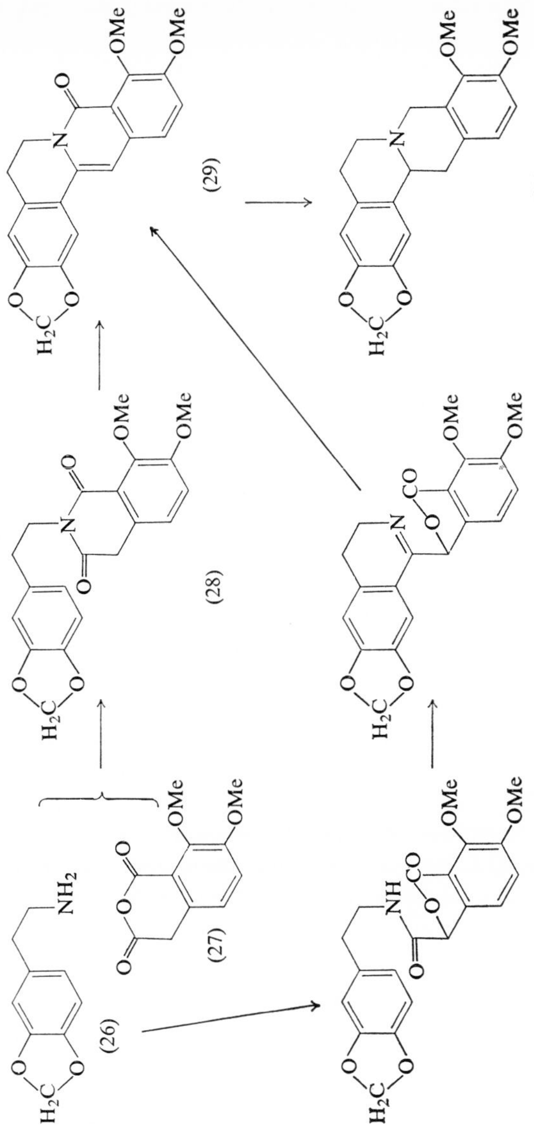
(26)
(27)
(28)
(29)
(30)
(31)
(32)
H$_2$C
NH$_2$
OMe
NH
CO
N

reaction occurs with canadine this alkaloid is always accompanied by berberine, although berberine is occasionally found alone.

Tetrahydropalmatine

This alkaloid has the structure (33, R = R′ = Me) and affords hemipinic acid (11) and *m*-hemipinic acid (35) on oxidation, together with corydaldine (34, R = R′ = Me). Corypalmine and isocorypalmine are a pair of isomeric monophenolic bases giving tetrahydropalmatine on *O*-methylation; the ethyl ethers of these

(33)   (34)   (35)

two bases yield respectively on oxidation the amides (34, R = Et, R′ = Me) and (34, R = Me, R′ = Et) showing that corypalmine is the base (33, R = H, R′ = Me) and isocorypalmine the base (33, R = Me, R′ = H). The berberine analogues of all three bases, namely palmatine, jatrorrhizine and columbamine, are known.

Corydaline

This alkaloid, from *Corydalis tuberosa*, has the composition $C_{22}H_{27}O_4N$ and occurs naturally in association with its oxidation product dehydrocorydaline $C_{22}H_{23}O_4N$, and the two bases have the same relationship as canadine and berberine or tetrahydropalmatine and palmatine. As corydaline contains four methoxyl groups and CH_2 more than tetrahydropalmatine it must bear a *C*-methyl group or must alternatively be a ring-B homologue of this base (the ready dehydrogenation to dehydrocorydaline, the ultraviolet absorption of which is identical with that of berberine,

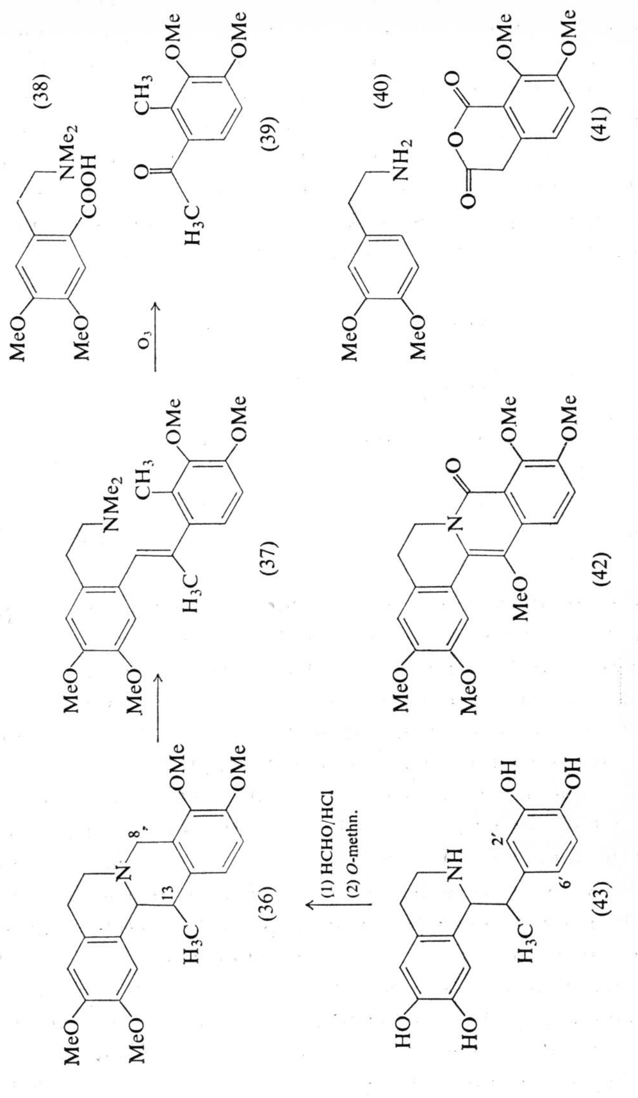
(36)
(37)
(38)
(39)
(40)
(41)
(42)
(43)
O₃
(1) HCHO/HCl
(2) O-methn.

rules out the possibility of an extra methylene group being present in ring-C). That it contains a *C*-methyl group is suggested by the fact that reduction of dehydrocorydaline gives not only (±)-corydaline but also the diastereoisomeric (±)-mesocorydaline, indicating the production of *two* asymmetric centres during the reaction. The oxidation of corydaline gives hemipinic acid (11) and corydaldine (34, R = R′ = Me), and this shows that the *C*-methyl group must be at position 8 or 13, and since dehydro-corydaline, like berberine, undergoes the Cannizzaro reaction as if

(44) (45) (46)

it were an aldehyde (giving oxodehydrocorydaline and dihydro-dehydrocorydaline) position 8 for this group can be eliminated, leading to structure (36) for corydaline. This has been confirmed by the ozonolysis of the base (37), produced by Hofmann and Emde degradations of the alkaloid, which furnishes the amino-acid (38) and 3,4-dimethoxy-2-methylacetophenone (39).

A synthesis of oxodehydrocorydaline (42) (and hence of corydaline and dehydrocorydaline) from homoveratrylamine (40) and the anhydride (41), follows lines analogous to those by which oxyberberine was prepared. Corydaline itself has also been synthesised from methyltetrahydropapaveroline (43) by condensation with formaldehyde followed by *O*-methylation, and in this case the base is accompanied by an isomer resulting from condensation with the formaldehyde at position 6′ instead of 2′. Methyltetrahydropapaveroline (43) was prepared from papaverine (44) by condensation of formaldehyde with the reactive methylene group, reduction of the product (45) to the tetramethoxy analogue of (43) and demethylation.

A number of other bases bearing a C-13 methyl group have been discovered; these differ from corydaline only in the substitution on the four oxygen atoms.

Corleximine

This alkaloid, from *Dicentra eximia*, contains two phenolic hydroxyl groups and gives a dimethyl ether isomeric with tetra-hydropalmatine. Oxidation of the dimethyl ether to a berberine-like quaternary hydroxide followed by reduction affords the racemic dimethyl ether, which is identical with norcoralydine (46, R = Me) obtained by the condensation of tetrahydropapaverine with formaldehyde, during which cyclisation occurs with position 6′ rather than 2′, and coreximine therefore belongs to a series isomeric with the main tetrahydroberberine group, though it is the only representative of this series so far discovered in Nature. Coreximine diethyl ether can be oxidised to 5-ethoxy-4-methoxy-phthalic acid and the amide (34, R = Me, R′ = Et) one of the phenolic hydroxyl groups must be at position 2, and on the assumption that in the plant cyclisation of a benzyltetrahydro-isoquinoline alkaloid with formaldehyde occurs *para* and not *meta* to hydroxyl, coreximine was assigned the structure (46, R = H). This assignment was shown to be correct by the synthesis of the diethyl ether (46, R = Et) by the conventional route.

Ophiocarpine

This alkaloid is the only known example of a hydroxytetra-hydroberberine, and represents the first oxidation step along the assumed biogenetic pathway from tetrahydroberberine to hydra-stine (see Chapter 14). It has the composition $C_{20}H_{21}O_5N$ and contains one alcoholic hydroxyl, one methylenedioxy and two methoxyl groups. It may be dehydrated by prolonged boiling with hydrochloric acid and oxidation of the anhydro-compound so obtained and subsequent reduction of the berberine-like base affords racemic tetrahydroberberine (30). Careful oxidation of the alkaloid affords the amide (12, R = H), showing that the hydroxyl group must be located at position 8, 13 or 14, and as it does not behave as a pseudo-base positions 8 and 14 need not be considered, and ophiocarpine is seen to be 13-hydroxytetrahydroberberine.

CHAPTER 9

Alkaloids Related to Cryptopine

THE alkaloids related to cryptopine and those discussed in the next two chapters are believed to arise in Nature by the oxidation of tetrahydroberberine bases, though the centres involved in the production of the cryptopines and the phthalideisoquinolines are different. The bases of the cryptopine group probably arise by oxidation at position 14, followed by N-methylation of the resulting carbinolamine to the keto tertiary base, and this process has been accomplished in the laboratory (see page 183). Most of the bases of this group have analogues with the same substitution pattern in the tetrahydroberberine group, but tetrahydroberberines are known that have no cryptopine equivalent.

Cryptopine itself is one of the minor alkaloids of opium, and also occurs in small quantities in certain *Corydalis* and *Dicentra* species. It has no value in medicine, although it has been found to be a central nervous system depressant. The elucidation of the structure of the alkaloid was reported by W. H. Perkin, Jnr., in a series of papers that are now regarded as perfect examples of classical structural studies and logical reporting, though some of the structural assignments in the pseudo- and epi-cryptopine series appear to need revision in the light of modern knowledge. As a result of this work the elucidation of the structure of any new base assigned with confidence to this series became a simple matter.

Cryptopine

Cryptopine has the composition $C_{21}H_{23}O_5N$ and contains one methylenedioxy, one *N*-methyl and two methoxyl groups. The fifth oxygen atom is not easily identified in cryptopine and many of its derivatives, but is clearly revealed as a carbonyl group by infrared spectral studies. The reduction of cryptopine metho-methylsulphate with sodium amalgam results in Emde reductive opening of the nitrogen-containing ring and simultaneous reduction of the carbonyl group, the product being the secondary alcohol tetrahydromethylcryptopine $C_{22}H_{29}O_5N$. Dehydration of this to the olefine anhydrotetrahydromethylcryptopine $C_{22}H_{27}O_4N$ followed by oxidation leads to the following products:

(a) 4,5-dimethoxy-2-(2′-dimethylaminoethyl)-benzaldehyde (1),
(b) 2-methyl-3,4-methylenedioxybenzaldehyde (2),
(c) the *N*-formyl acid (3) resulting from further oxidation of the aldehyde (1),
(d) the acid (4) resulting from further oxidation of the aldehyde (2).

The structure of the base (1) was determined by Hofmann degradation to trimethylamine and the olefine $C_{11}H_{12}O$ (5), which gives *m*-hemipinic acid (6) with the loss of one carbon atom on oxidation. The aldehyde (2) on oxidation gave the acid (4) which was converted into hemipinic acid (7) by demethylenation, *O*-methylation and oxidation, and the dihydroxy-compound from the acid (4) gave isohomocatechol (8) on decarboxylation; these reactions determine the structure of the aldehyde (2).

As both aldehydes (1) and (2) together contain all the carbon atoms of anhydrotetrahydromethylcryptopine from which they are derived, this base may confidently be given the structure (9), and tetrahydromethylcryptopine must be either the alcohol (10) or the isomeric base bearing the hydroxyl group at the position marked in (10) with an asterisk. Further Hofmann degradation of anhydrotetrahydromethylcryptopine (9) yielded the corresponding vinyl compound, which on oxidation gave the aldehydes (2) and (5).

Since tetrahydromethylcryptopine (10) arises from cryptopine by the reduction of a carbonyl group, *N*-methylation and Emde reduction, cryptopine may be assigned the structure (11) or that of the 13-keto isomer. That the carbonyl group is indeed located at C-14 and not C-13 was suggested by the fact that dihydrocryptopine, the product of sodium amalgam reduction of the alkaloid, may be converted into two diastereoisomeric quaternary chlorides (12) closely resembling the two isomeric tetrahydroberberine methochlorides (13) in all their reactions. The same conclusion was

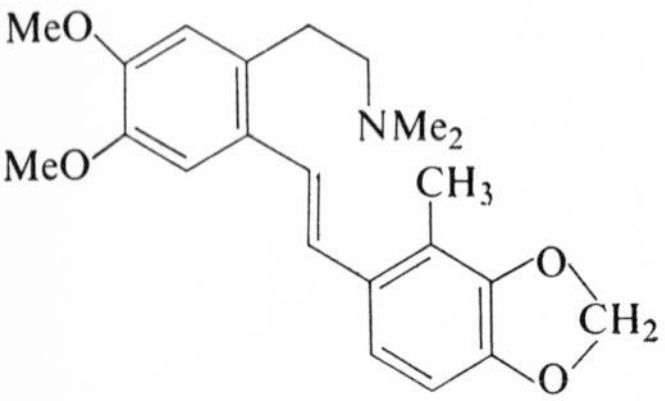

(9)

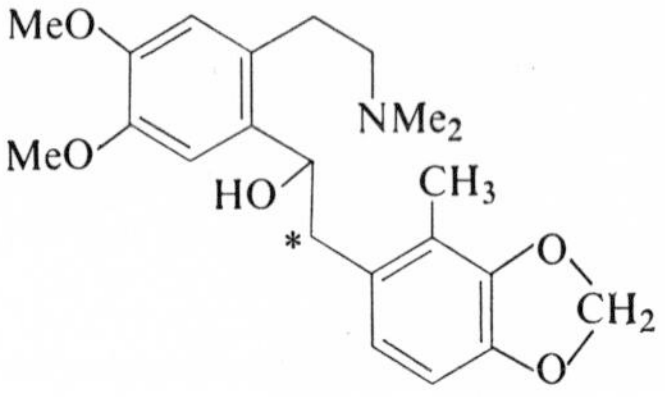

(10)

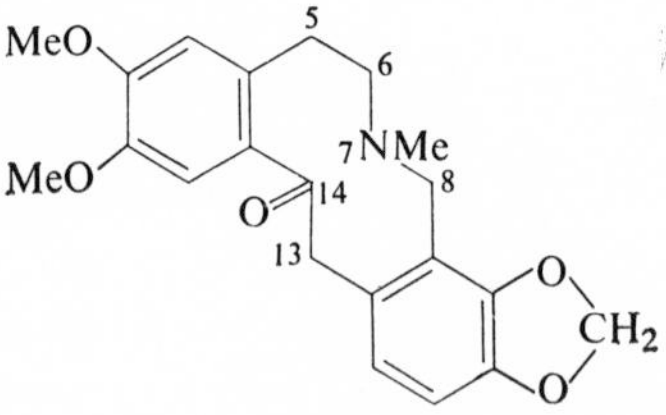

(11)

drawn from the conversion of cryptopine on treatment with phosphorus oxychloride (presumably by way of the enol chloride) into isocryptopine chloride (14) and the *N*-demethylation and oxidation of this to epiberberine (15), identical in all of its reactions with berberine (16) from which it differs only in the reversal of the methoxy–methylenedioxy substitution pattern. When this work was begun the structure of berberine had already been elucidated, and accordingly cryptopine was allotted the constitution (11). It should be noted that although a quaternary salt of the type (17) could possibly arise from a 13-keto analogue of the base (11), such a system could not be converted into a quaternary hydroxide analogous to berberine (16).

Exhaustive methylation of cryptopine affords in the first step a mixture of the ketonic γ-methylcryptopine (18) (which is the

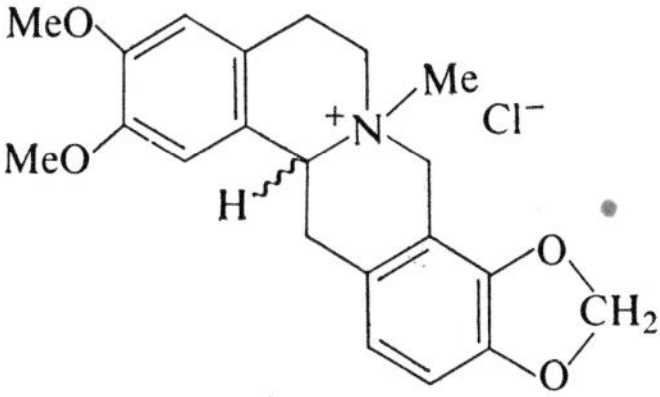

(12)

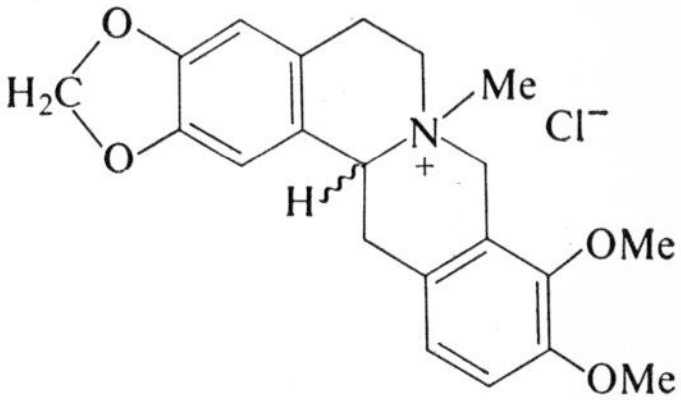

(13)

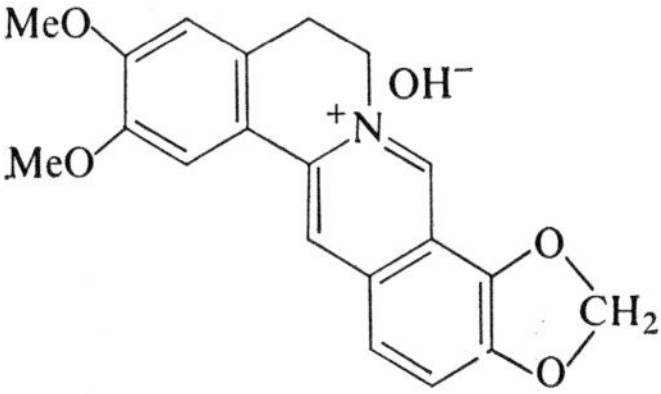

(15)

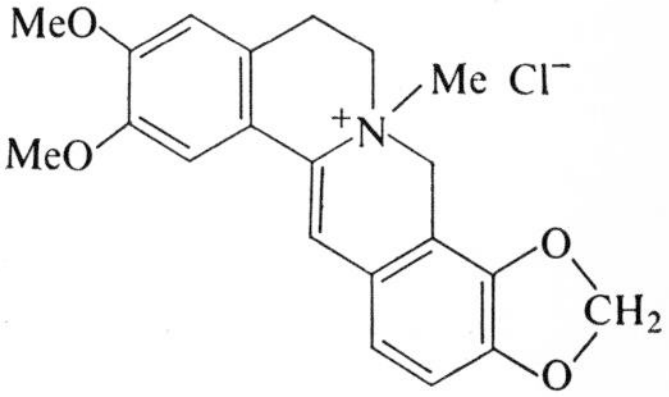

(14)

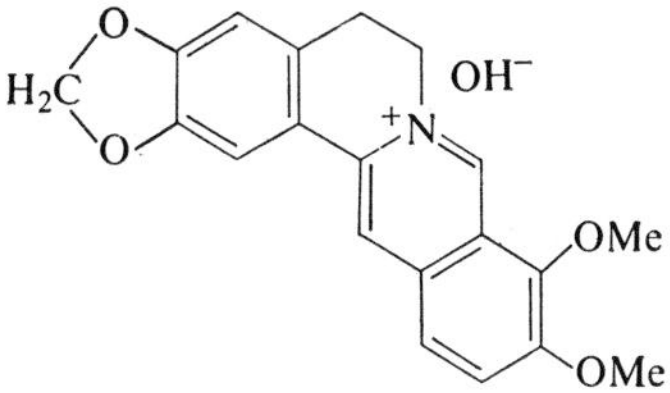

(16)

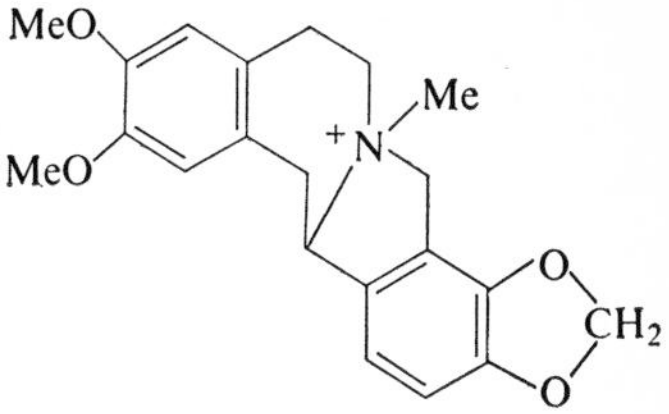

(17)

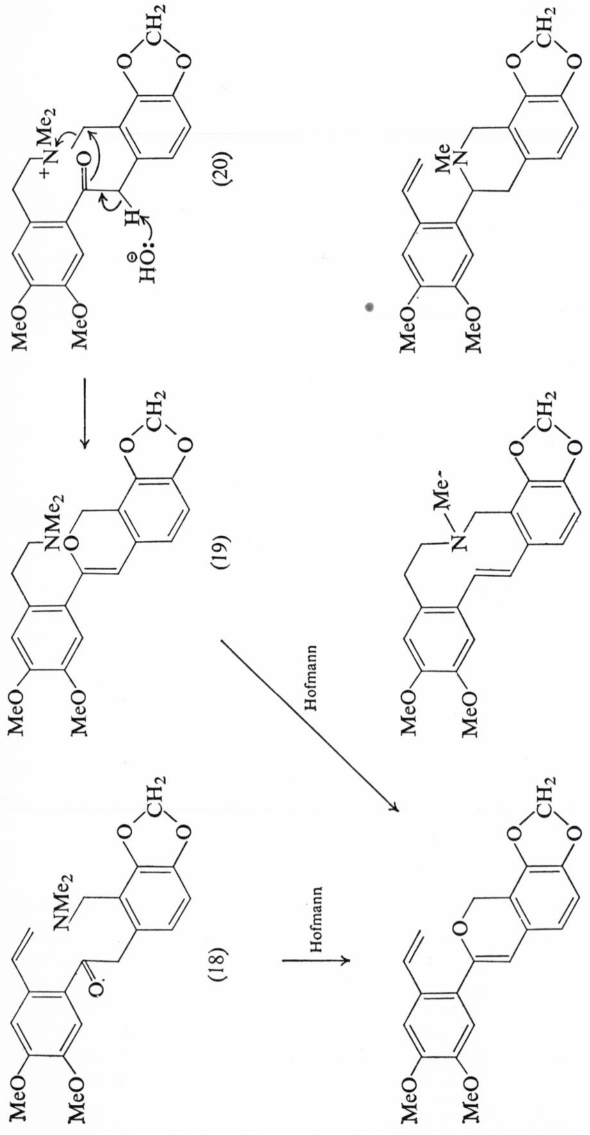
(18)
(19)
(20)
(21)
(22)
(23)
Hofmann
Hofmann

simplest derivative of the alkaloid to yield normal carbonyl condensation products) and the non-ketonic β-methylcryptopine (19). Of these the former arises by the normal elimination reaction, whereas the latter is the product of a displacement reaction involving the enolate ion of the carbonyl group as shown in (20). The second stage Hofmann degradation with either β or γ-methylcryptopine yields the same nitrogen-free product, anhydrocryptopidiol (21), in one case by elimination and in the other by displacement through the enolate ion.

The Hofmann degradation of the quaternary salts (12) affords a mixture of the two olefines (22) and (23), which are analogous to the two primary degradation products of canadine (see formulae (31) and (32) of Chapter 1), and of these the stilbene (22), anhydrodihydrocryptopine-A, is also accessible by the sodium amalgam reduction of cryptopine and dehydration of the resulting alcohol (24). The quaternary salt (12) may be reconstructed from the methine base (22) by heating with acids, and presumably the isomerisation of the base (22) to the stable base (23) by boiling in ethanol proceeds also via the quaternary salt. The ready reformation of the salt from the methine base is presumably due in this case, as in the case of canadine discussed in Chapter 1, to the close proximity in which the *N*-methyl group and the double bond are held in the ten-membered ring. The further degradation of either base (22) or (23) yields methylisoanhydrodihydrocryptopine (25) and finally the alcohol α-isocryptopidol (26) by a primary displacement reaction of the type discussed in Chapter 1. The further degradation of the two canadine methines follows an exactly similar course.

The quaternary salt isocryptopine chloride (14), obtained from the alkaloid and phosphorus oxychloride, on Hofmann degradation yields the methine base anhydrocryptopine (27), the quaternary salts of which are resistant to further elimination (methanol is displaced from the hydroxide when degradation is attempted, and this was the first recorded instance of such a displacement during Hofmann degradation) but they readily undergo Emde reduction with fission of the benzylamine system to give dihydroanhydro-methylcryptopine (28). The quaternary salts of this last-named base on boiling with alkali yield the nitrogen-free hydroxy-cryptopidine, represented by Perkin in the enol form (29) though

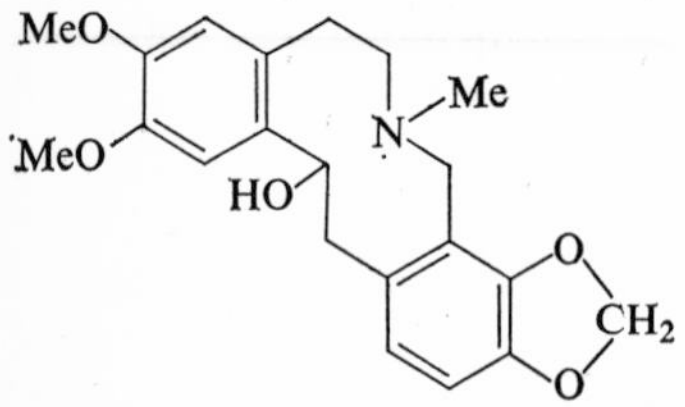

(24)

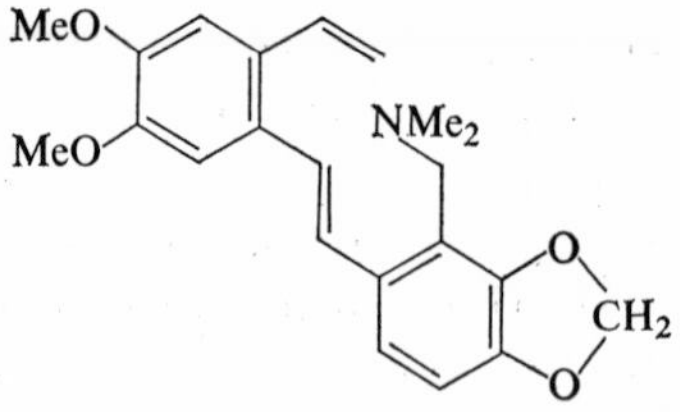

(25)

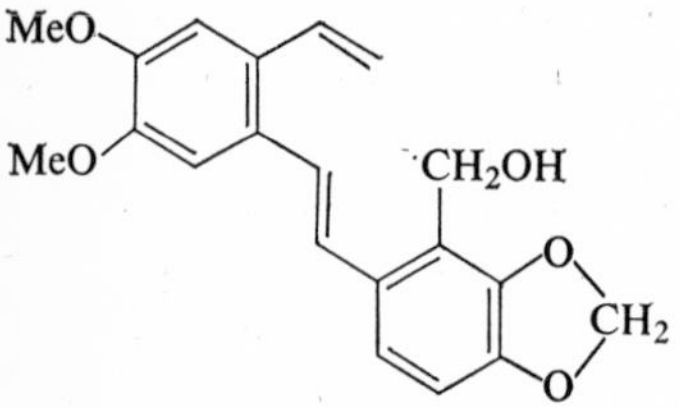

(26)

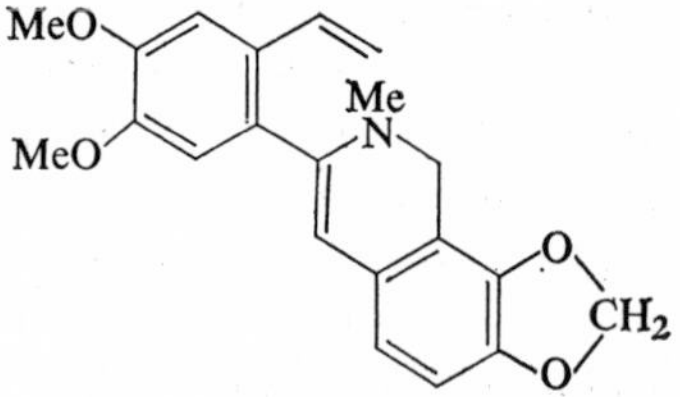

(27)

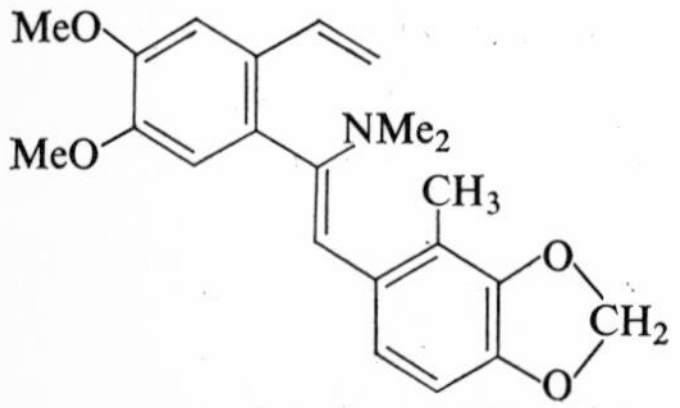

(28)

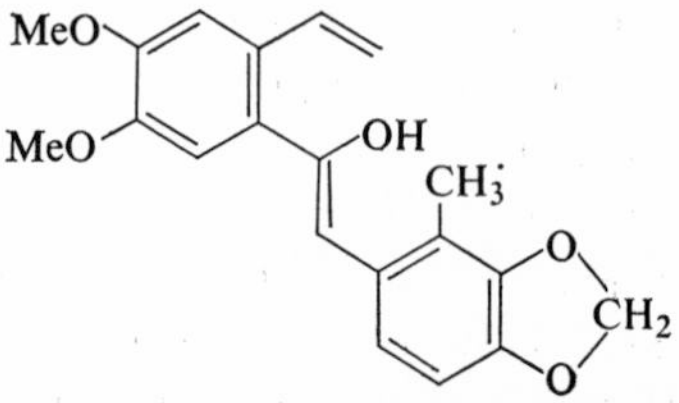

(29)

the keto-form seems more likely, and this may be regarded as either a displacement reaction of the same type as is involved in the production of α-isocryptopidol (26) or as the hydrolysis of a vinylamine.

Both the amine (27) and the ether (21) can be oxidised at the methylene group to give a lactam and a lactone respectively, and the amine, being a dihydroisoquinoline can be oxidised by aerial oxygen in methanol to the carbinolamine ether (30, R = Me), from which yellow quaternary salts of the type (31) can be generated by the action of mineral acids, and these salts are converted by alkalis into the parent carbinolamine (30, R = H), which yields the methyl ether again on boiling with methanol.

(30)   (31)

A number of reactions of anhydrocryptopine reported by Perkin do not permit entirely rational explanation on the basis of the data available in the literature, and re-examination of these with the use of modern spectroscopic aids and the redetermination of all relevant analyses would prove an instructive and useful exercise. For example anhydrocryptopine on heating with concentrated hydrochloric acid affords a base isomeric with cryptopine and named epicryptopine-A, and this is allegedly isomerised with hot methanol to epicryptopine-B, the reverse change being accomplished through the hydrochloride by hydrochloric acid. The two compounds give identical acetyl derivatives, though this is obtained from epicryptopine-A with much greater ease than from epicryptopine-B. Epicryptopine-A is converted into epicryptopine-C by dilute acetic acid and this third compound also gives the same acetyl derivative which is believed, because of its stability to acid hydrolysis, to be an *N*-acetyl compound. Perkin's explanation of these unusual reactions involved hydration of the double bond of the dihydroisoquinoline system of anhydrocryptopine to give a 13-keto base (33) which, together with its enol form represented epicryptopine-A and B; the third isomer, epicryptopine-C, was regarded as probably the cyclic base (33*a*), but it is difficult to see how all three compounds could give the same *N*-acetyl-derivative.

A more plausible hypothesis is that epicryptopine-A is the carbinolamine (34, R = H) resulting from hydrolysis of the vinyl-amine system of anhydrocryptopine (32) and that the allegedly isomeric epicryptopine-B is the methyl ether (34, R = Me), which would be converted back into the parent carbinolamine through the salt (35) by treatment with mineral acid and then with alkali. Epicryptopine-C could then be the open-chain tautomeric keto-base (36) from which the common *N*-acetyl compound could be derived; this *N*-acetyl derivative would probably be obtained with greater difficulty from the carbinolamine ether than from the carbinolamine itself. Perkin rejected the structure (36) for one of the isomers on the grounds that the *supposed N*-methyl analogues of the epicryptopines, namely the "epimethylcryptopines", pre-pared by the action of hot concentrated hydrochloric acid on γ-methylcryptopine (18) were not identical with γ-methylcrypto-pine! No attempt to correlate the two series, which differ in certain respects, by *N*-methylation of any of the epicryptopines was made.

Epicryptopine-A is converted by phosphorus oxychloride into a deep red, apparently quaternary, salt, epicryptorubin chloride, the precise nature of which remains obscure, though the participation of the vinyl group of the carbinolamine (34, R = H) in the forma-tion of a salt of the ψ-cryptopine chloride type (see below) with concomitant aerial oxidation is an attractive possibility.

Similar mystery surrounds the nature of the "hydroxyiso-anhydrodihydrocryptopines A and B" obtained from anhydro-cryptopine by the action of dilute acid, and their dehydration

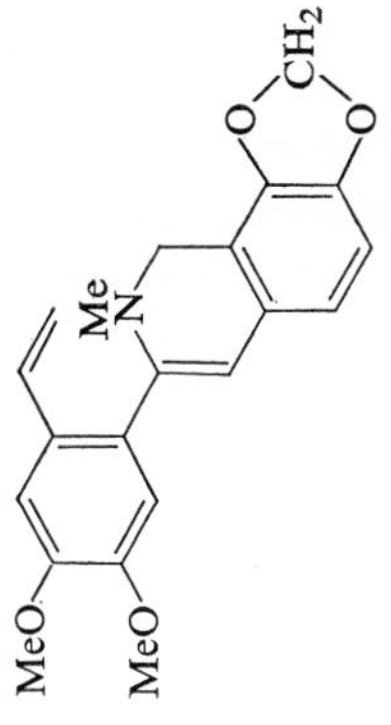

(33a)

(36)

(33)

(34)

$$\xrightleftharpoons[\text{OH}^-]{\text{H}^+}$$

(32)

Anhydrocryptopine

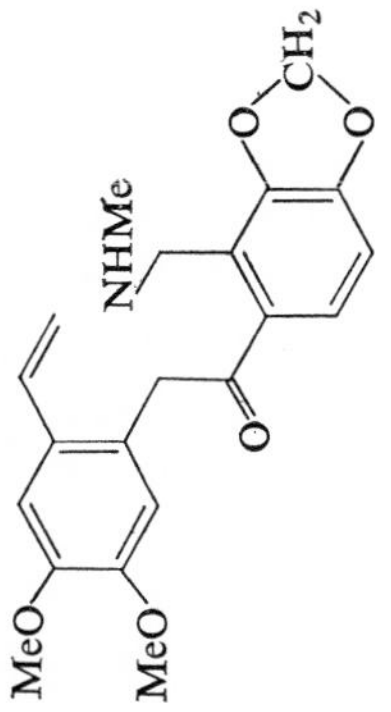

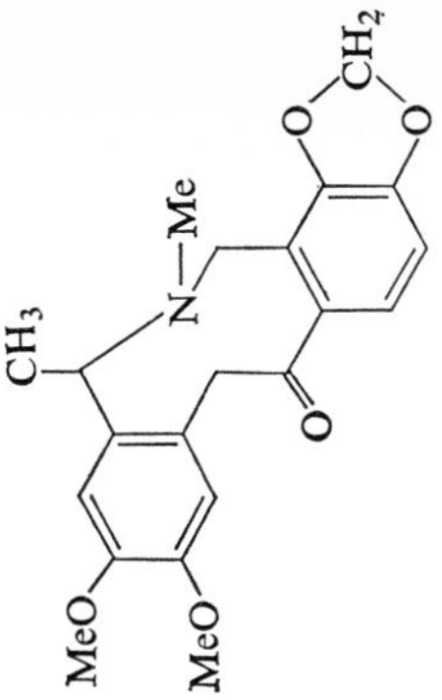

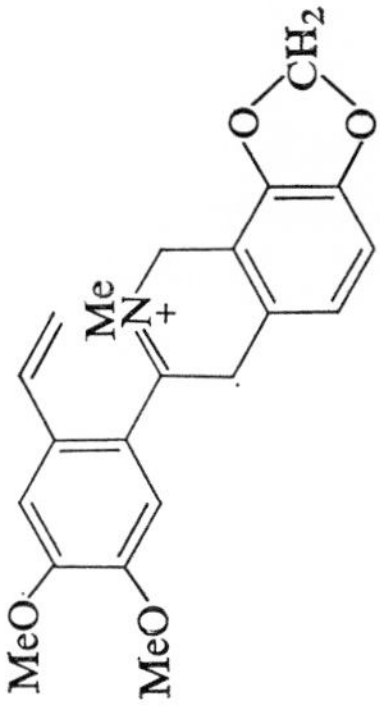

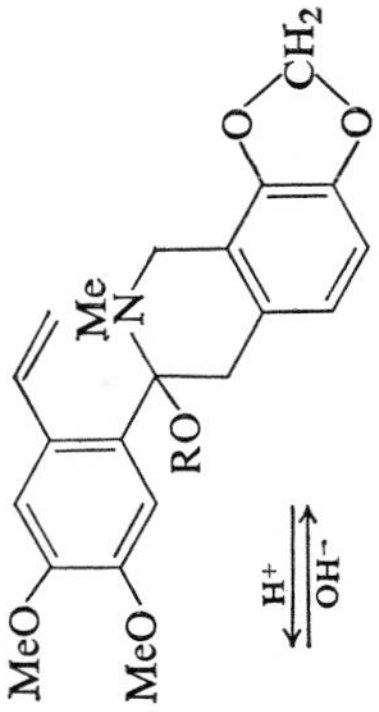

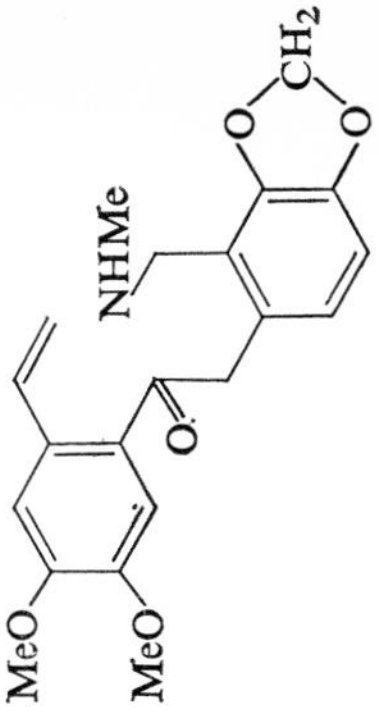

(35)

(37)

(38)

(39)

(40)

(41)

(42)

product "isoanhydrocryptopine", spectral data for which would seem to be essential before confident structural assignments can be made.

The *N*-methyl quaternary salts of anhydrocryptopine are also affected by hot concentrated hydrochloric acid, the product in this case being the quaternary salt ψ-cryptopine chloride (37), which

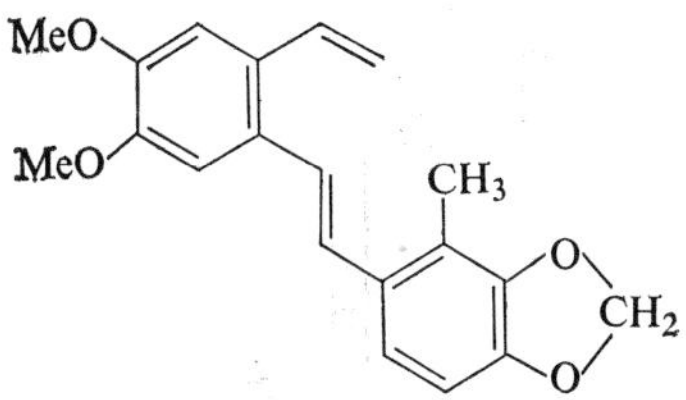

(43)

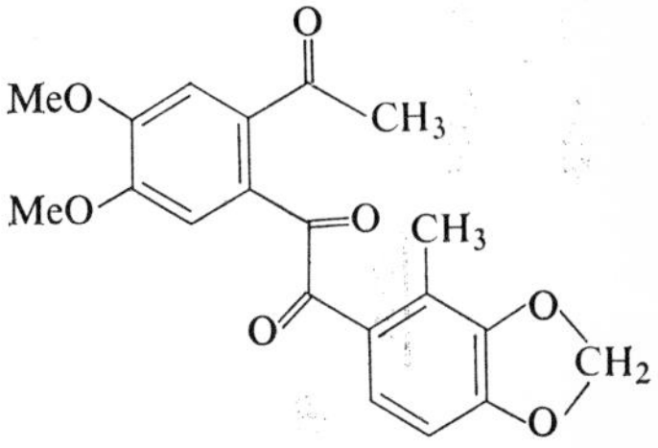

(44)

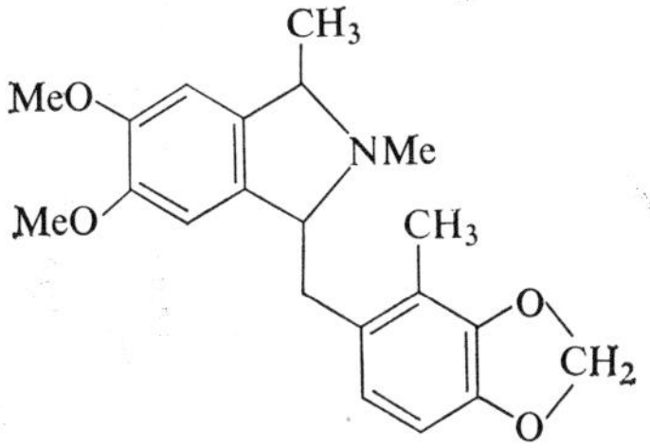

(45)

presumably arises by the loss of methyl alcohol or chloride from the starting material, protonation of the vinyl group and addition to it of the tertiary amino group. The quaternary salt can be *N*-demethylated by heat to give the parent tertiary base, the ultra-violet spectrum of which has recently been shown to be stilbenoid. However, in this series also some of Perkin's structures for the products of further transformation of ψ-cryptopine chloride appear to require revision. For example sodium amalgam reduction of the

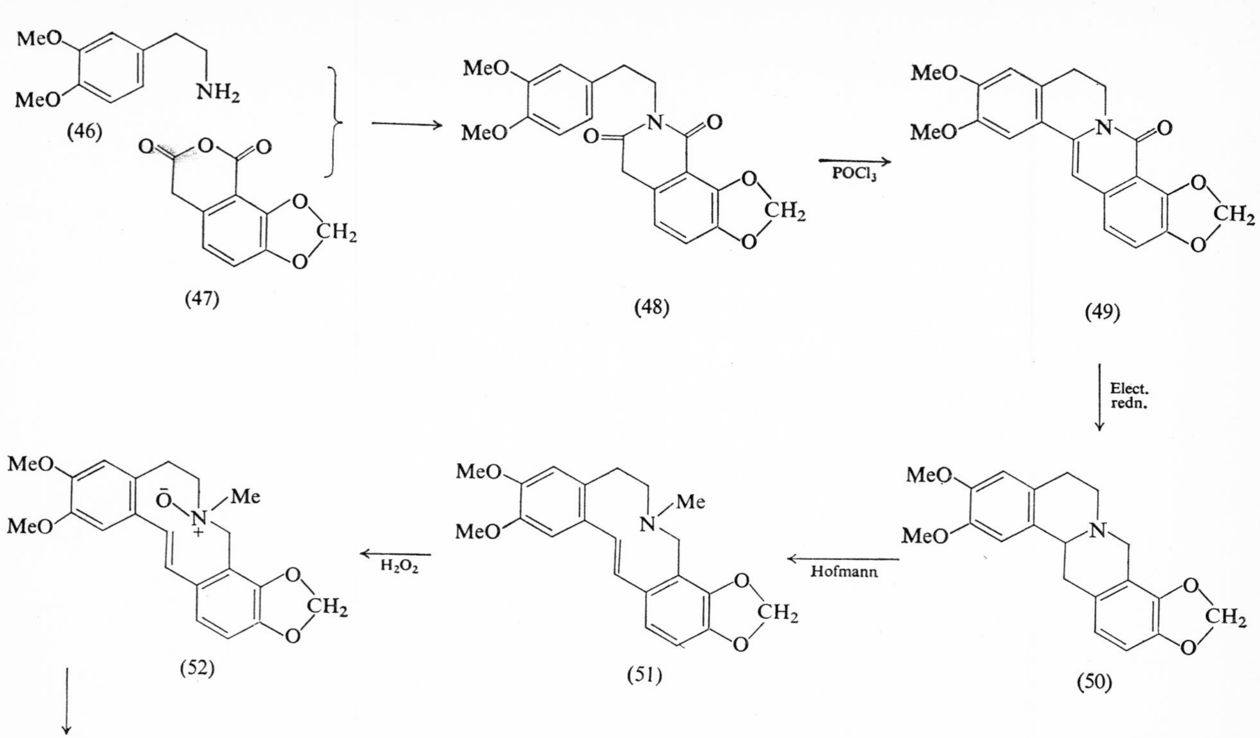

(46)

(47)

(48)

(49)

(50)

(51)

(52)

POCl₃

Elect. redn.

Hofmann

H₂O₂

(54) (58)

(55) (56)

(53) (57)

K_2CrO_4

MeOH

MeI

CNBr

HCl

chloride in alkaline solution yields ψ-anhydrodihydrocryptopine, to which Perkin assigned the structure (38), but for which either (39) or (40), with fission of either of the benzylamine linkages rather than of the vinylamine, is preferable; as no methylenedioxy-toluic acid has been isolated from the products of oxidation of this base the structure (39) is most likely. Further reduction of the quaternary salts of this base proceeds in an unusual fashion with complete loss of the nitrogen and yields ψ-cryptopidene, allegedly isomeric with cryptopidene (43), the product of Hofmann degradation of anhydrotetrahydromethylcryptopine (9), but which must surely be a dihydrocryptopidene (41). Oxidation of this N-free product gives methylenedioxy-o-toluic acid, a "dioxy-ψ-crypto-pidene" which is detectably ketonic and may well be the benzil (42), and a "trioxy-ψ-cryptopidene" which is probably the further oxidation product (44) derived from the benzil (42).

The reduction of ψ-cryptopine chloride with sodium amalgam in acid solution or catalytically, yields dihydroanhydro-ψ-cryptopine, which does not show stilbenoid absorption in the ultraviolet, and oxidation of this base affords methylenedioxy-o-toluic acid showing that it must have the constitution (45). A second product of the sodium amalgam reduction is, however, the nitrogen-free "iso-ψ-cryptopidene", produced by a highly unusual complete loss of the nitrogen atom and allegedly isomeric with cryptopidene (43) and the above-mentioned ψ-cryptopidene; it is presumably identical with ψ-cryptopidene, though further work is obviously necessary to confirm this and to elucidate the other structural problems in the series.

The synthesis of cryptopine was achieved via a berberine-like intermediate, by a trans-annular oxidation that provides no evidence regarding the position of the carbonyl group in the final product. The amide (48), prepared from homoveratrylamine (46) and the anhydride (47), was cyclised by the Bischler–Napieralsky method to oxyepiberberine (49), electrolytic reduction of which gave tetrahydroepiberberine (50). Hofmann degradation of this base then gave a mixture of methine bases from which the stilbene

(51) was separated, and the *N*-oxide (52) of this base on heating was isomerised to cryptopine (53). The mechanism of this isomerisation remains obscure. A more recent synthesis of cryptopine follows closely the biogenetic pathway by which the alkaloids of this group are believed to be formed from bases of the tetrahydroberberine series. This was accomplished by the isomerisation of

(59)   (60)   (61)

(62)   (63)

the *N*-oxide (54) of tetrahydroepiberberine (50) to the carbinolamine (55) by treatment with potassium chromate. Methylation of the carbinolamine with methyl iodide then gave cryptopine (53). It is of interest to note that the same carbinolamine (55) is obtained, presumably via the tautomeric secondary base (56), by hydrolysis of *N*-cyanonorcryptopine (57), which is the product of interaction of cryptopine and cyanogen bromide; *N*-demethylation in preference to a possible benzylamine fission in the reaction of a base with cyanogen bromide is most unusual. The carbinolamine (55) is easily converted into the corresponding *O*-methyl ether (58) by boiling with methanol.

Using both synthetic processes other alkaloids of the cryptopine group, including some that have so far not been found in Nature, have been prepared.

The formation of the carbinolamine (55) from the amine oxide (54) on treatment with potassium chromate is analogous to the production of norcodeine (61) from codeine *N*-oxide (59) presumably via the carbinolamine (60), and of ψ-strychnine (63) from strychnine *N*-oxide (62) by the action of the same reagent. The utility of the reaction is, however, limited by the fact that when an *N*-methyl group is present in a base the *N*-oxide in this way suffers demethylation in preference to carbinolamine formation in any other direction.

OTHER ALKALOIDS OF THE GROUP

Allocryptopine

This base, which occurs in a number of species of Papaveraceae, is isomeric with cryptopine and as on treatment with phosphorus oxychloride it gives dihydroberberine methochloride (65), obtainable from berberine (66), it must have the structure (64). This has been confirmed by the synthesis of allocryptopine by a route analogous to that used for the synthesis of cryptopine, and its preparation from tetrahydroberberine via the *N*-oxide and carbinolamine.

Hunnemanine

Hunnemanine is a monophenolic alkaloid giving allocryptopine on *O*-methylation, and since the *O*-ethyl ether when subjected to a sequence of degradations analogous to those used in the elucidation of the structure of cryptopine (*N*-methylation, sodium amalgam reduction, dehydration and oxidation) finally yields 3-ethoxy-4-methoxy-2-methylbenzoic acid, it must have the hydroxyl group in the position marked in formula (64) with an asterisk.

Protopine

This base appears to be the most widely distributed of all alkaloids, though the amount present at any one time in any plant is very small. It has the composition $C_{20}H_{19}O_5N$, and undergoes reactions similar in every respect to those of cryptopine, which

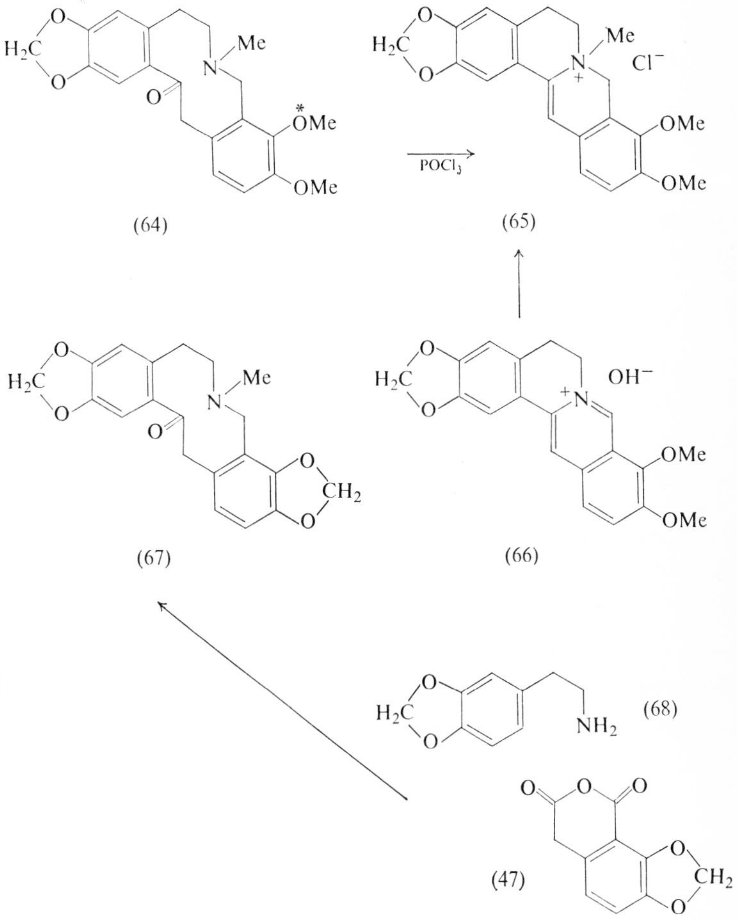

(64)

(65)

POCl₃

(67)

(66)

(68)

(47)

contains CH_4 more. As the alkaloid is non-phenolic it was reasonably formulated as the bis-methylenedioxy analogue of cryptopine, i.e. (67), and this was finally confirmed by a synthesis of protopine exactly analogous to the first synthesis of cryptopine, starting from homopiperonylamine (68) instead of homoveratrylamine (46).

Corycavine

This base is a *C*-methylated protopine obtained from *Corydalis tuberosa*, which also contains the *C*-methylated tetrahydroberberine corydaline, and it is not unreasonable to expect that the

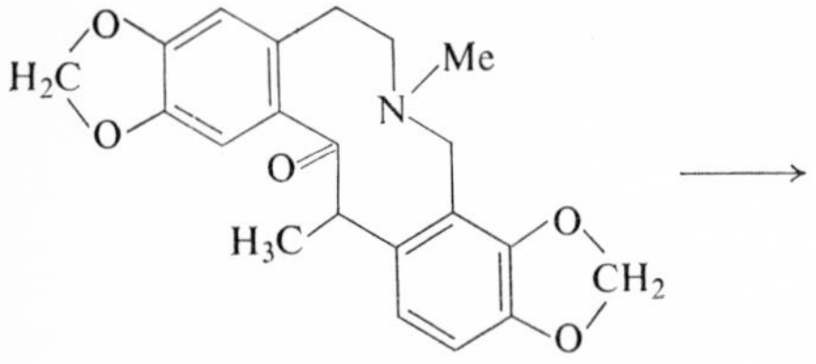

(69)

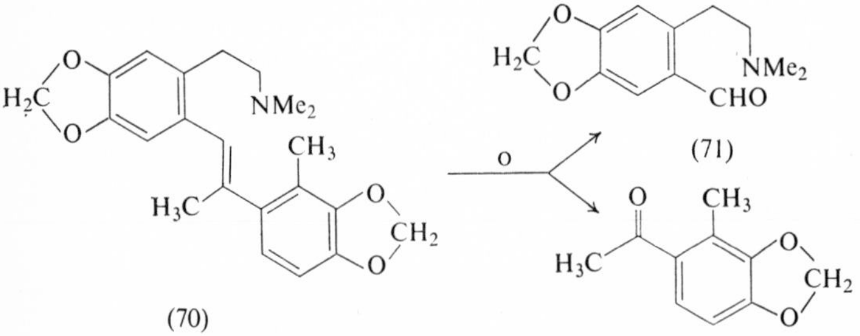

(70)

(71)

(72)

C-methyl group occupies the same position in the two bases. It is, however, not the protopine analogue of corydaline as it has the composition $C_{21}H_{21}O_5N$ compared with $C_{22}H_{27}O_4N$ for that base. It clearly belongs to the cryptopine group as it may be reduced with sodium amalgam to a dihydro-compound that readily gives a tetrahydroberberine-like quaternary salt with phosphorus oxychloride. Unlike cryptopine and allocryptopine, which have the same carbon content, it contains no methoxyl groups and was readily assumed to be a *C*-methylprotopine. Reduction of the methosulphate with sodium amalgam effected ring fission and keto group reduction and the resulting secondary alcohol was dehydrated to anhydrotetrahydromethylcorycavine, analogous to anhydrotetrahydromethylcryptopine (9) obtained in the same way from cryptopine. This base must have the structure (70) since it may be oxidised by potassium permanganate to 2-(2'-dimethylaminoethyl)-4,5-methylenedioxybenzaldehyde (71), obtainable in the same way from protopine, and 3,4-methylene-dioxy-2-methylacetophenone (72). Corycavine must therefore have the structure (69). The analogous tetrahydroberberine alkaloid, from which corycavine may be assumed to arise, is worenine, obtainable from *Coptis japonica*.

Cryptocavine

This base, originally tentatively formulated as the 13-keto isomer of cryptopine, has been shown to be identical with the latter alkaloid.

CHAPTER 10

Rhoeadine

RHOEADINE, the main alkaloid of the red corn-field poppy, *Papave rhoeas*, from which the well-known cultivated Shirley poppy is derived, may be regarded as an interesting half-way stage between the bases of the tetrahydroberberine and phthalideisoquinoline groups.

It has the composition $C_{21}H_{21}O_6N$ and contains at least one methylenedioxy group, one O-methyl and one N-methyl group and no active hydrogen, but on treatment with mineral acid it is readily converted into rhoeagenine $C_{20}H_{19}O_6N$, which contains one active hydrogen atom, one carbonyl group and no methoxyl group,

the demethylation of which in rhoeadine doubtless accounts for the loss of CH_2 during this process. Such behaviour would be explicable if rhoeadine contained the mixed ketal or acetal system (1), since hydrolysis of this would result in the production of methanol and an aldehyde or ketone containing a primary alcoholic group which contains an active hydrogen atom (2). On this assumption and the further assumption that rhoeadine bears some

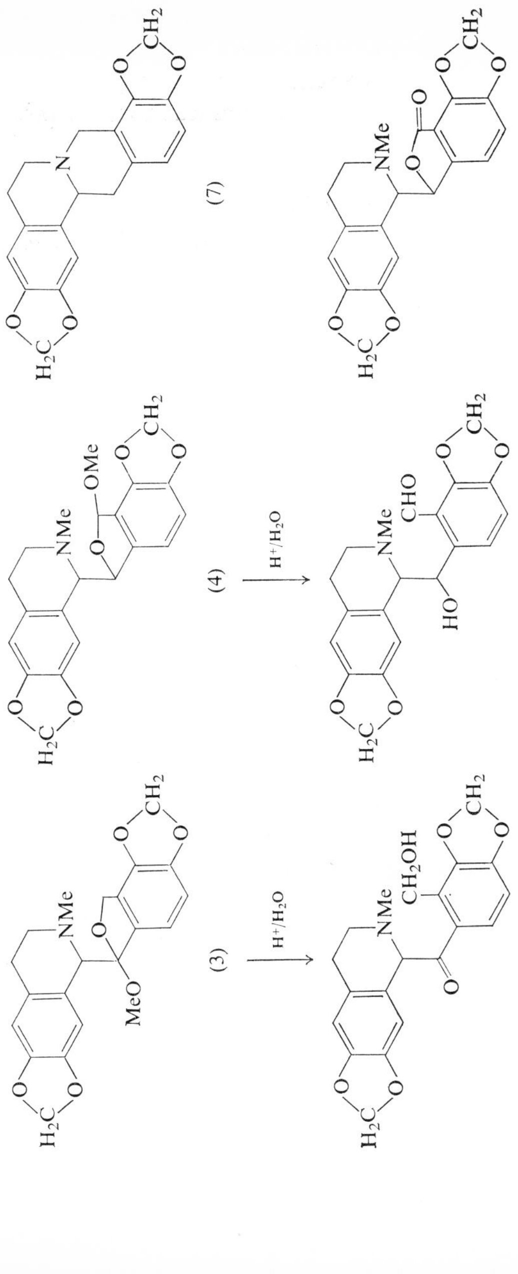

(7)

(8)

(4) $\xrightarrow{\text{H}^+/\text{H}_2\text{O}}$ (6)

(3) $\xrightarrow{\text{H}^+/\text{H}_2\text{O}}$ (5)

structural resemblance to the opium alkaloids papaverine, laudanosine and narcotine, the alkaloid must contain two methylenedioxy groups and two rational structures (3) and (4) may be advanced for it. These two structures lead to the expressions (5) and (6) for rhoeagenine. Either structure would place rhoeadine between the tetrahydroberberine alkaloid stylopine (7) and the phthalideisoquinoline alkaloid bicuculline (8) in the accepted biogenetic relationships of the bases, and on this basis the methylenedioxy groups are placed as shown in formulae (3) and (4).

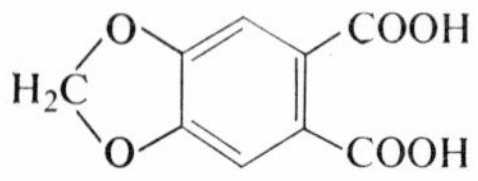

(9)

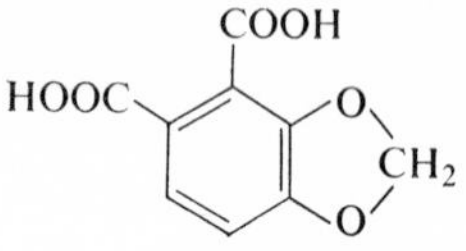

(10)

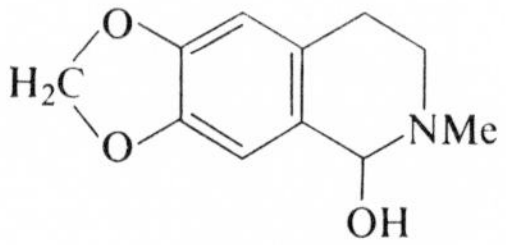

(11)

Support for either of these possible structures, and confirmation of the orientation of the substituents was provided by the oxidation of rhoeadine by alkaline potassium permanganate to hydrastic acid (9) and isohydrastic acid (10), and by nitric acid to hydrastininine (11), obtained in the same way from the alkaloid hydrastine (see Chapter 11). These results reveal the positions of all substituents on the aromatic nuclei and the linkage at position 1 of the dihydroisoquinoline (11) of the portion of the rhoeadine molecule that gives rise to isohydrastic acid.

Hofmann degradation of rhoeadine methiodide affords a methine base $C_{23}H_{23}O_6N$, the further degradation of which by the

Hofmann or Emde process yields an *N*-free product $C_{20}H_{16}O_6$ and both of these degradation products can be hydrolysed to the corresponding derivatives of rhoeagenine $C_{21}H_{21}O_6N$ and $C_{19}H_{14}O_6$ respectively, though these are not accessible by the direct degradation of that base. Since two successive Hofmann degradations can only occur in a base having at least one hydrogen atom on the β-carbon atom on each side of the nitrogen, rhoeadine

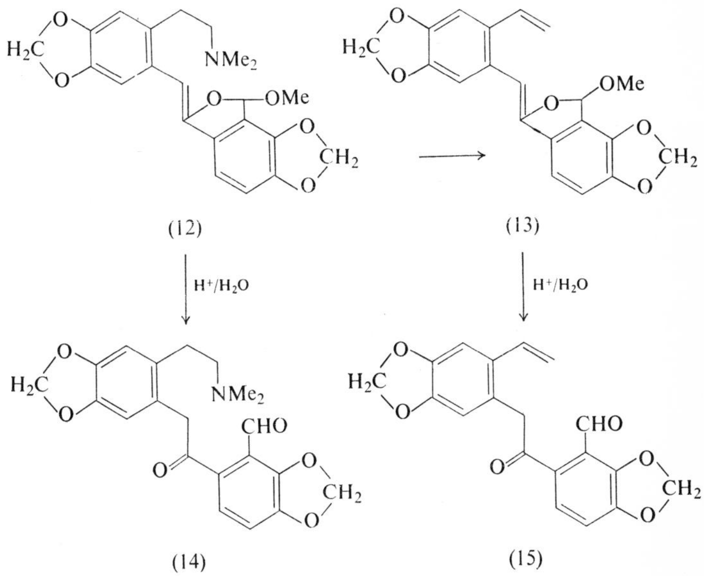

(12)   (13)

(14)   (15)

must have the structure (4), on the basis of which the methine base may be assigned the structure (12) and the nitrogen-free product the structure (13), the corresponding derivatives of rhoeagenine obtained by hydrolysis being the ketones (14) and (15). If rhoeadine had the structure (3) the first-stage Hofmann degradation product would be the base (16), from the quaternary hydroxide of which trimethylamine could only be removed by a displacement reaction (see Chapter 1) leading to the alcohol (17).

It may be noted that rhoeagenine (6) has a structure analogous to that of hydroxylaudanosine (18), which suffers molecular fission on attempted Hofmann degradation (see Chapter 1), and the failure of rhoeagenine to yield simple elimination products on degradation is easily understood.

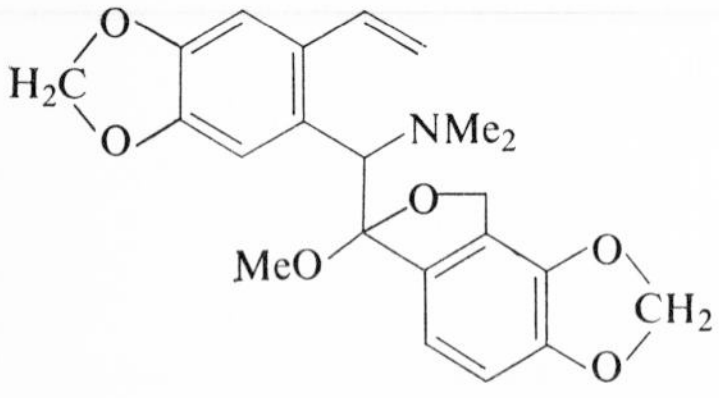

(16)

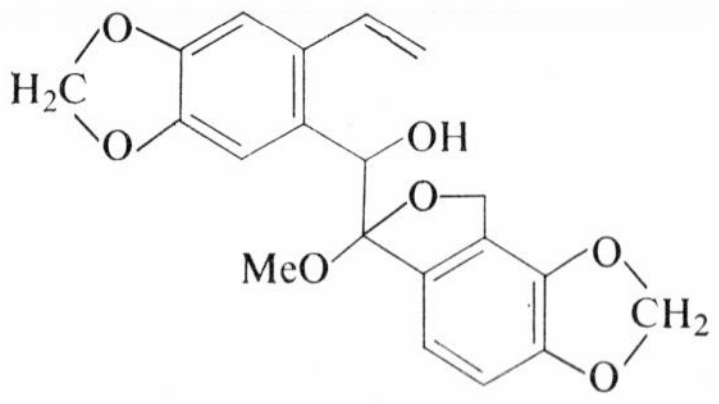

(17)

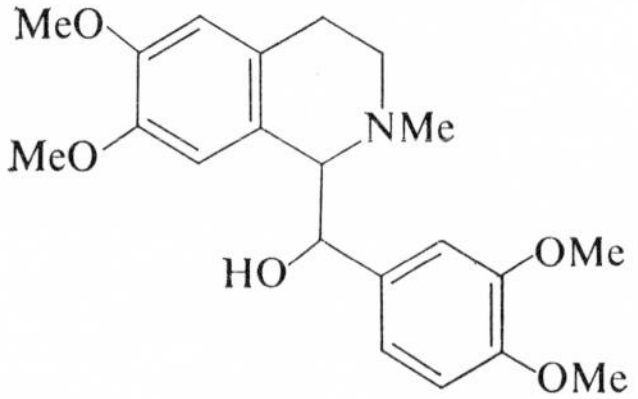

(18)

CHAPTER 11

The Phthalideisoquinolines

THE phthalideisoquinoline group of alkaloids comprises a series of eleven bases of the general structure (1), some of which are further substituted by hydroxyl or methoxyl at the position marked with an asterisk. They are believed to originate in Nature by the oxidation of bases of the tetrahydroberberine group (2) at the

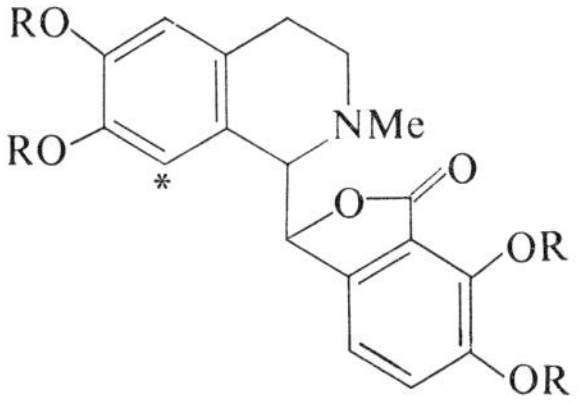

(1)

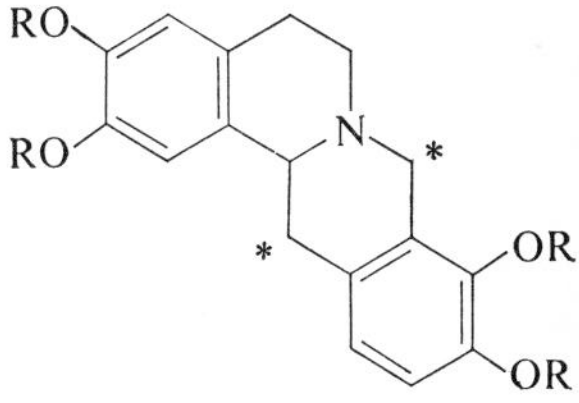

(2)

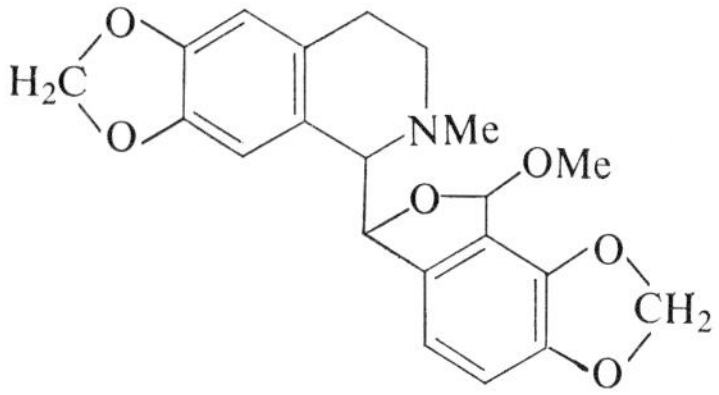

(3)

193

carbon atoms marked with an asterisk, before or after *N*-methylation, and it is interesting to note that rhoeadine (3) represents an intermediate stage in this process. All of the bases are easily cleaved into two readily recognisable fragments, and this feature makes the elucidation of the structure of any new member of the group a relatively simple process.

Narcotine

This alkaloid, which is one of the minor alkaloids of opium, and has recently attained a certain, probably undeserved, reputation as an antitussive, is a typical example of the group. It has the composition $C_{22}H_{23}O_7N$ and contains three methoxyl groups, one methylenedioxy and one *N*-methyl group; the two remaining oxygen atoms not accounted for in this way are present in a hydrolysable lactone ring. It may be cleaved in three ways, and in each of these the two cleavage fragments together account for all of the 22 original carbon atoms of the alkaloid.

(a) Oxidative hydrolysis of the base with sulphuric acid yields opianic acid $C_{10}H_{10}O_5$ and the base cotarnine $C_{12}H_{15}O_4N$.

(b) Hydrolysis alone with water at 150° gives opianic acid $C_{10}H_{10}O_5$ and the base hydrocotarnine $C_{12}H_{15}O_3N$, also obtainable by the reduction of cotarnine.

(c) Reductive hydrolysis with zinc and sulphuric acid also yields hydrocotarnine together with meconine $C_{10}H_{10}O_4$, also obtainable by the reduction of opianic acid.

The elucidation of the structures of these fission products led to the solution of the structural problem presented by the parent alkaloid.

Opianic acid, $C_{10}H_{10}O_5$, is a monobasic acid containing two methoxyl groups; on reduction it yields the lactone meconine $C_{10}H_{10}O_4$ corresponding to a hydroxy acid of composition $C_{10}H_{12}O_5$, and on oxidation it affords hemipinic acid (4). This behaviour is what would be expected of an aldehydo-acid, and, since its oxidation product is hemipinic acid (4), opianic acid can only be the acid (5) or (6). As meconine, its reduction product (7), can be synthesised from 2,3-dimethoxybenzoic acid (8) by the action of formaldehyde and hydrochloric acid, it must have the structure (6); the acid (5), ψ-opianic acid which gives ψ-meconine (9) on reduction, is obtainable from berberine (see Chapter 8).

Cotarnine, $C_{12}H_{15}O_4N$, may be reduced catalytically with zinc and hydrochloric acid to hydrocotarnine $C_{12}H_{15}O_3N$ with loss of oxygen, and the reverse change can be accomplished by oxidising hydrocotarnine with iodine and alcohol. Cotarnine contains one *N*-methyl, one methoxyl and one methylenedioxy group. Oxidation of the base with permanganate yields cotarnic acid $C_8H_6O_3(COOH)_2$ which is an *ortho*-dicarboxylic aromatic acid since it readily gives an anhydride; on demethylation with hydriodic acid it gives gallic acid and must therefore be one of the isomeric acids (10) or (11), and of these (11) was shown to be correct by the synthesis of cotarnic acid from the indanone (12) via the intermediates (13)–(17).

Cotarnine behaves as a pseudo-base, forming salts with loss of water when treated with mineral acids, being regenerated from these salts by the action of alkali, and condensing with aromatic amines and reactive methylene compounds as if it were an aromatic aldehyde. These properties are consistent with formulation of the base as a carbinolamine of the type (18), which can give the salts of the cation (19) with acids and can also react in the tautomeric

amino-aldehyde form (20). It was for some time believed to exist normally in the amino-aldehyde form, but ultraviolet absorption studies reveal that none of this form exists in neutral solution. Cotarnine itself is colourless in the solid state and in non-hydroxylic solvents, but its salts are yellow, and this is in accord with the formulation of the base as (18) and the salts as (19); in hydroxylic media it is present largely as the yellow quaternary hydroxide corresponding to (19) rather than as the pseudo-base (18).

On the above evidence cotarnine could have either structure (21) or (22) and of these (22) was thought to be more likely since the anil (23), formed by condensation with aniline, gives a quaternary methiodide that suffers loss of aniline and *O*-demethylation on heating with hydrochloric acid, and resembles in this way the anil of *ortho* but not *meta* or *para* methoxybenzaldehyde. This assignment of structure to cotarnine has been supported by synthesis by

oxidation of the benzyltetrahydroisoquinoline (26), itself prepared by a synthesis analogous to that of laudanosine (see Chapter 3) from the amine (24) and phenylacetic acid, via the amide (25). The process, however, does not exclude the structure (21), which is available by the oxidation of the base (27), also produced during the synthesis.

As would be expected of a carbinolamine cotarnine reacts with methyl iodide to give a mixture of the quaternary salts (28) and (29), and of these the latter may be degraded by Hofmann's method to the aldehyde cotarnone (30). It also reacts with Grignard reagents in the general manner of Schiff base quaternary salts to give *C*-alkylated or arylated bases of structure (31).

Hydrocotarnine, the reduction product of cotarnine, is the tetra-hydroisoquinoline (32). This on Hofmann degradation suffers nitrogen-ring fission on the only side of the nitrogen atom where there is a β-hydrogen atom, the product being the methine base (33), which is then stable to further degradation. Emde reduction of the quaternary salt of hydrocotarnine, however, results in

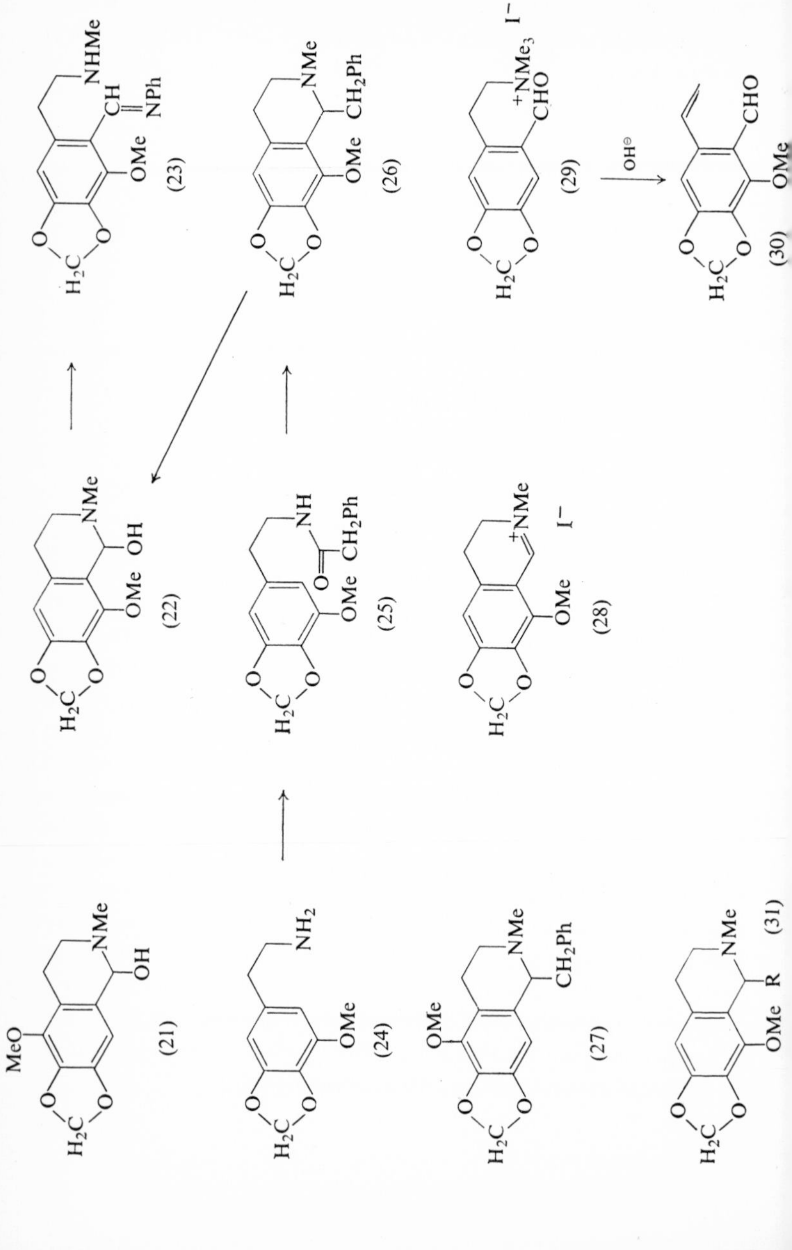
(21)
(22)
(23)
(24)
(25)
(26)
(27)
(28)
(29)
OH⊖
(30)
(31)

fission of the benzylamine system, giving the base (34), which may then be subjected to Hofmann degradation to obtain the *N*-free vinyl compound.

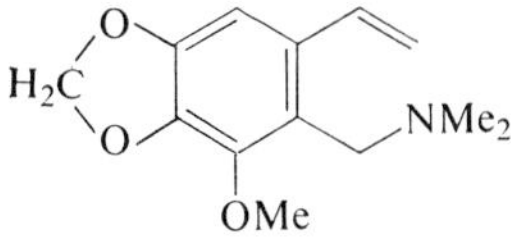

(33)

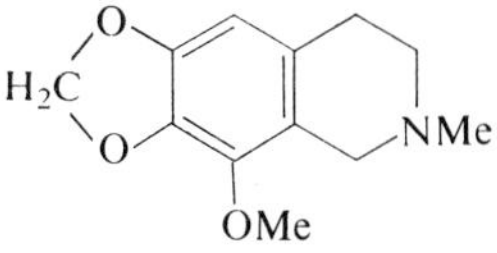

(32)

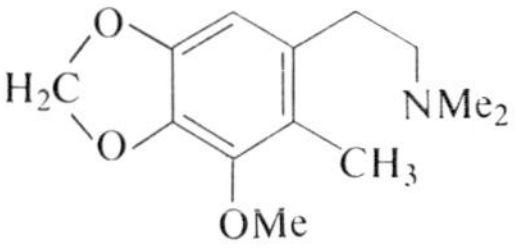

(34)

As the hydrolysis of narcotine affords hydrocotarnine and opianic acid it may be deduced from the structures of these that narcotine has the constitution (35). The reconstitution of the base from the hydrolysis products cannot be effected but a synthesis of racemic narcotine (gnoscopine) has been effected from cotarnine and meconine (36) and (37), that is by a reversal of the oxidation states of the two hydrolysis fragments. As narcotine contains two asymmetric carbon atoms four stereoisomers, which may be paired to give two racemates, are possible; the product of the above synthesis was identical with gnoscopine, obtainable from opium. The reactivity of the methylene group of meconine is increased by the introduction of the electron-withdrawing nitro group in the *ortho* position, and nitromeconine readily condenses with cotarnine to give the nitro-base (38), but this belongs to a series diastereoisomeric with that to which narcotine belongs, the difference between the two series being in the relative dispositions of the hydrogen atoms at the two asymmetric centres.

Hofmann degradation of narcotine leads to a normal methine base, narceine (41), which results from hydrolysis of the initially formed enol lactone (40); of the two hydrogen atoms β to the nitrogen, that which is activated by both aromatic nuclei is preferentially removed. The structure of narceine is readily elucidated

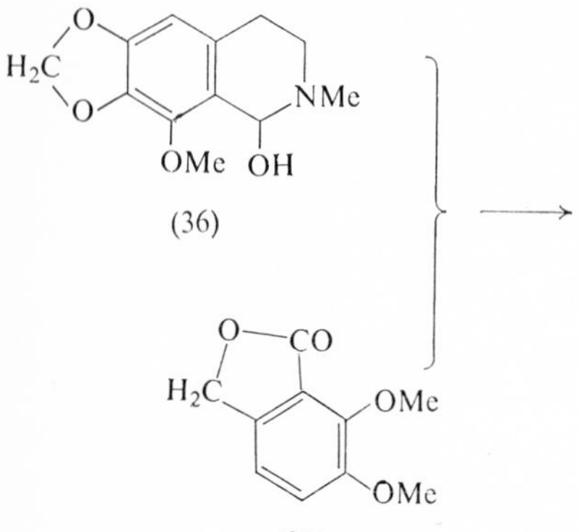

(36)

(37)

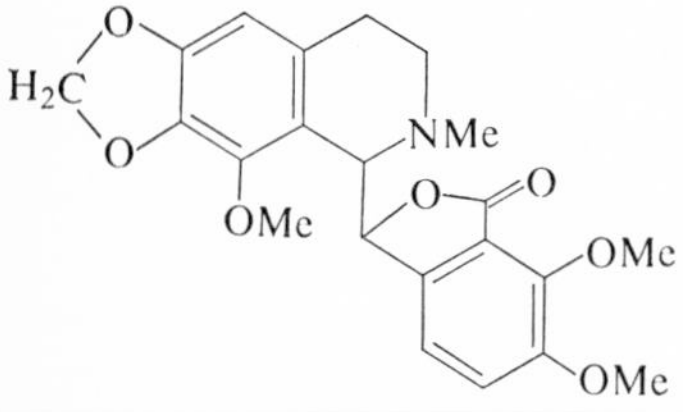

(35)

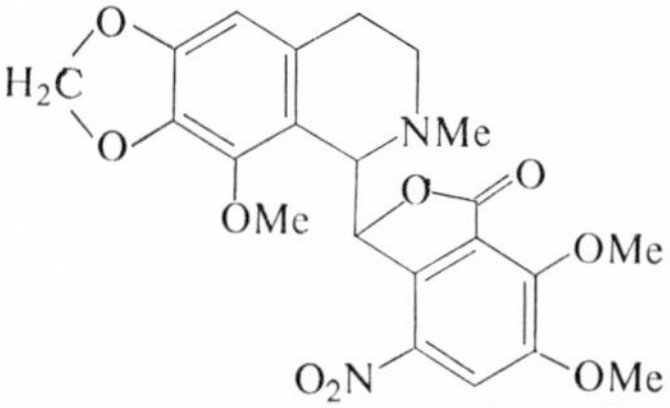

(38)

in the following way. It clearly contains the system —CH_2—CO— since it gives a phenylhydrazone and an isonitroso-compound (42), and the last of these when heated splits into hemipinic acid (44) and a base (43) that gives cotarnonitrile (45) on Hofmann degradation. As cotarnonitrile is also obtained by the Hofmann degradation of *N*-methylcotarnine oxime methochloride (46) it must have the

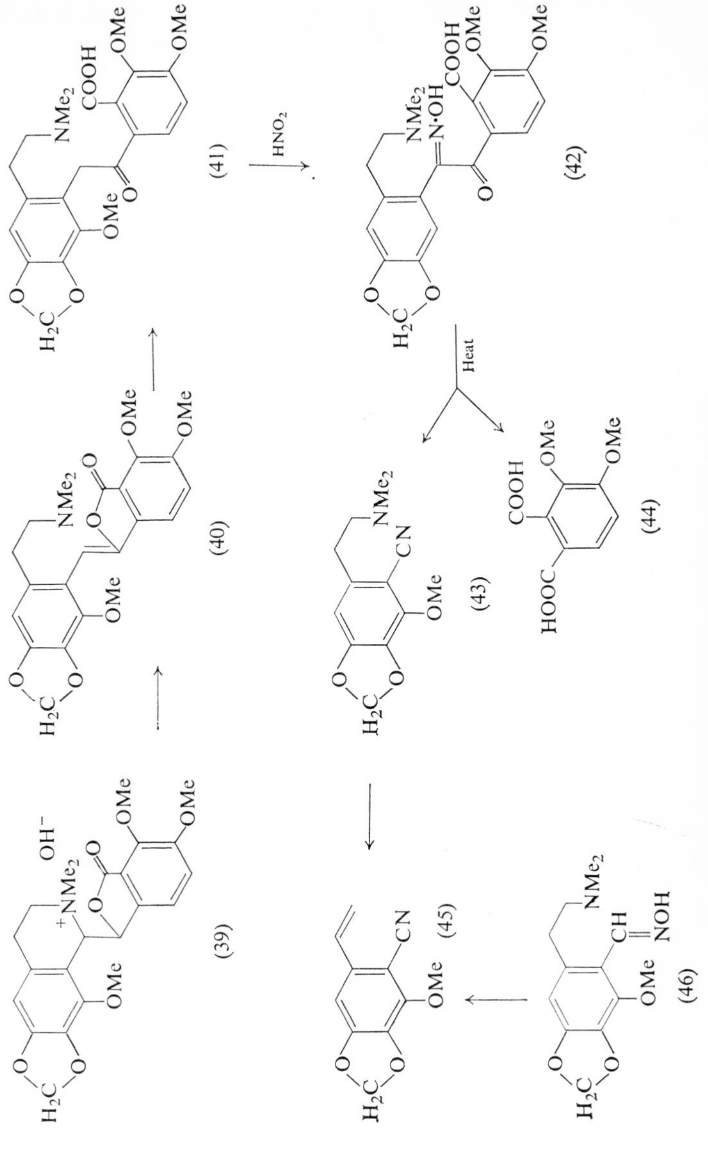
(39)
(40)
(41)
HNO2
(42)
Heat
(43)
(44)
(45)
(46)

structure (45) and the base from which it was derived must have the constitution (43), in which case isonitrosonarceine is correctly represented by (42) and narceine by (41).

Pyrolysis of the amine oxide of narcotine (47) follows a similar course to the Hofmann degradation, but as the conditions are not such as would be expected to cause hydrolysis the enol lactone (48) may be isolated and hydrolysed separately to the narceine analogue (49).

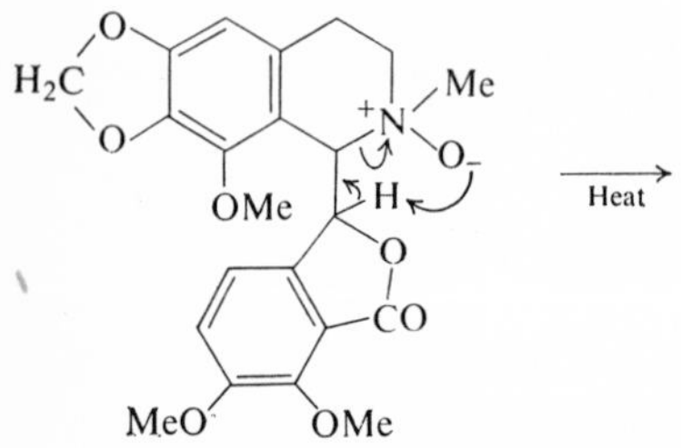

(47)

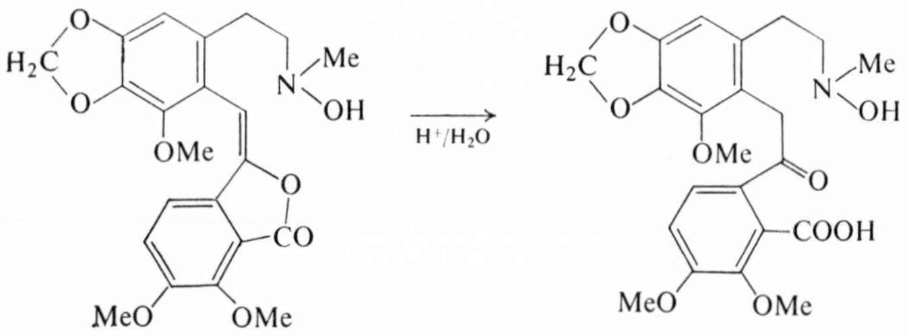

(48)   (49)

Reduction of narcotine with lithium aluminium hydride affords the diol (50), the methiodide of which, unlike that of narcotine in which the hydroxyl group is bound up in a lactone ring, on Hofmann degradation suffers attack at the hydrogen atom of the hydroxyl group with fission of the molecule to the aldehyde (51) and the transitory ylid (52). Under the conditions of the reaction these are further transformed into ψ-meconine (53) (by Cannizzaro reaction

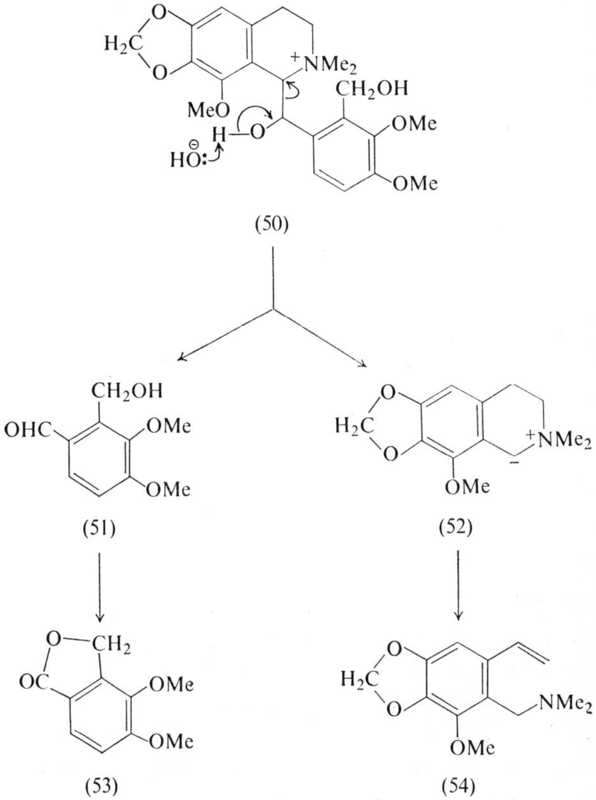

(50)

(51)

(52)

(53)

(54)

or autoxidation) and the vinylbenzylamine (54) (by Hofmann degradation). Narcotine diol in this way resembles hydroxy-laudanosine (see Chapter 3) and the molecular fission appears to be dependent on the ease of formation of the ylid (52), which is increased by the positive charge on the nitrogen atom in the quaternary salt; the free base is stable to prolonged boiling with alkali, as is β-hydroxylaudanosine under the same conditions. The pyrolysis of the amine oxide of narcotine diol follows a course similar to that of the Hofmann degradation.

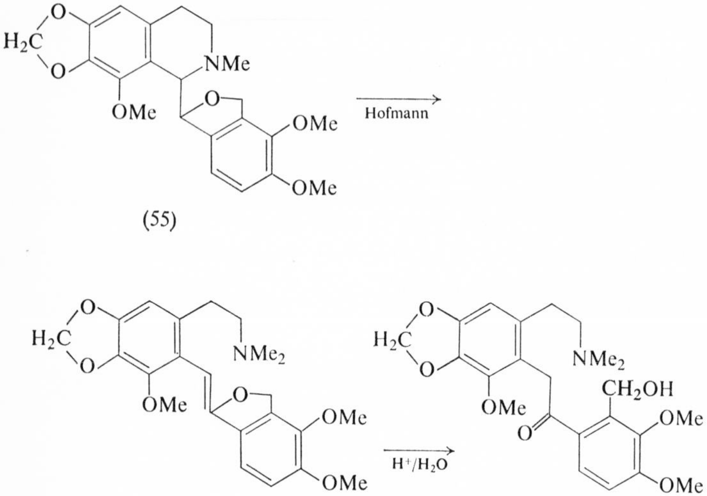

(55)

(56)

(57)

Unlike β-hydroxylaudanosine, however, narcotine diol is not oxidised under the conditions of the Oppenauer oxidation, the product of the reaction being the cyclic ether (55), the structure of which follows from its Hofmann degradation to the enol ether (56) and the hydrolysis of this to the ketone (57). This ketone on reduction with lithium aluminium hydride yields the same diol as is obtained in the same way from narceine ethyl ester.

Hydrastine

This base, from *Hydrastis canadensis*, has the composition $C_{21}H_{21}O_6N$ and contains one methylenedioxy and two methoxyl groups. It is a close relative of narcotine and on oxidative hydro-

lysis yields hydrastinine and opianic acid, although, unlike narcotine, it is stable to hydrolysis and reductive hydrolysis. Hydrastinine bears a close resemblance to cotarnine in all of its reactions;
it is colourless, but gives coloured salts with loss of water on

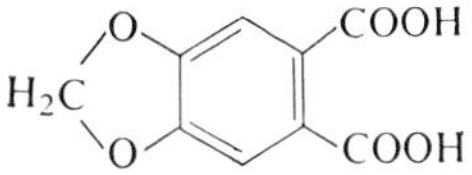

(58) 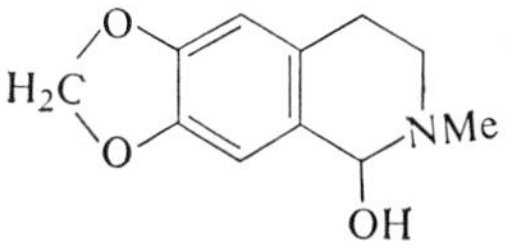   (59)

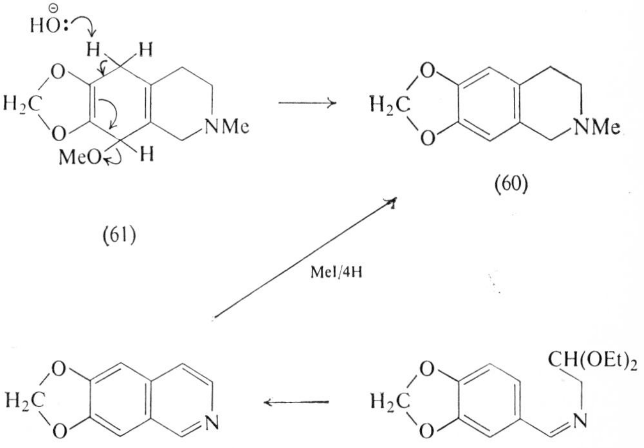

(61) $\longrightarrow$ (60)

MeI/4H

(62) $\longleftarrow$ (63)

treatment with mineral acids, and is regenerated from these salts
by treatment with alkali; it condenses with hydroxylamine and
with substances such as acetone and nitromethane that contain
reactive methylene groups, and behaves like a carbinolamine in
that it gives an *O*-methyl ether with hot methanol and an aldehydic
quaternary salt (analogous to (30)) on treatment with methyl

iodide. On oxidation it is converted into the symmetrical hydrastic acid (58), which leads to the reasonable belief that hydrastinine is the carbinolamine (59), and this is confirmed by reduction to hydrohydrastinine (60), which is obtainable by the reductive demethoxylation of hydrocotarnine (32) by sodium and alcohol; this latter reaction presumably proceeds by way of the 5,8-dihydro-compound (61). Hydrohydrastinine (60) has also been synthesised by the reduction of the methiodide of 6,7-methylenedioxyiso-quinoline (62), produced by the cyclisation of the imino-acetal (63), which is the product of condensation of piperonal and amino-acetal. Hydrohydrastinine may be oxidised back to hydrastinine to complete the synthesis of this base.

Hydrastinine, like berberine which is also a carbinolamine (see Chapter 8), can be made to undergo the Cannizzaro reaction, the products being hydrohydrastinine (60) and oxyhydrastinine (64). The condensation products of acetone and nitromethane with hydrastinine previously mentioned have the structures (65) and (66) respectively.

(64)   (65)   (66)

By analogy with narcotine hydrastine clearly has the structure (67) and a synthesis of the alkaloid has been achieved by the condensation of hydrastinine with nitromeconine, followed by reduction of the nitro-base and deamination. In this way a mixture of two racemic amino-bases was obtained and the deamination of racemate-*a* and resolution of the product afforded (−)-hydrastine-*a*, identical with the alkaloid; the second racemate differs from the first in the relative disposition of the hydrogen atoms at the two asymmetric carbon atoms.

Hydrastine, being a lactone, is, like narcotine, reduced by lithium aluminium hydride to a diol (68), and when this is treated with thionyl chloride the presumed intermediate dichloro-compound cyclises to a quaternary salt (69), with simultaneous loss of hydrogen chloride, the product being dihydroanhydroberberinium methochloride. This salt on heating dry loses methyl chloride and gives the parent tertiary base, dihydroanhydroberberine, identical with material prepared from berberine. This represents a laboratory reversal of the conversion of the tetrahydroberberine alkaloid into the phthalideisoquinolines, believed to occur in the plant.

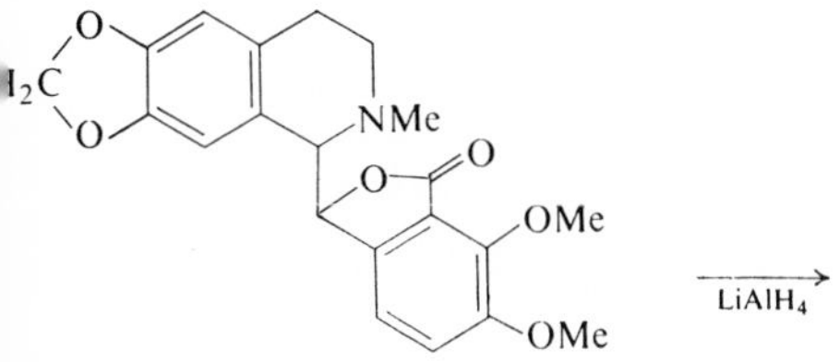

(67)

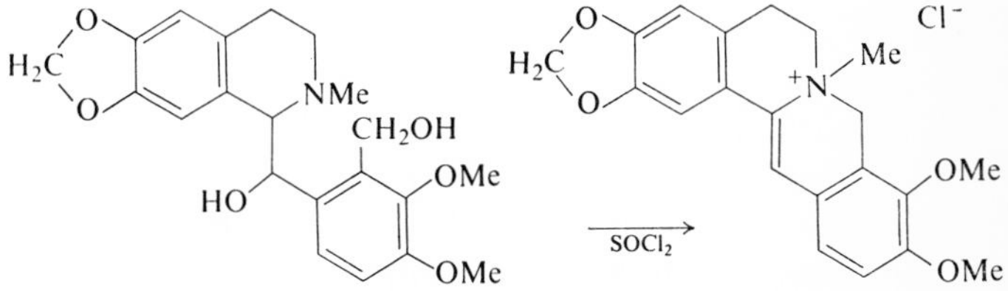

LiAlH₄

(68)

SOCl₂

(69)

The diol (68) behaves in the same way as narcotine diol (50) on Hofmann degradation or pyrolysis of the *N*-oxide, molecular fission occurring in both reactions.

CHAPTER 12

The α-Naphthaphenanthridines

THE bases of this group are characterised by the ring system (1); in all the alkaloids the two terminal rings are aromatic and bear oxygen substituents (methoxyl or methylenedioxy) at the positions shown, and in some of the bases the middle rings are also aromatic. They are not clearly derived from benzylisoquinolines, as are the bases of the groups so far discussed, and the orientation of oxygen

(1)   (2)

substituents in the isoquinoline portion of the molecule is different from that otherwise universally found in the other bases discussed in this book, but their appearance in papaveraceous plants, to which they are almost completely restricted, makes their derivation from the tetrahydroberberine system seem probable. One possible route for such a transformation would be fission at the dotted line in structure (2), and linkage of the two asterisked carbon atoms after rotation of the molecule about the C—C bond; the subject is discussed further in Chapter 14.

The bases of this group have not been found to have any useful pharmacological properties; they have been shown to bring about considerable increases in intra-ocular pressure, and have been cited as causative agents in glaucoma, when accidentally ingested over a lengthy period.

As examples of the series the alkaloids chelidonine, sanguinarine and chelerythrine may be selected. All three bases occur in *Chelidonum majus*. Chelidonine has the composition $C_{20}H_{19}O_5N$ and sanguinarine the composition $C_{20}H_{15}O_5N$, and both alkaloids contain one *N*-methyl and two methylenedioxy groups, chelidonine containing in addition one esterifiable alcoholic hydroxyl group. The two alkaloids are closely related, and sanguinarine may be prepared from chelidonine by oxidation of the *O*-acetyl ester, hydrolysis and dehydration to dihydrosanguinarine and further aerial oxidation. Hofmann degradation of chelidonine yields a methine base, $C_{21}H_{21}O_5N$, which may be oxidised with fission of the double bond to a mixture of hydrastic acid (3) and 2-dimethyl-aminomethyl-3,4-methylenedioxybenzoic acid (4). The second of these products was initially formulated as the 4,5-methylenedioxy-isomer of (4), indicating that the two aromatic nuclei had the same substitution pattern in the alkaloid, or that the phthalic acid (3) is simply a further oxidation product of the amino-acid (4). This ambiguity was resolved when the same amino-acid (4) was prepared by the oxidation of the methine base (5) obtained by the Hofmann degradation of the Emde reduction product (6) of isodihydrocryptopine chloride (7) (see Chapter 9). Had the base (6) been derived from the tetrahydroberberine alkaloid stylopine instead of from the cryptopine derivative (7) the two methoxyl groups would have been replaced by a methylenedioxy group, and the resulting methine base would have given both acids (3) and (4) on oxidation. Accordingly on the assumption that chelidonine differs from a hydroxylated stylopine only in the mode of closure of the fourth ring the structure (8) was advanced for the alkaloid;

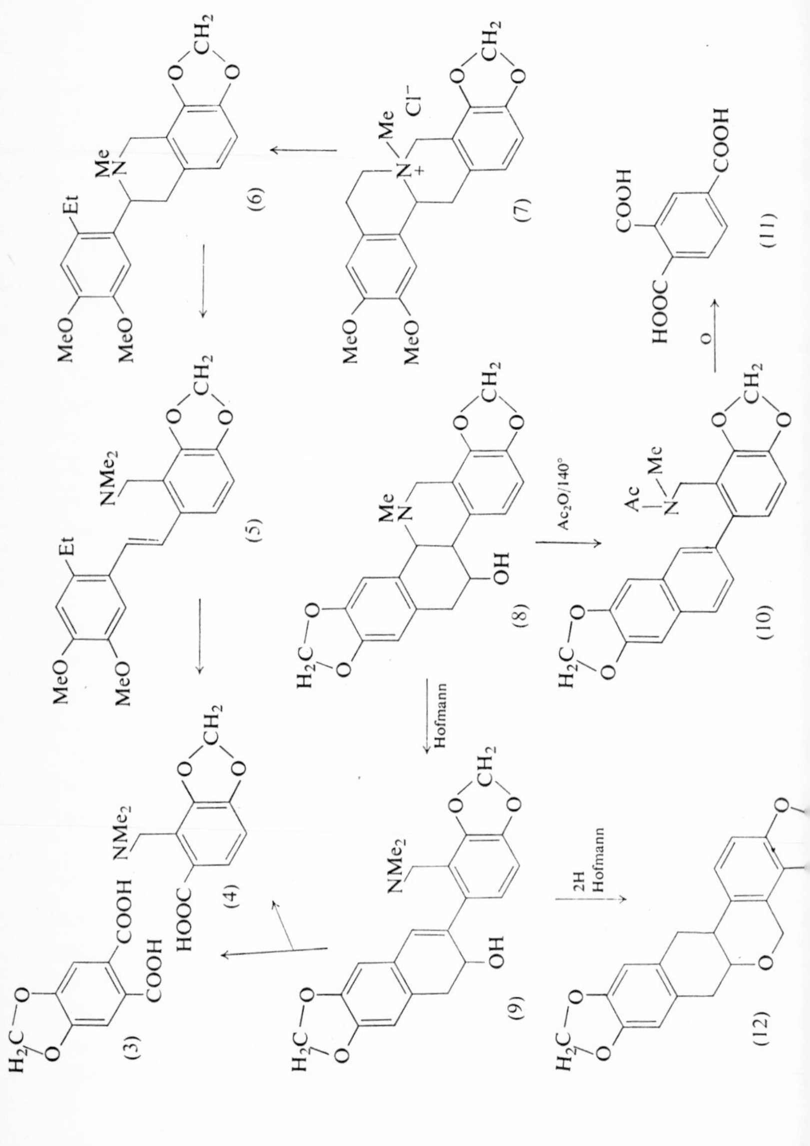

(3)
(4)
(5)
(6)
(7)
(8)
(9)
(10)
(11)
(12)
Hofmann
2H Hofmann
Ac₂O/140°
O

on this basis the methine base would be formulated as (9), and the production of the acids (3) and (4) by the oxidation of this is easy to understand.

That the skeleton of (8) is present in chelidonine is further indicated by dehydration and nitrogen ring fission at 140° with acetic anhydride to an *N*-acetyl compound (10) (compare the behaviour of the aporphine alkaloids under the same conditions, reported in Chapter 6) that may be oxidised under vigorous conditions to benzene-1,2,4-tricarboxylic acid (11). During this oxidation the aromatic nuclei bearing the hydroxyl groups are obviously destroyed, and the production of the acid (11) indicates that they must be separated in the *N*-acetyl compound (10) by a trisubstituted aromatic nucleus. However, the structure (10) is not uniquely derived from (8), it could equally well be formed from the ring system (13), but as the zinc dust distillation of sanguinarine (already related to chelidonine) yields α-naphthaphenanthridine (14) the presence of the basic skeleton of (8) in chelidonine is confirmed. The location of the methylenedioxy groups on the skeleton is, of course, unambiguously revealed by the oxidation of the methine base to the acids (3) and (4).

The precise position of the hydroxyl group in chelidonine has not been conclusively proved, but as the group is easily esterified it is unlikely to be tertiary and as chelidonine shows none of the properties of a carbinolamine only two positions for it are possible, and that shown in formula (8) is chosen to account for the very ready formation of a cyclic ether (12) during the Hofmann degradation of the dihydro-derivative of the methine base (9); the easy formation of a seven-membered ring during such a process is considered unlikely.

The composition of sanguinarine and the orange-yellow colour of its salts indicate that it has the fully-aromatic quaternary base structure (15), though as it behaves in some of its reactions as if it contains a carbonyl group it must also be capable of existing in the carbinolamine form (16), the situation in this series being similar to that in the berberine group (see Chapter 8). The stages in the

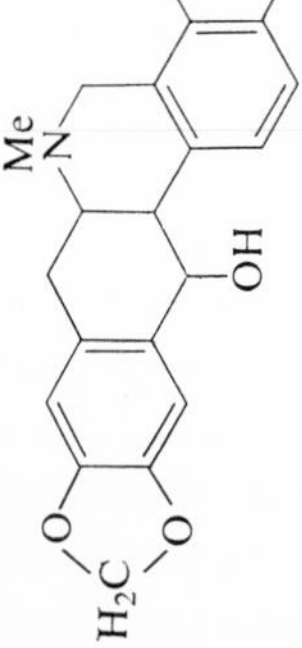

(15)

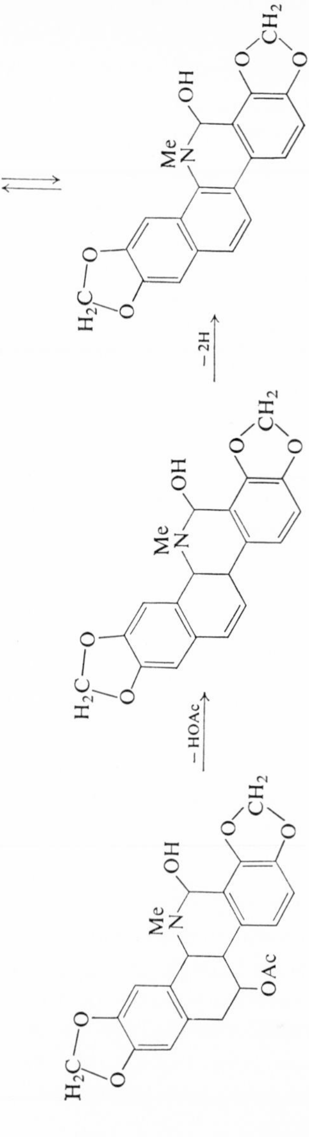

$\rightleftharpoons$

(16)

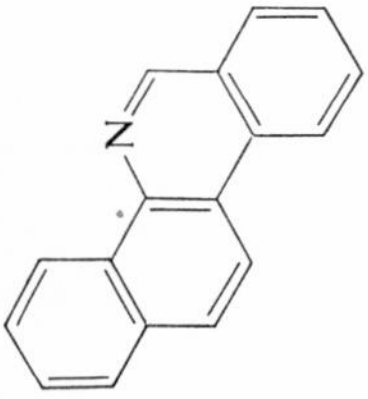

(14)

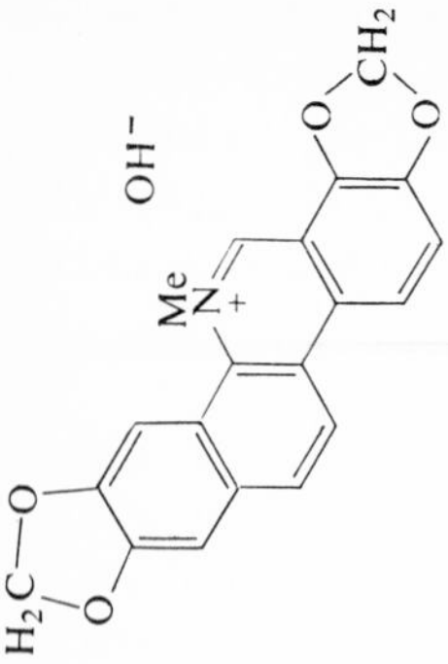

(18)

(13)

(17)

$-2H$

$-HOAc$

conversion of chelidonine into sanguinarine may be represented as involving the production of the carbinolamine (17) by the mercuric acetate oxidation of *O*-acetylchelidonine, the hydrolysis and dehydration of this to dihydrosanguinarine (18) and the easy atmospheric oxidation of the dihydro-base to sanguinarine (16).

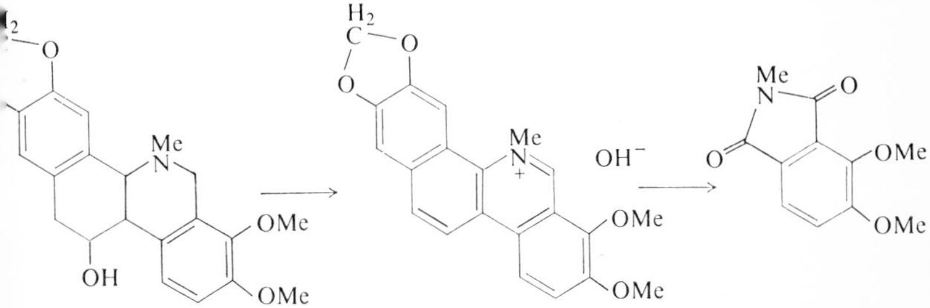

(19) (20) (21)

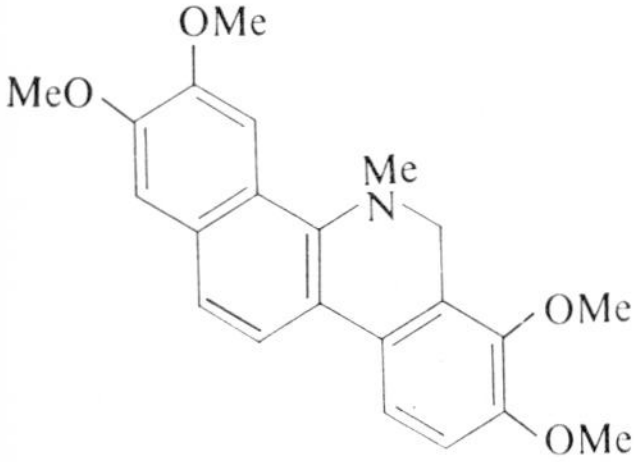

(22) 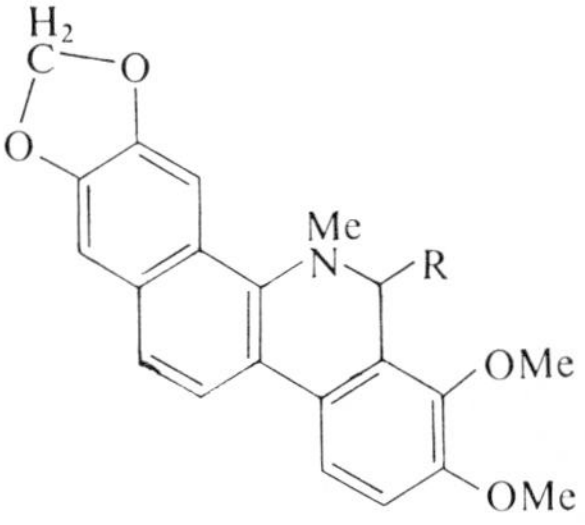 (23)

Homochelidonine, which occurs with chelidonine, contains CH_4 more than the latter, and the difference is accounted for by the presence in this base of two methoxy groups in place of one of the methylenedioxy groups of chelidonine. It must have the structure (19) since the mild oxidation of chelerythrine (20), the sanguinarine analogue derived from homochelidonine, yields

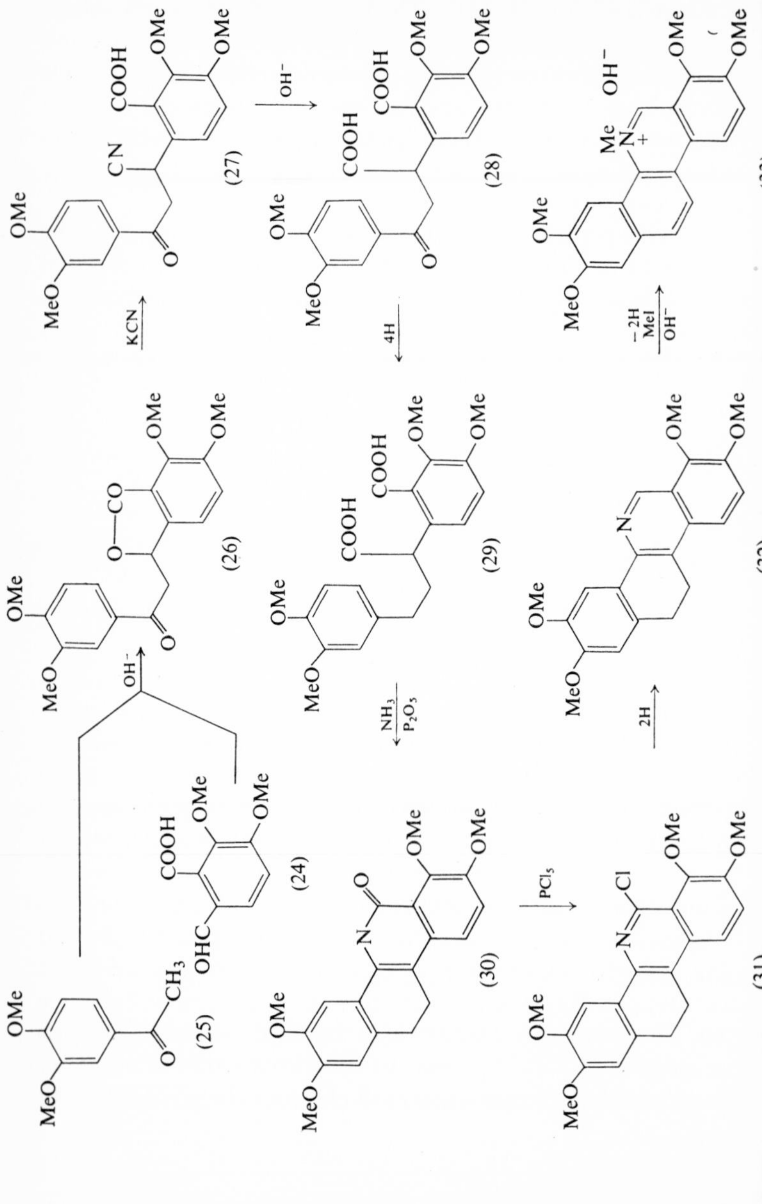

MeO
OMe
CH3
OHC
COOH
OMe
OMe
(25)
(24)
OH⁻
O—CO
(26)
KCN
CN
COOH
(27)
OH⁻
COOH
(28)
4H
(29)
NH3
P2O5
N
O
(30)
PCl5
Cl
(31)
2H
(32)
−2H
MeI
OH⁻
Me
N+
OH⁻
(33)

N-methylhemipinimide (21). The location of the oxygen substituents in the same places on the basic skeleton in chelerythrine and sanguinarine was confirmed by the conversion of the respective dihydro-bases into the same tetramethoxy-compound (22) by hydrolytic fission of the methylenedioxy groups and methylation of the resulting phenols, thus placing the relationship of the two sets of alkaloids beyond doubt.

As in the berberine series the quaternary isoquinolininium salts will react with Grignard reagents to give *C*-alkylated or arylated dihydro-bases, e.g. chelerythrine (20) yields bases of the type (23) in this way.

(34)   (35)   (36)

In spite of the apparent simplicity of the ring system involved the synthesis of alkaloids of this group proved difficult, and has only recently been successfully accomplished. The first base to be synthesised was the tetramethoxy-analogue of sanguinarine and chelerythrine (33), which was prepared as follows. Aldol condensation of opianic acid (24) with acetoveratrone (25) yielded the lactone (26), which with potassium cyanide gave the nitrile (27). Alkaline hydrolysis of the nitrile yielded the ketodicarboxylic acid (28), the reduction of which by Clemmensen's method led to the acid (29), and the imide of the latter acid was cyclised to the amide (30). The conversion of the amide to the dihydro-base (32) through the chloride (31) was followed by dehydrogenation to a tertiary base from which the quaternary salt (33) could be prepared.

The synthesis of chelerythrine chloride (36) then followed similar lines. The appropriate methylenedioxy analogue of the acid (28) was too sensitive to acids to be reduced by Clemmensen's method and was instead converted into the analogue of the acid (29) by catalytic reduction over palladium in acetic acid containing perchloric acid. The acid chloride of the dicarboxylic acid was then cyclised with stannic chloride to give the enol-lactone (34), which, with ethylene glycol and ammonia, gave the amide (35), and this was converted into chelerythrine chloride (36) by the method used in the tetramethoxy series.

CHAPTER 13

Emetine and Related Compounds

"IPECAC ROOT", the root of *Cephaelis ipecacuanha* Rich (*Psychotria ipecacuanha* Stokes) and certain other plants of the same species, has been used for over three centuries as an emetic and, more recently, as a specific remedy against amoebic dysentery. The principal alkaloid found in the root, to which it owes its pharmacological importance, is emetine, although the related bases emetamine, cephaeline, psychotrine and *O*-methylpsychotrine have also been isolated.

Emetine has the composition $C_{29}H_{40}O_4N_2$ and contains four methoxyl groups, one *C*-methyl and one secondary amino group; the second nitrogen atom is clearly present in a tertiary amino group, but no *N*-methyl group is present. As there are no reducible double bonds in the alkaloid, assuming the presence of two aromatic nuclei the base must be pentacyclic. Oxidation of the alkaloid yields 6,7-dimethoxyisoquinoline-1-carboxylic acid (1), *m*-hemipinic acid (2) and the amide corydaldine (3) (obtainable from tetrahydropalmatine, Chapter 8), according to the conditions used. The yield of *m*-hemipinic acid from emetine when compared with that obtained from papaverine (Chapter 3) under the same conditions indicates that the alkaloid contains two 6,7-dimethoxy-isoquinoline units in the molecule.

The Hofmann degradation of the dimethiodide of the bis-tertiary base *N*-methylemetine yields a methine base ($C_{32}H_{46}O_4N_2$)

with fission of both nitrogen-containing rings. The saturation of the two double bonds introduced during this degradation gives a tetrahydromethine ($C_{32}H_{50}O_4N_2$) which can be converted into a monomethiodide, the Hofmann degradation of which proceeds with the loss of trimethylamine and the production of des-*N*(*a*)-emetinetetrahydromethine ($C_{30}H_{43}O_4N$). Oxidation of this base with fission of the double bond introduced during the second Hofmann degradation affords 6-ethylveratric acid (4) and an acid $C_{18}H_{28}O_2N$—COOH (5), showing that des-$N(a)$-emetinetetrahydromethine may be assigned the part-structure (6), and from this it may be deduced, bearing in mind the proved presence of 6,7-tetrahydroisoquinoline nuclei in emetine, that the product of the

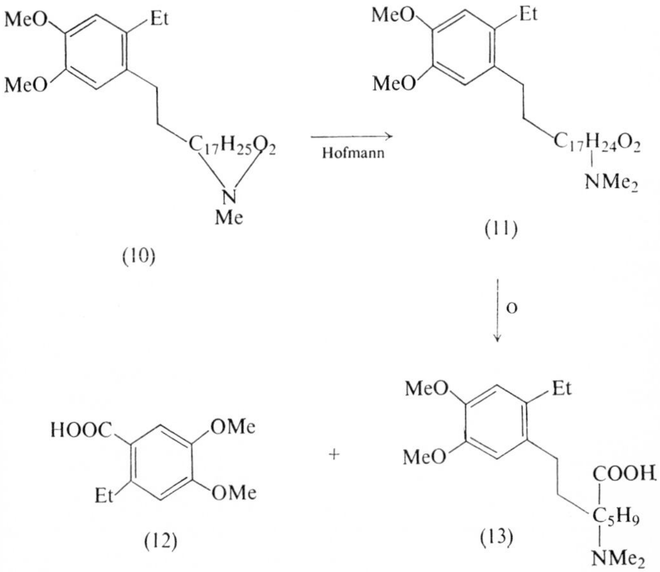

(10)

(11)

(12) + (13)

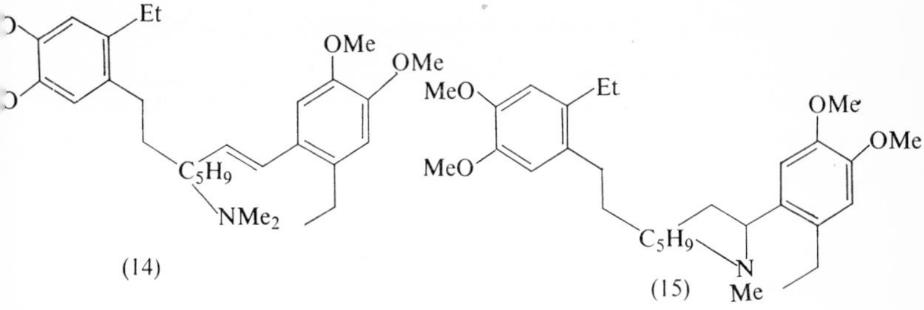

(14)

(15)

first Hofmann degradation must have the structure (7) and emetine itself the structure (8). The alternative part-structure (9) for the alkaloid would, as will become obvious from the degradations described below, lead finally to a structure containing at least one *C*-methyl group more than can be detected by analysis.

The hydrogenation of des-*N*(*a*)-emetinetetrahydromethine (6) leads to a hexahydromethine which may be represented by the part-structure (10), since Hofmann degradation of the methiodide yields a base (11), indicating that the nitrogen atom must be part of a ring, and since the reduced methine base (10) is itself derived from emetine by processes involving degradation around that nitrogen atom it must be common to two rings in the parent alkaloid. Further information concerning the structure of the Hofmann degradation product (11) may be obtained from the oxidation of the base at the double bond to 6-ethylveratric acid (12) and an amino-acid $C_{20}H_{33}O_4N$. Since the ethylveratric acid cannot be derived from the known portion of the molecule as the double bond in that section has been reduced, the amino-acid $C_{20}H_{33}O_4N$ may be assigned the part-structure (13) and the part-structure (11) for the Hofmann degradation product from the hexahydromethine may be expanded to (14).

The double bond in the Hofmann degradation product (14) is introduced by the fission of a ring during the degradation, and accordingly the structure of the reduced methine (10) may be expanded to (15), which in turn leads to the expansion of structures (7) and (8) to (16) and (17) for *N*-methylemetinebismethine and emetine respectively. The alternative structure (18) for emetine can be discounted as it can be shown by the degradations about to be described that the only *C*-methyl group that can be detected in the alkaloid by analysis is present in the so far undiscussed C_5H_9 system.

It may be noted here that on the basis of part of the evidence presented above, the correct structure was deduced for emetine on the hypothesis of a plausible biogenetic conversion of a tetrahydro-berberine base into an intermediate for a laudanosine-like synthesis with dihydroxyphenylethylamine or its equivalent, further details of which are given in Chapter 14.

The structure of the system —CH_2—$C_5H_9NMe_2$—CH= in the reduced methine base (14) was elucidated in the following manner.

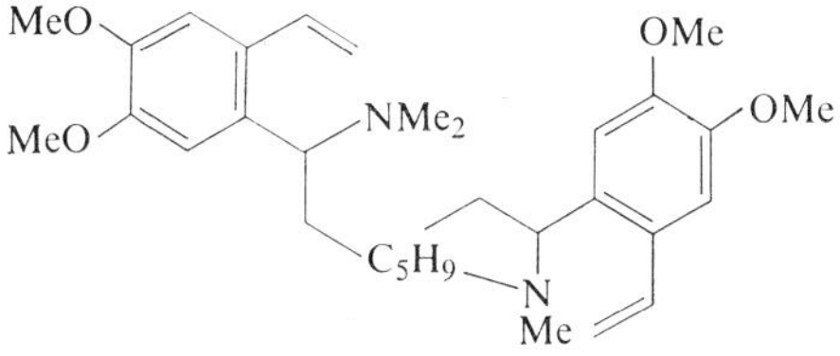

(16)

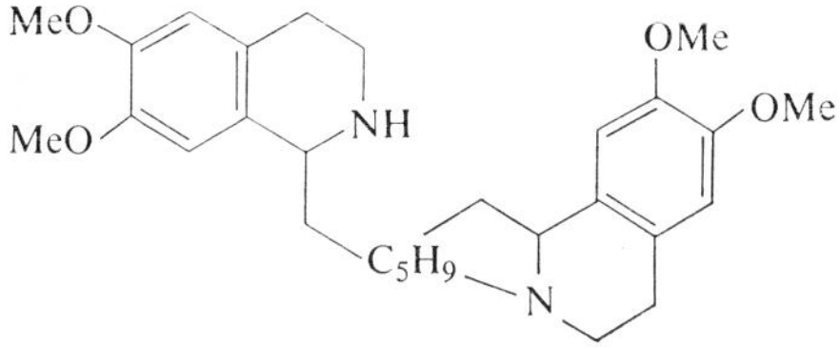

(17)

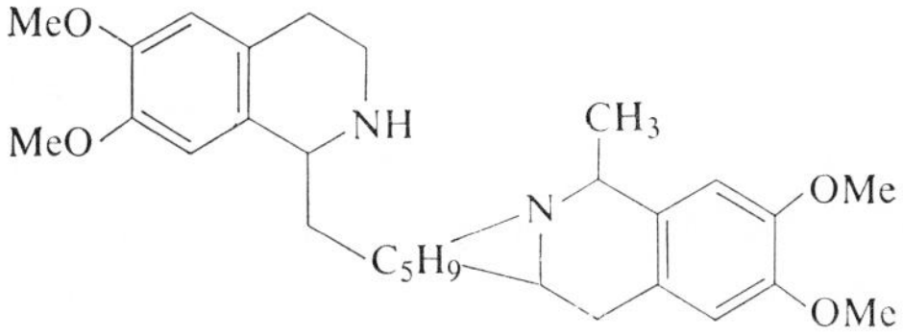

(18)

The reduction of the double bond of the methine followed by further Hofmann degradation results in the elimination of tri-methylamine and the production of a nitrogen-free product that must contain a vinyl group since it yields formaldehyde on ozonolysis. The group $C_5H_9NMe_2$ may thus be expanded to C_4H_7—CH_2NMe_2 or C_3H_6—CMe—NMe_2. The Hofmann degradation of the base (14) without prior reduction of the double bond results in the formation of a conjugated diene that must be represented by the complete structure (19) since on ozonolysis it

(19)   (20)

(21)

gives an $\alpha\beta$-unsaturated aldehyde (20) that may be reduced to the saturated aldehyde (21), identical with material prepared by synthesis.

The conjugated diene (19) could be produced either directly by elimination of trimethylamine from the quaternary salt containing the system (22) or by degradation of either system (23) or (24) to a 1,4-diene and subsequent migration of the double bond into conjugation with that already present under the strongly alkaline conditions of the reaction. (Such a double-bond migration occurs during the exhaustive methylation of *N*-methylpiperidine to pent-1,3-diene.)

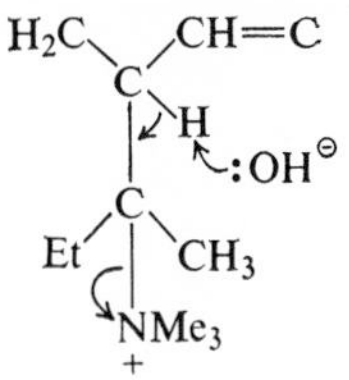

(22)

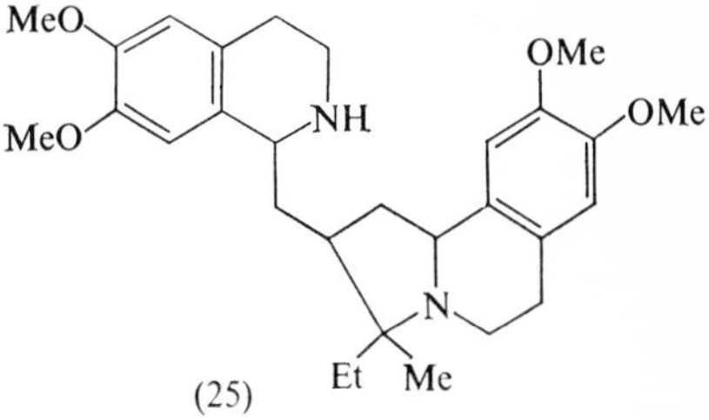

(25)

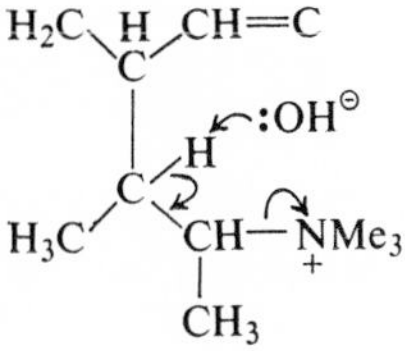

(23)

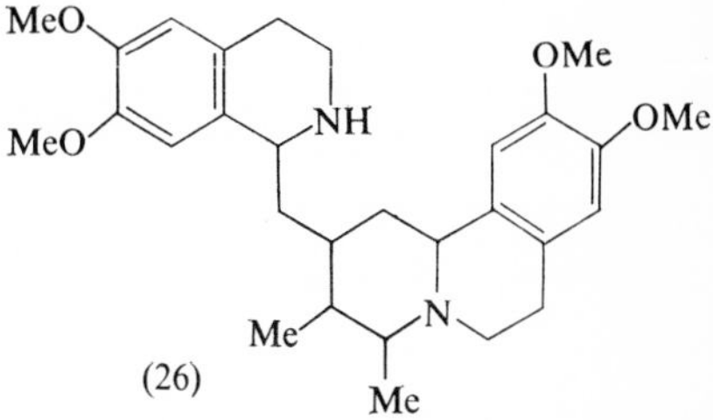

(26)

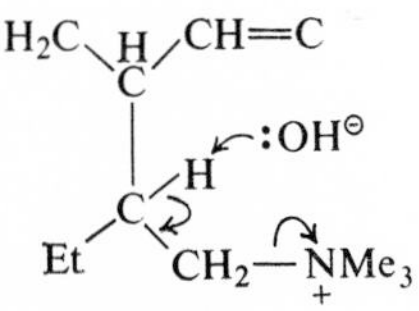

(24)

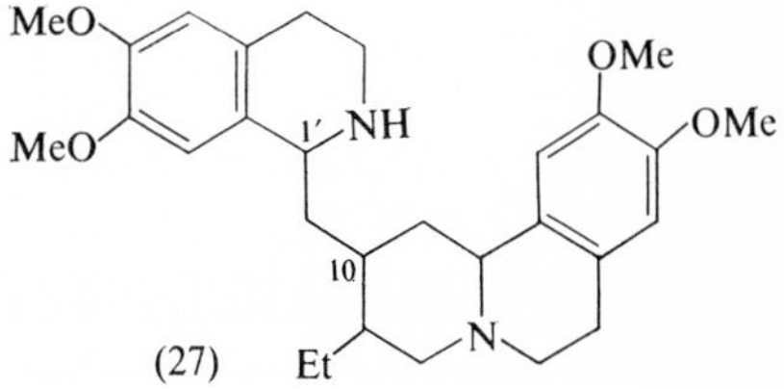

(27)

The part-structures (22), (23), and (24) lead to the alternative structures (25), (26) and (27) respectively for emetine, and of these only (27) is in accord with the presence in the alkaloid of one *C*-methyl group, and this structure has been amply confirmed by synthesis.

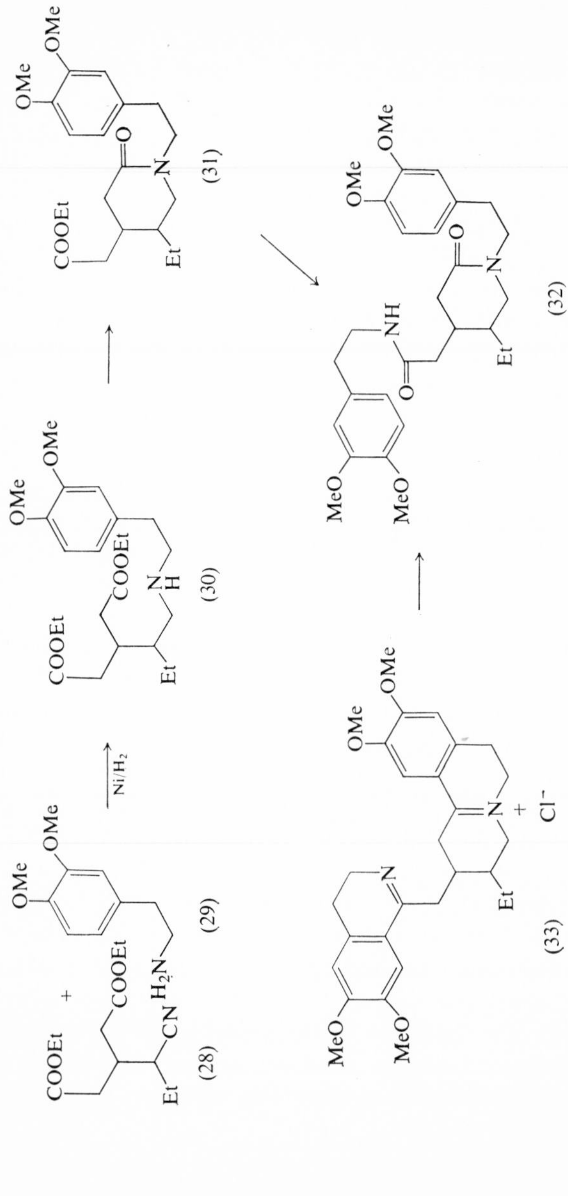

(31)

(32)

(30)

(29)

(28)

(33)

Ni/H₂

The synthesis of emetine

A non-stereospecific synthesis that gave a mixture of emetine and its various stereoisomers was achieved by the Bischler–Napieralsky isoquinoline cyclisation of the diamide (32), followed by reduction of the resulting imine-quaternary salt (33). The diamide (32) was prepared by the reduction of the nitrile (28) in the presence of an excess of homoveratrylamine (29), followed by lactamisation of the resulting symmetrical diester (30) and the condensation of the lactam ester (31) with homoveratrylamine.

This synthesis, however, is not stereospecific, and some knowledge of the stereochemistry was necessary for the planning of a stereospecific synthesis of the alkaloid, and this knowledge was obtained in the following way.

The stereochemistry of emetine

The alkaloid psychotrine is a phenolic base of composition $C_{28}H_{36}O_4N$. It is unsaturated and on reduction affords a mixture of the alkaloids cephaeline and isocephaeline, showing that the saturation of the double bond generates a new asymmetric centre, and these two alkaloids on *O*-methylation yield emetine and isoemetine respectively; emetine and isoemetine differ at the asymmetric carbon atom C-1'. *O*-Ethylation of psychotrine and oxidation of the ethyl ether yields the lactam (34), and the oxidation of *N*-benzoyl-*O*-methylpsychotrine with perphthalic acid and ozone yields the *N*-benzoyllactam (35), and these two reactions indicate the positions of the phenolic hydroxyl group and the double bond in psychotrine, which thus has the structure (36).

Successive Hofmann degradations of *N*-acetylemetine, with reduction at the first stage only, results in elimination of the tertiary nitrogen atom and the production of a diene (37), ozonolysis of which yields the (+)-acid (38). The configuration of this acid has been confirmed by the conversion into the base (39) of known stereochemistry by reactions that do not involve the asymmetric centre at any step. The variation of optical rotatory power with solvent polarity of the product of each step in the transformation of the acid (38) into the base (39) confirmed the stereochemical assignment. These results clearly fix the stereochemistry at C-1′ in emetine.

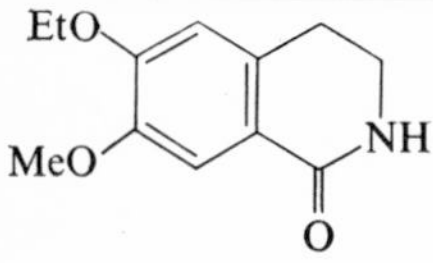

(34)

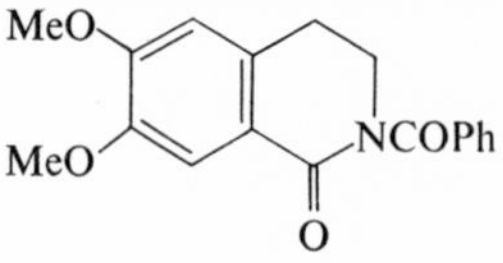

(35)

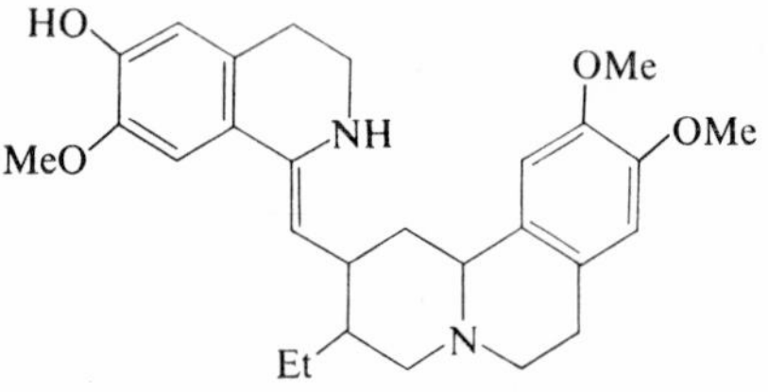

(36)

Oxidation of the bisbenzochloride of *O,N*-dimethylpsychotrine affords a quaternary betaine (40), which may be hydrogenolysed to the amino-acid (41) and in this the carboxyl group must be equatorial since the ethyl ester is stable under vigorous equilibrating conditions. It was shown that there is no inversion at the asymmetric carbon atom to which the carboxyl group is joined during this degradation, by the conversion of the acid (41) into the homologue (42) by the Arndt–Eistert reaction, and the conversion of this homologue into *O*-methylpsychotrine via the homoveratrylamide.

The same acid (42) has also been prepared from the simpler alkaloid protoemetine (43) also found in certain *Ipecacuanha* species, and Wolff–Kishner reduction of this aldehydic base yields the *trans* diethyl compound (44) the racemic form of which has been synthesised as shown in stages from racemic *trans*-3,4-di-ethylcyclopentanone (45), via the intermediates (46)–(49). The addition of hydrogen in the final step of this synthesis is assumed to occur from the least hindered side of the molecule, that is *trans* to the nearest ethyl group, leading to the stereochemistry at the point of ring fusion shown in (44) and hence (40).

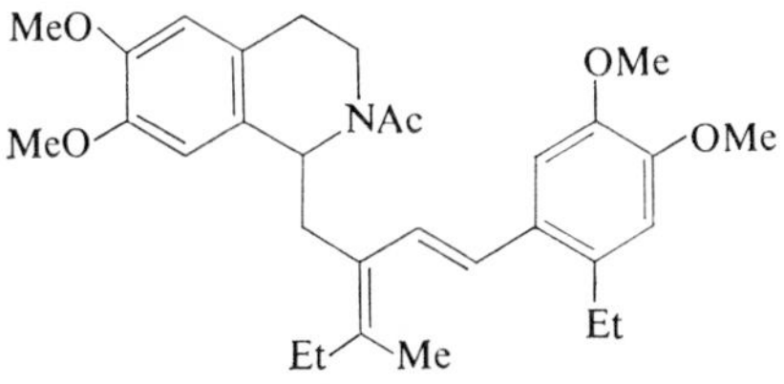

(37)

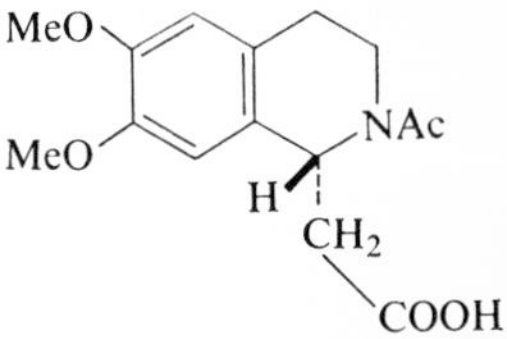

(38)

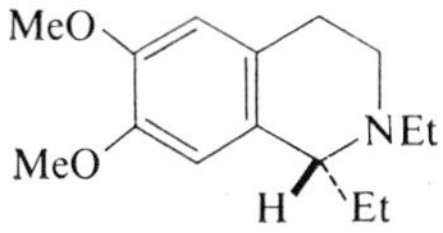

(39)

These reactions thus fix steric arrangements at the three asymmetric centres in the second half of the molecule, but it is not possible to determine from them the relative dispositions of the hydrogen atoms at the asymmetric centres C-1' and C-10. A stereospecific synthesis has been devised which also leaves this final point unsettled, as follows.

The amine (50) was converted into the ethylmalonyl derivative (51) and thence by Dieckmann condensation into the keto-lactam (52), sodium borohydride reduction of which to the β-hydroxy-lactam (53), followed by base-catalysed elimination yielded the $\alpha\beta$-unsaturated lactam (54). Michael addition of ethyl malonate

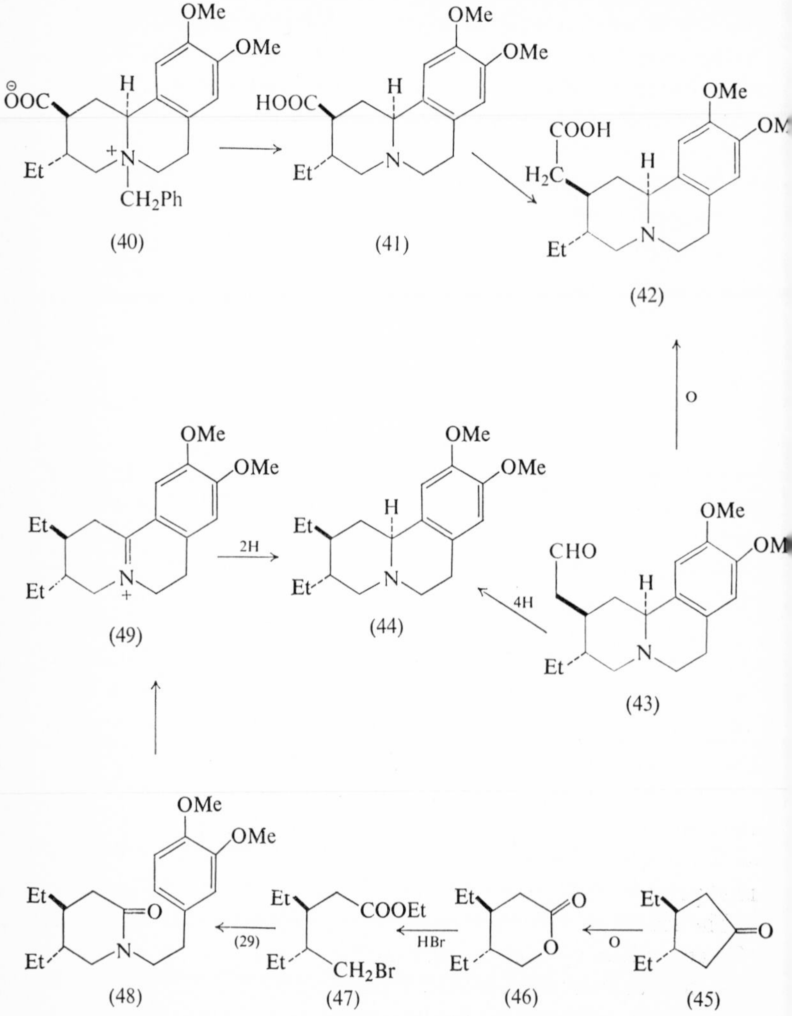

(40)

(41)

(42)

(49)

(44)

(43)

(48)

(47)

(46)

(45)

to this unsaturated lactam, being reversible, gave the thermo-dynamically more stable *trans* product (55), which was converted by simple stages through the mono-ester (56) and cyclised quaternary salt (57) into the basic ester (58), identical with the ethyl ester of the acid (42) obtained as described above from *O*-methyl-psychotrine and protoemetine. The cyclisation of the homo-veratrylamide (59) obtained from the ester (58) then yielded *O*-methylpsychotrine (60), from which emetine was prepared.

An alternative stereospecific synthesis does, however, allow the establishment of a direct relationship between C-1′ and C-10. The starting point for this synthesis is the *meso* ketone (62), obtained together with the racemic form from the pseudo-base (61) and acetone dicarboxylic acid. (Compare the condensation of cotarnine and hydrastinine with acetone and nitromethane, Chapter 11.) The bis-*N*-butyryl derivative of the *meso* ketone gives two diastereo-isomeric alcohols (63) on reduction with sodium borohydride, and is in this way distinguished from the racemate which gives only one such alcohol. In this way the relative stereochemistry at carbon atoms 1′ and 11*b* in the final alkaloid is established; the *meso* ketone (62) yields ($\pm$)-emetine and the racemic isomer yields ($\pm$)-isoemetine.

Treatment of the diamino-ketone (62) with methyl vinyl ketone gives the base (64, $R = CH_2CH_2COCH_2$), cyclisation of which with sodium hydride leads to the pentacyclic base, (65, $R = CH_2CH_2COCH_3$), and this on dehydration gives the un-saturated ketone (66, $R = CH_2CH_2COCH_3$). Reduction of the unsaturated ketone with lithium and liquid ammonia results in the production of the base (67, $R = CH_2CH_2CHMeOH$) with kinetic control giving the less stable isomer at the α-carbon atom and thermodynamic control giving the more stable isomer at the β-carbon atom. Epimerisation at the α-carbon in acid to the more stable form (68) followed by reduction of the ethylenethioketal of the ketone gives the ethyl compound having the stereochemistry shown in (69). The product (69, $R = CH_2CH_2CHMeOH$) on Oppenauer oxidation yields presumably the ketone (69,

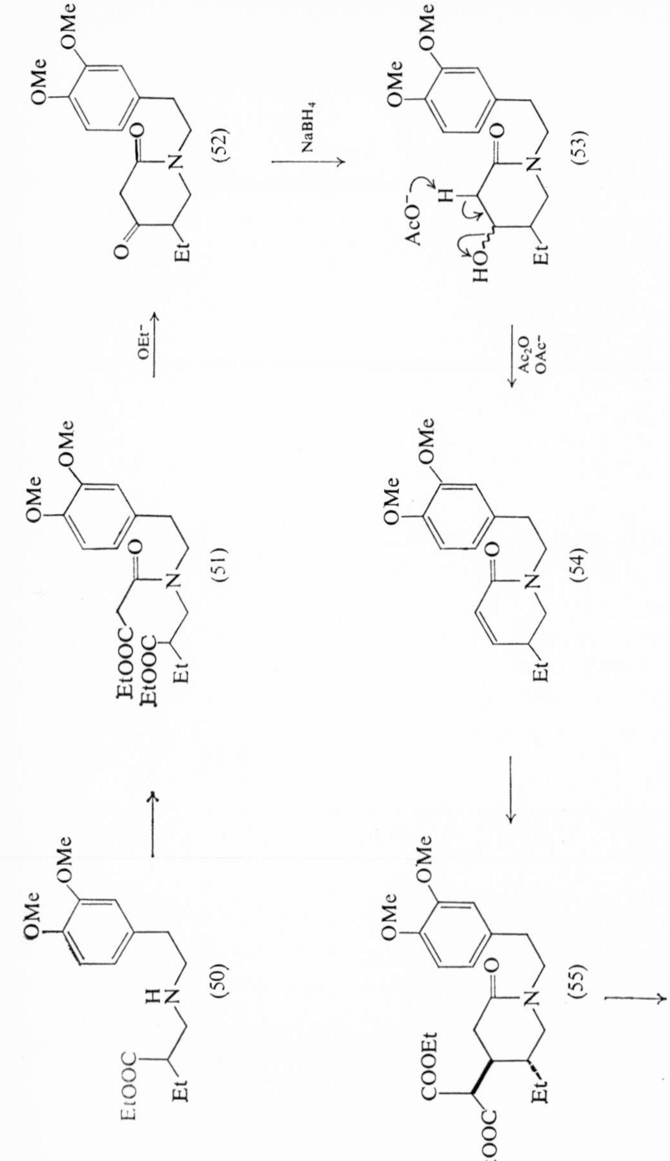
OEt⁻
NaBH₄
Ac₂O
OAc⁻
AcO⁻
(50)
(51)
(52)
(53)
(54)
(55)

COOEt
OMe
OMe
Et
O
N
(56)
POCl$_3$
COOEt
OMe
OMe
Et
N
+
Cl$^-$
(57)
2H
COOEt
OMe
OMe
H
N
Et
(58)
(29)
MeO
MeO
O
NH
OMe
OMe
H
N
Et
(59)
MeO
MeO
NH
OMe
OMe
H
N
Et
(60)

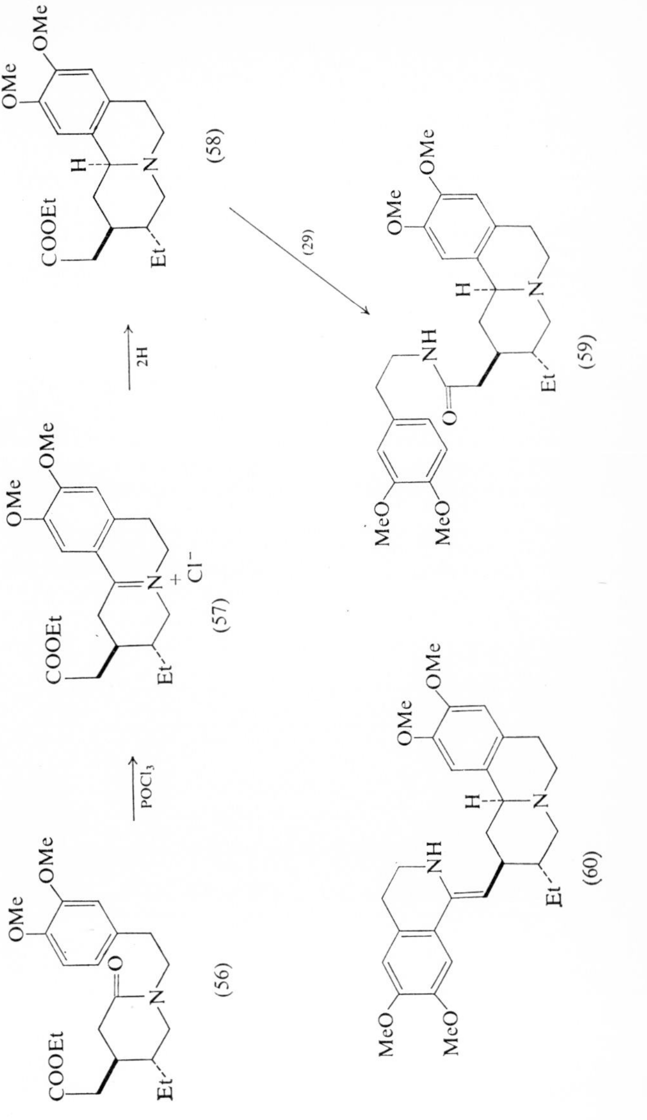

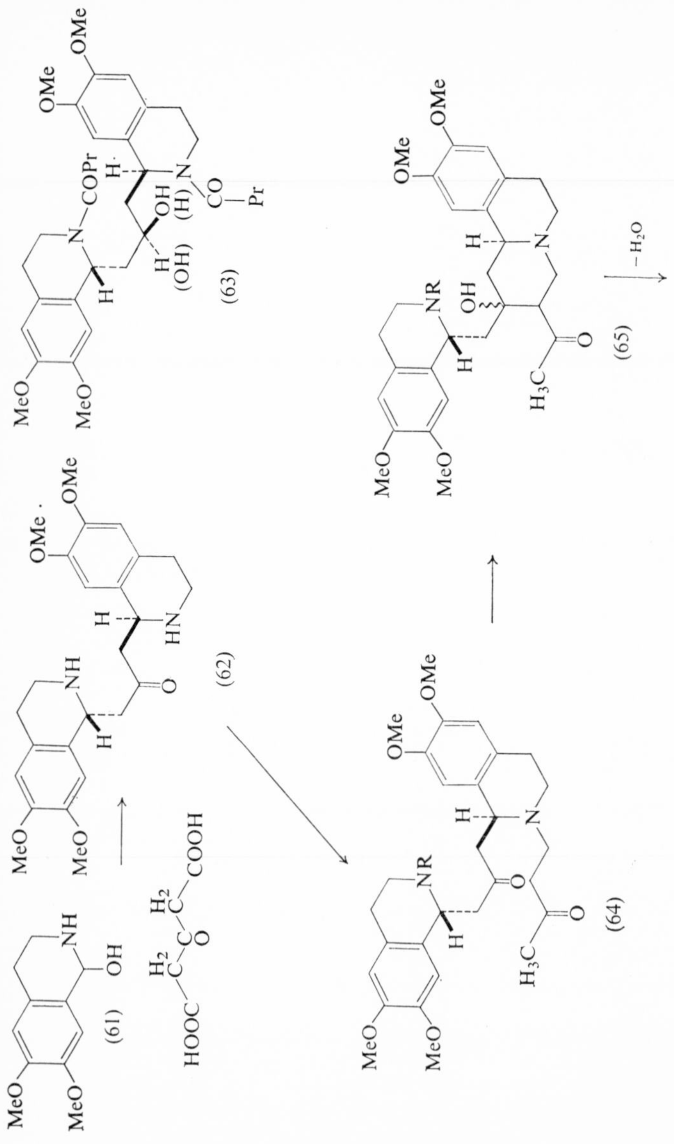
MeO
MeO
NH
OH
(61)
HOOC
H_2
C
C
O
H_2
C
COOH
MeO
MeO
H
NH
O
H
HN
OMe
OMe
(62)
MeO
MeO
H
NR
O
H
N
OMe
OMe
H_3C
O
(64)
MeO
MeO
H
N—COPr
H
(OH)
OH
(H)
H
N
CO
Pr
OMe
OMe
(63)
MeO
MeO
H
NR
OH
H
N
OMe
OMe
H_3C
O
(65)
− H_2O

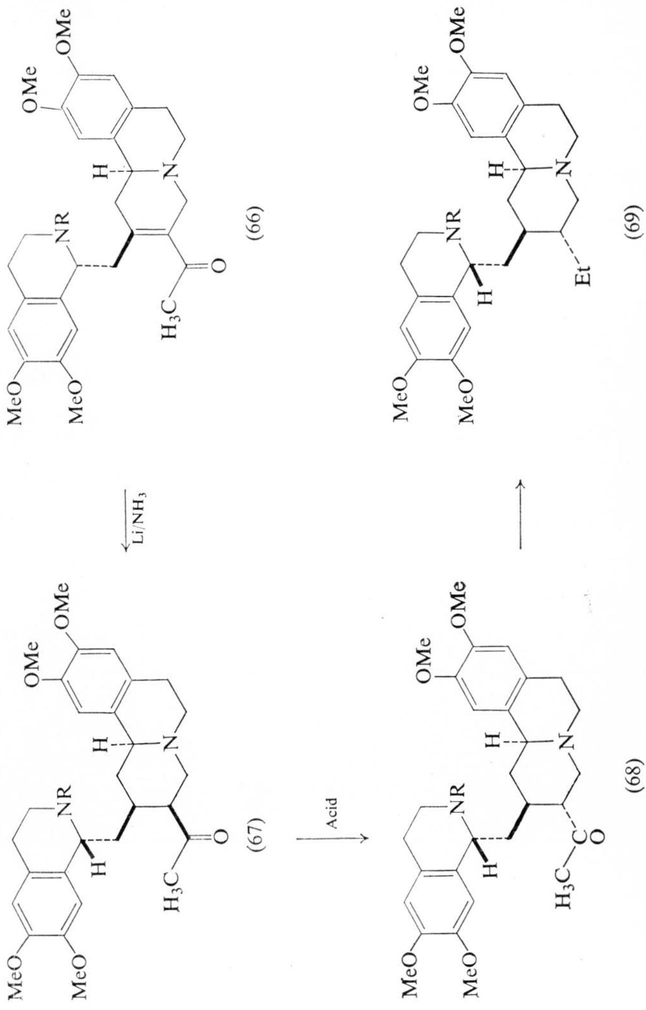

(66)

(67)

(68)

(69)

Li/NH₃

Acid

(71)

(72)

(70)

(73)

R = $CH_2CH_2COCH_3$), which loses methyl vinyl ketone under the vigorous alkaline conditions of the reaction to give ($\pm$)-emetine.

The rubremetinium salts

The dehydrogenation of emetine catalytically yields the iso-quinoline base (70), which is the alkaloid emetamine, but mild oxidation with iodine affords the quaternary rubremetinium salts. These salts are intensely coloured and contain the cation $C_{29}H_{33}O_4N_2^+$. They may be reduced to dihydro-derivatives which are readily oxidised back to the rubremetinium salts by atmospheric oxygen. To explain these facts and the loss of basicity of the non-quaternary nitrogen atom the structure (71) was proposed for rubremetinium bromide. The salt owes its colour to the existence in the molecule of a resonating charged system analogous to that in the cyanine dyes; the positive charge can reside on either nitrogen atom, and the canonical structures are (71) and (72). Reduction of such a salt would be expected to stop at the stable pyrrole (73), oxidation of which to the more stable extended conjugated system of the original salt would be expected to be easy.

The structure (71)–(72) is supported by the very close similarity between the ultraviolet absorption spectra of rubremetinium bromide and the salt (75), prepared by the oxidation of the base (74) and by the synthesis of *C*-bisnorrubremetinium bromide (80) by the self-explanatory route set out in formulae (76)–(80).

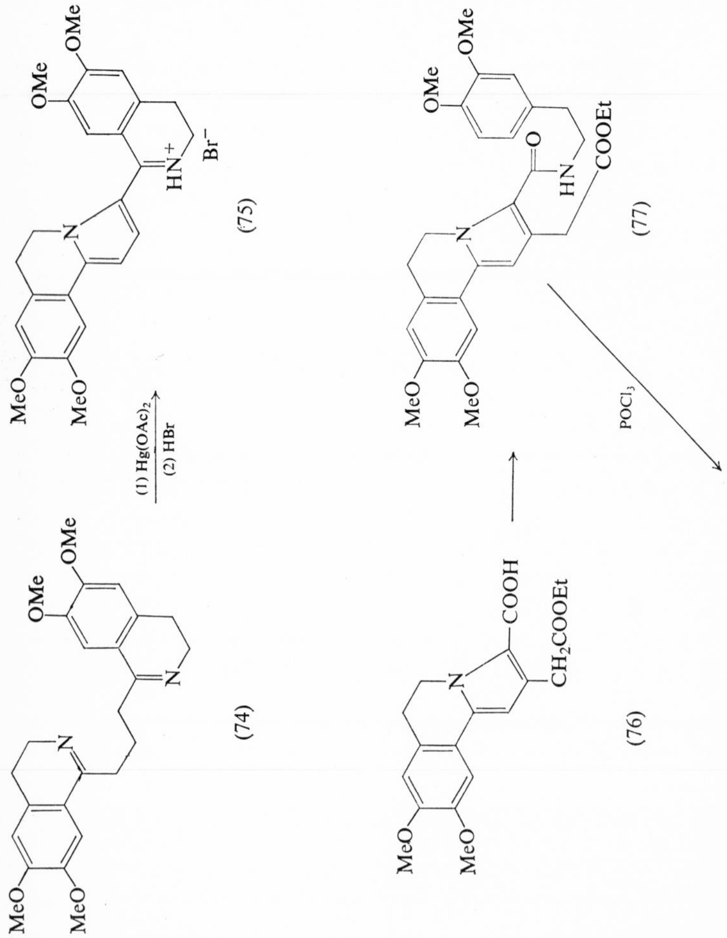

(74)

(75)

$\xrightarrow[\text{(2) HBr}]{\text{(1) Hg(OAc)}_2}$

(76)

(77)

POCl₃

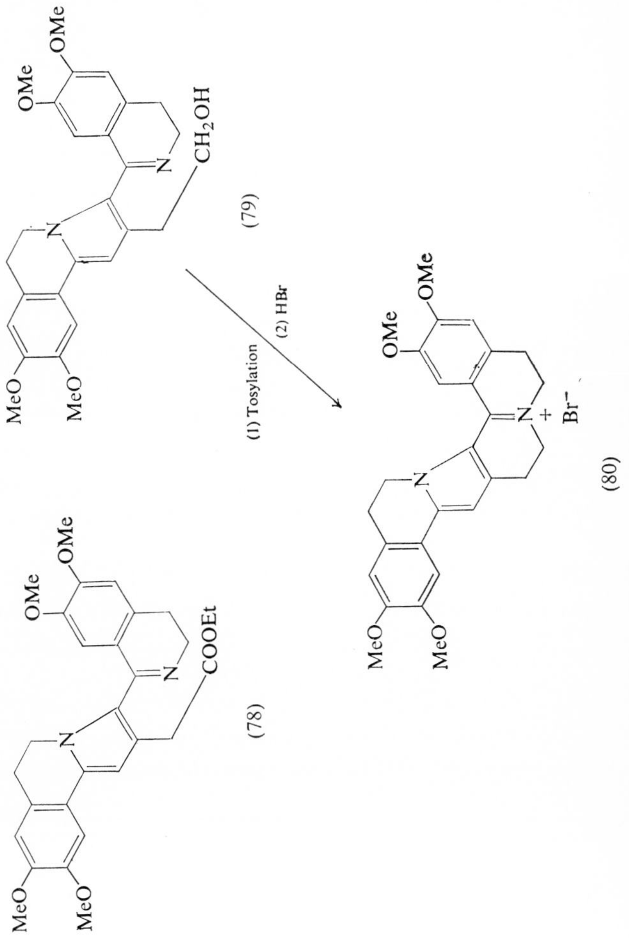
MeO
MeO
OMe
OMe
N
N
COOEt
(78)
CH2OH
(79)
(1) Tosylation
(2) HBr
N
N+
Br−
(80)

The Biogenesis of the Isoquinoline Alkaloids

CERTAIN structural relationships can be traced through the sub-groups of the isoquinoline alkaloids, and the processes whereby the bases of the various groups are formed in a rational sequence from bases of the benzylisoquinoline series have been deduced with reasonable certainty, though only recently has convincing experimental evidence been produced in support of these theories by a study of the results of the feeding of presumed alkaloid precursors labelled at specific points in the molecule with radio-active ^{14}C to growing plants.

The principal building blocks from which the alkaloids are constructed were early assumed to be the amino-acids tyrosine (1) and its oxidation product 3,4-dihydroxyphenylalanine (2). The latter acid could by decarboxylation yield the amine (3), from which arise such bases as hordenine and, by further oxidation, mescaline. The acid (2) could by oxidation yield also the aldehyde (4), and condensation of the amine (3) with the aldehyde (4) under mild conditions in the cell could then lead to norlaudanosine (5), which is believed to be one of the essential precursors of all the other alkaloids of the group. If acetaldehyde or its equivalent were to condense with the amine (3) the product would be the base (6) from which such bases as anhalonidine could be derived.

In the biosynthesis of alkaloids N-methylation, O-methylation and O,O-methylation are subsidiary processes accomplished by formaldehyde or its equivalent (e.g. methionine) and can probably

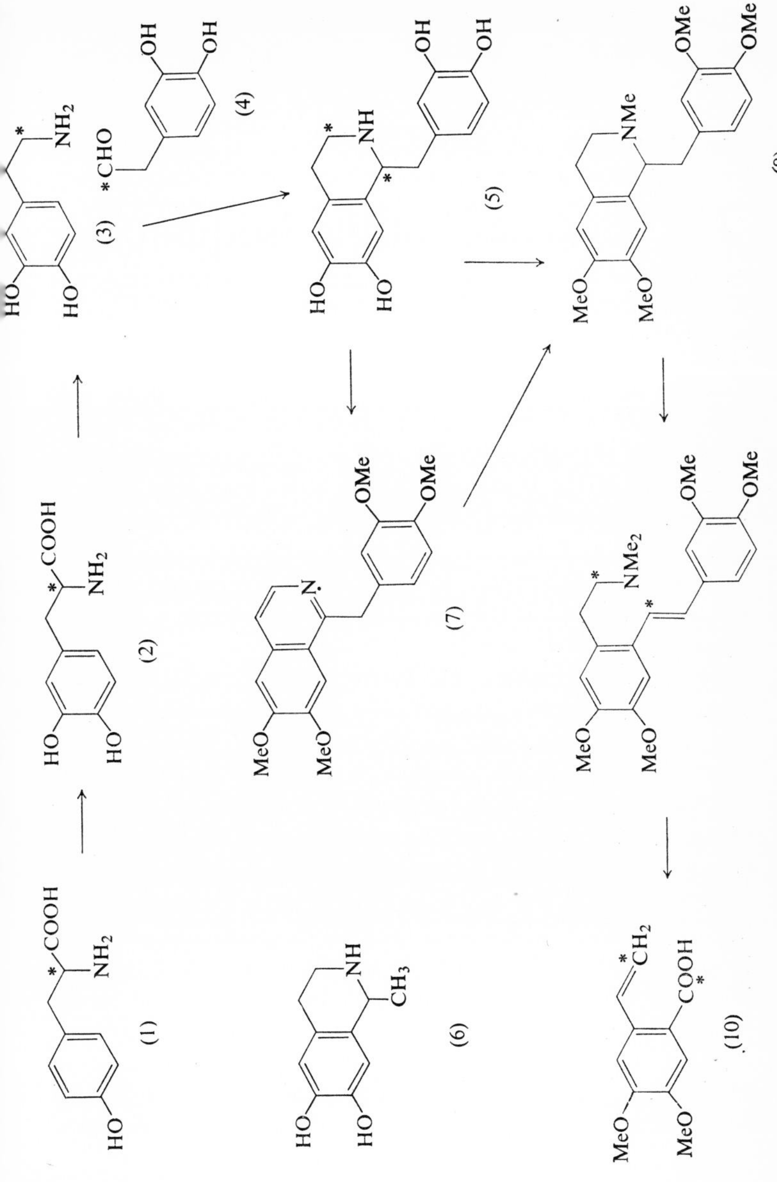
(1)
(2)
(3)
(4)
(5)
(6)
(7)
(8)
(9)
(10)

occur at any stage along the route to a particular alkaloid, as long as phenolic hydroxyl groups necessary for oxidative coupling reactions are not in this way masked. For example (+)-laudanosine probably arises in the plant by *O*,*N*-methylation of the phenolic base (5), and papaverine presumably also arises from the reduced base (5) by dehydrogenation and *O*-methylation. Similarly the introduction of the third oxygen atom in the anhalonium bases also is a secondary process, and can occur before or after closing of the isoquinoline ring system, though the presence of mescaline (3,4,5-trimethoxyphenylethylamine) in the same plants as the anhalonium bases suggests that the oxidation precedes cyclisation; it is likely that isoquinoline ring closure only occurs in phenols, and that *O*-methylation in mescalines prevents this reaction from taking place.

These theories have been put to the experimental test of feeding ^{14}C labelled tyrosine to poppy plants. Using tyrosine specifically labelled as shown by the asterisk in structure (1) radioactive papaverine was obtained, and *N*-methylation and reduction of this (see Chapter 3) gave racemic laudanosine (8), which was degraded by way of the methine base (9) to the acid (10) and this retained all of the original radioactivity present in the papaverine. Ozonolysis of the vinyl group of the acid (10) removed one of the radioactive carbon atoms, while decarboxylation removed the other, and the activity was found to lie wholly at these two centres and to be equally distributed between them, from which it can be concluded that the papaverine obtained in this way is exclusively labelled at the positions shown in (7), in accord with the biogenetic theories.

The elaboration of the other alkaloid sub-groups from the precursor (5) or a methylated derivative of this, occurs by two main processes:

(a) oxidation,
(b) condensation with formaldehyde or its equivalent with subsequent oxidation.

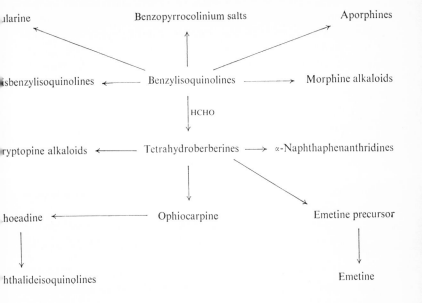

A. Oxidations

The oxidative processes occurring during the conversion of the benzyltetrahydroisoquinoline alkaloids into bases of the bis-benzylisoquinoline, cularine, aporphine and morphine groups may be illustrated by reference to the oxidation of *p*-cresol. This reaction results in the production of a non-phenolic $\alpha\beta$-unsaturated ketone $C_{14}H_{14}O_2$. When one electron is removed from the phenate anion (11) the product is a neutral radical for which the canonical structures (12*a*)–(12*d*) may be written (of these (12*b*) and (12*d*) are identical as *p*-cresol is symmetrical, but in unsymmetrical phenols these two structures are different), and the structure (13), arising from the pairing of the radicals in the forms (12*a*) and (12*c*), followed by addition of the phenolic nucleus to the dienone system, was first proposed for the oxidation product. Subsequent work, however, established for this ketone the structure (14*c*), which arises by the pairing of radicals in the forms (12*b*) and (12*c*), to give the diketone (14*a*) in which only one dienone system can achieve greater stability by enolisation to an aromatic form (14*b*), and this

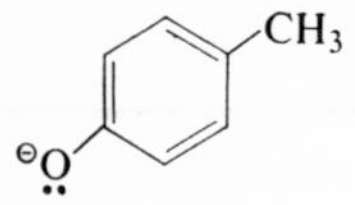

(11)

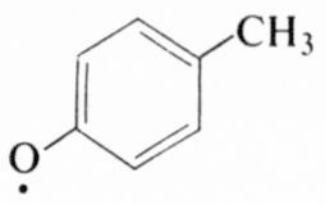

(12*a*)

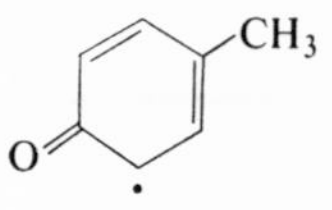

(12*b*)

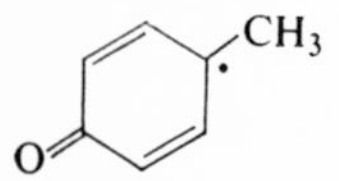

(12*c*)

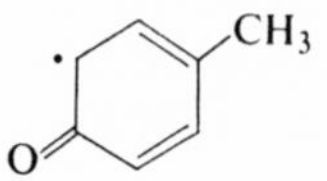

(12*d*)

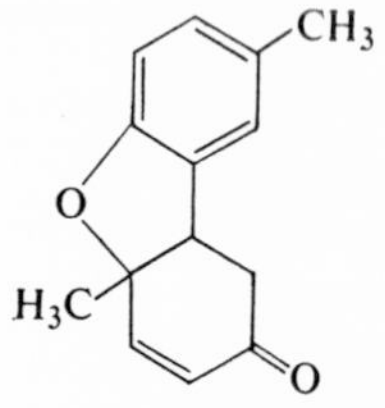

(13)

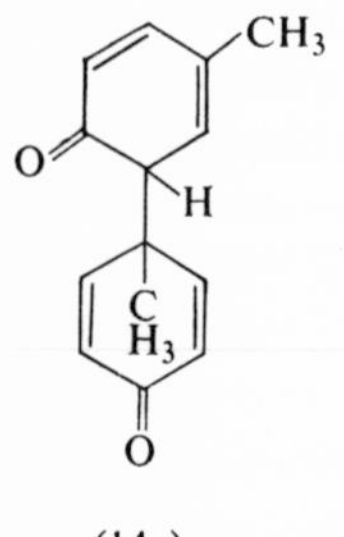

(14*a*)

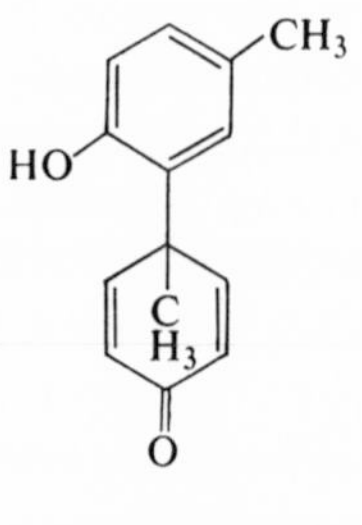

(14*b*)

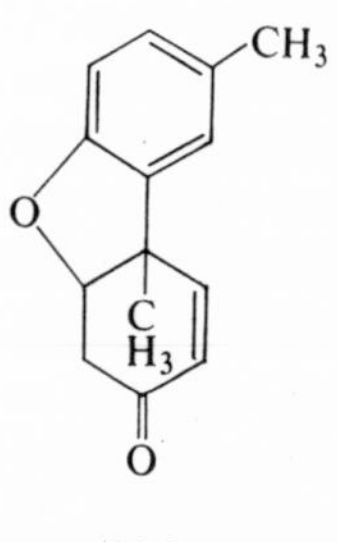

(14*c*)

phenol then adds to the adjacent dienone system to give (14*c*). It is this type of radical pairing that is believed to be involved in the biogenesis of the morphine alkaloids.

By processes analogous to those set out above the hypothetical precursor of morphine, the base (15) (this is selected as the likely immediate precursor rather than the tetra-phenolic base (5) as the alternative coupling possibilities are in that way reduced to a minimum) could be oxidised to the diradical (16) pairing of which internally would afford the phenol (17) analogous to the phenol (14*b*). It has been argued that this phenol is then transformed into the non-phenolic ketone (18), which yields thebaine by reduction and dehydration or some similar process. A more plausible hypothesis, and one for which there is believed to be some experimental support is that the phenolic ketone (17) is first reduced to the alcohol (19, R = H), in some suitable derivative of which such as the phosphate ester the 4,5-oxygen bridge can be closed with elimination of the C-7 oxygen substituent and the direct production of thebaine. This provides a satisfactory explanation of why the bases of this group that contain a 4,5-oxygen bridge have no substituent at C-7, whereas the bases sinomenine (22) and hasubanonine, as well as the alkaloids of *Croton linearis* (see Chapter 7), which contain no 4,5-bridge, bear no substituents at this point. Methylation of the alcohol (19, R = H) to the ether (19, R = Me), followed by double-bond migration would give the base (21), in which closure of the ether bridge by the process given in (19) is no longer possible, and simple hydrolysis of one of the two enol ether systems in this would give sinomenine (22).

The cases of hasubanonine and metaphenine are interesting. The former may be assigned either structure (26) or (27) on the available chemical evidence, and biogenetic theory is unable to differentiate between them. The structure (26) could most simply arise from the base (23), through the intermediate (25), which only requires *O*-methylation and reduction to yield the desired product. Since coupling of phenolic nuclei by oxidation can only occur *ortho* or *para* to hydroxyl the base (27) would have to arise through the coupled intermediate (28), presumably via the reduction product (29, R = H), and this would be expected to afford a 4,5-cyclised base by the process already mentioned. However,

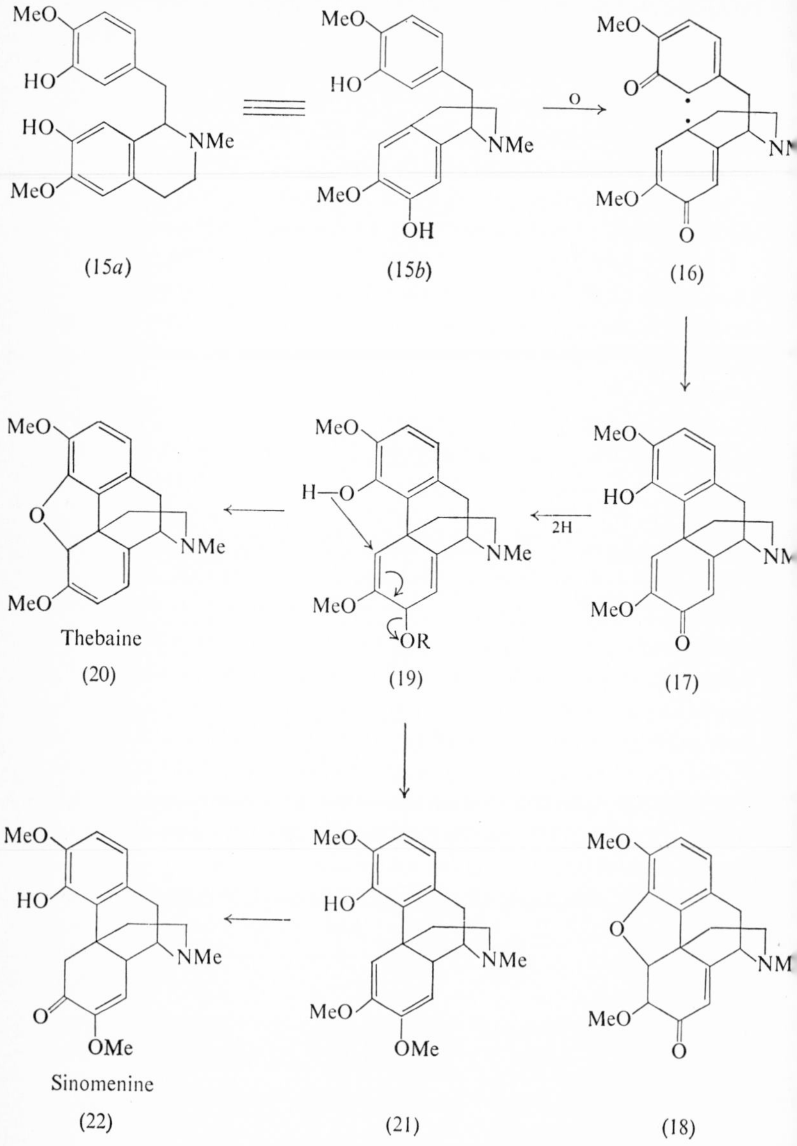

(15a)   (15b)   (16)

Thebaine

(20)   (19)   (17)

Sinomenine

(22)   (21)   (18)

hasubanonine is a 4-methoxy-compound, and if methylation of the 4-hydroxyl group of the phenol (28) precedes reduction 4,5-ether bridge formation would be effectively prevented. In any case *Stephania japonica* Miers, from which hasubanonine is isolated, also produces metaphenine, for which the structure (30) has been proposed, and the relationship of this to the hypothetical base (29, R = H) is obvious, though it is clear that its derivation from the dienone (25) via the reduced base (31) is no less plausible.

It will be seen from the foregoing discussion that the morphine alkaloids are believed to arise from bases of the benzyltetrahydro-isoquinoline group, which are themselves in turn derived from tyrosine, and that the first recognisable alkaloid of the morphine structure to be formed from the diphenolic precursor (15) is the-baine, which must be subsequently transformed into codeine and morphine in the plant in that order. Chemical evidence from the feeding of ^{14}C labelled precursors to opium poppy plants entirely support these conclusions.

The feeding of ^{14}C labelled tyrosine (31*a*) to *Papaver somniferum* results in the production of ^{14}C labelled morphine (33), the radio-activity of which was found to be restricted entirely to the carbon atoms maked with asterisks, and to be equally divided between them. This was demonstrated by the degradation of morphine by stages to the *N*-free 13-vinyl compound (34), which lost half of its radioactivity as formaldehyde on ozonolysis, and by degradation also to the phenanthrene (36) (during which half of the activity is lost with the side-chain) and the subsequent conversion of this through the acid (37) and the lactone (38) into the acid (39), which then lost all of its radioactivity on decarboxylation.

The feeding of specifically labelled norlaudanosoline (32, R = H) and reticuline (32, R = Me) to the opium poppy also afforded the same specifically labelled morphine, the incorporation of activity in the final alkaloid in these cases being much higher than with tyrosine as precursor, and the highest incorporation was achieved with reticuline, suggesting that this base is indeed the favoured precursor.

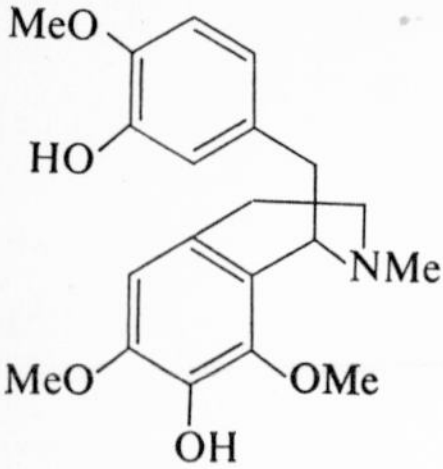

(23)

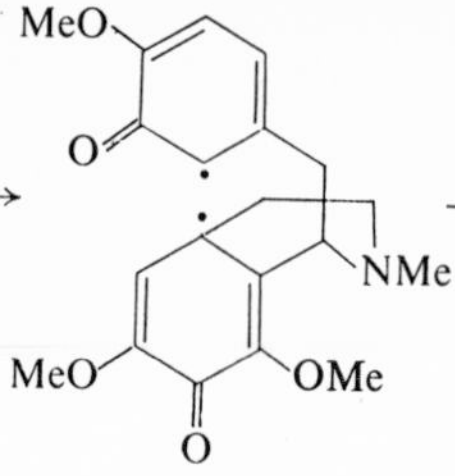

(24)

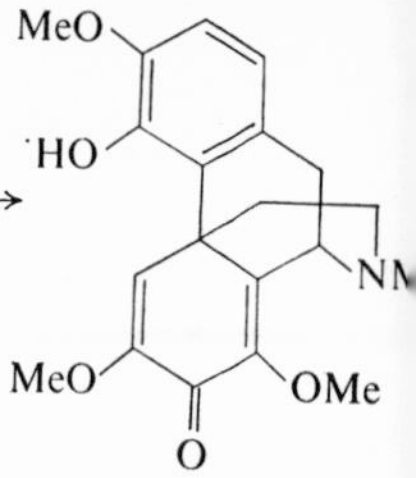

(25)

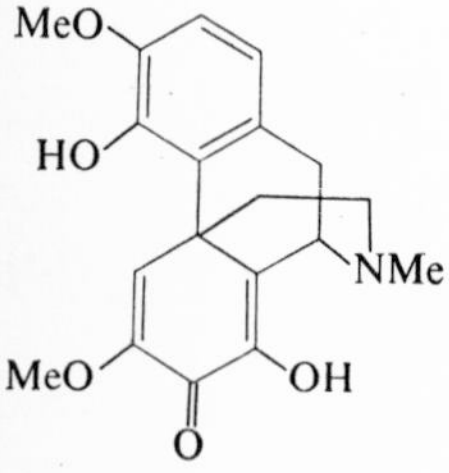

(28)

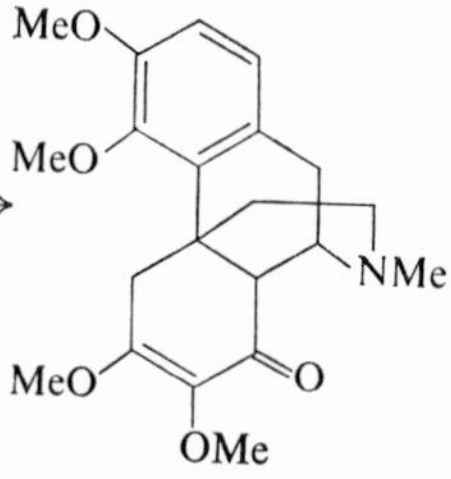

(27)

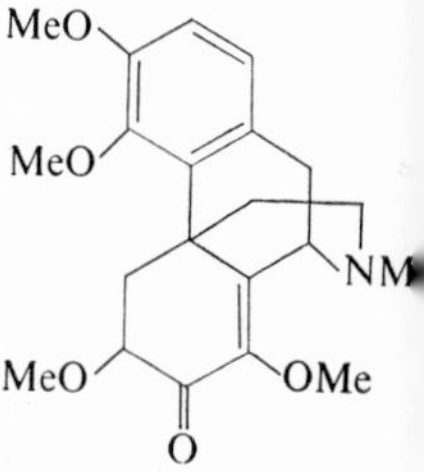

(26)

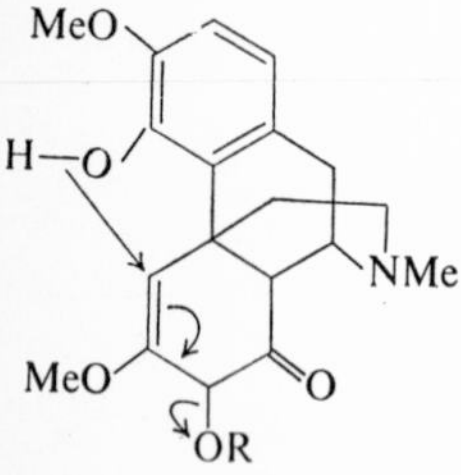

(29)

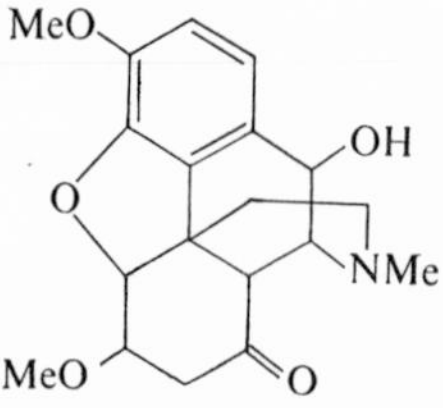

(30)

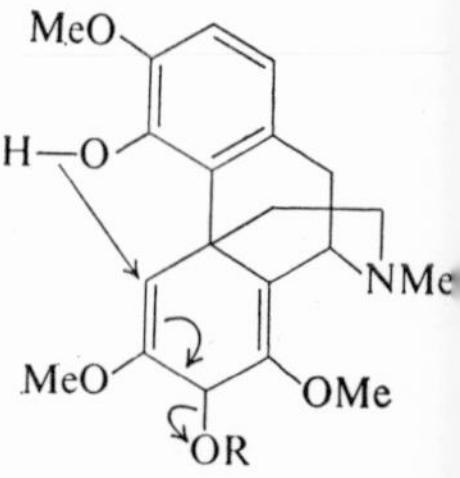

(31)

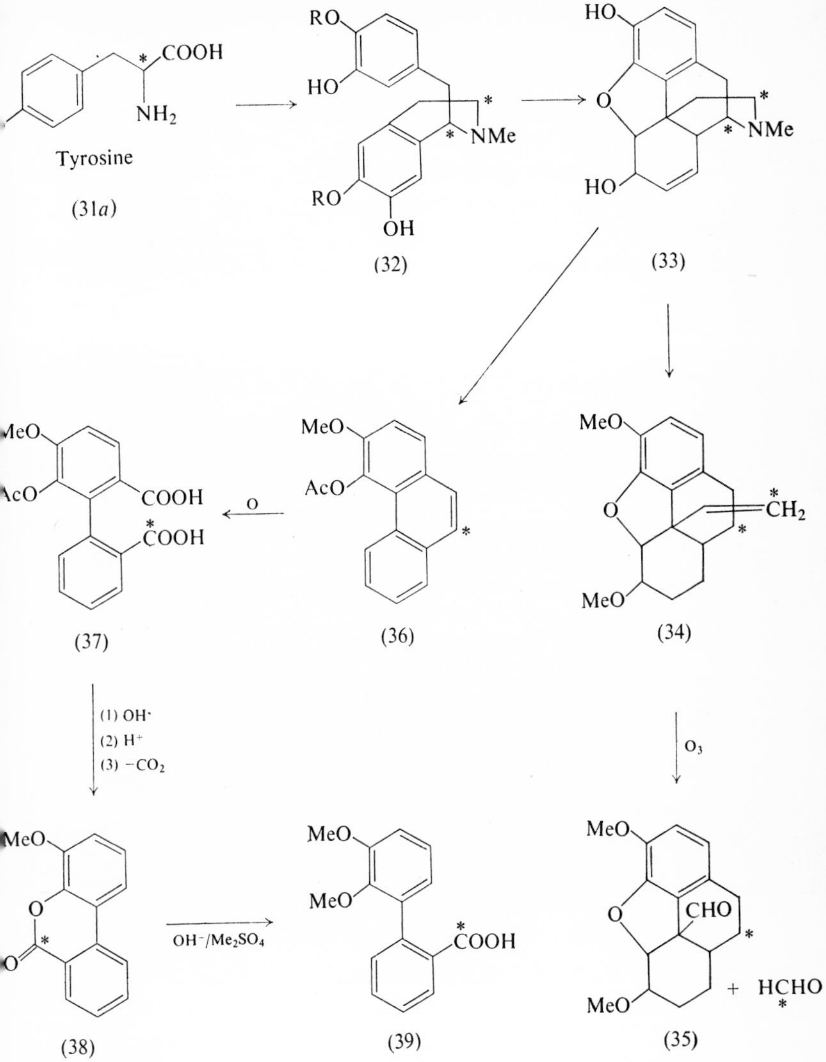

Tyrosine

(31a)

(32)

(33)

(34)

(35)

(36)

(37)

(38)

(39)

The rate of incorporation of radioactivity into the alkaloids in plants growing in an atmosphere containing $^{14}CO_2$ and the rate of incorporation of activity from labelled tyrosine have been measured, and in both cases the activity has been found first in thebaine, then in codeine and finally in morphine, indicating that this is the order in which the bases are formed in the plant. This has been confirmed by feeding the unspecifically labelled alkaloids (obtained from the $^{14}CO_2$ feeding experiment) back to new growing poppy plants; in this way the activity from thebaine was transmitted to codeine and morphine, that from codeine was transmitted to morphine only and no transfer of activity from morphine to codeine or thebaine could be detected.

The aporphine alkaloids

There is no reason why oxidative coupling of benzyltetrahydro-isoquinolines should necessarily occur in the manner given above, and other forms of coupling can be envisaged, and indeed the products of such coupling are found widely distributed in Nature. By reference to the radicals (12a)–(12d) it will be seen that the coupling in such a way as to avoid the production of a quaternary carbon atom would result in structures in which complete aromatisation is possible by enolisation of both dienone systems. For example the pairing of the radicals (12b) and (12d) could give the dienone (40), enolisation of which could afford the diphenol (41), and coupling of (12a) with (12d) could lead through the ether (42) to the oxygen-linked phenol (43). These are examples of two variants of the coupling process by which the aporphine, bis-benzylisoquinoline and cularine alkaloids presumably arise.

The application of these principles to the benzyltetrahydro-isoquinoline (44), which may also be represented in the form (44a), leads through the coupled products (45) and (45a) to the aporphine alkaloids with the two fundamental substitution patterns (46) and (46a), though the final pattern of substitution in individual alkaloids may be modified by subsequent changes. In a recent publication it has been alleged that thebaine is converted into the aporphine

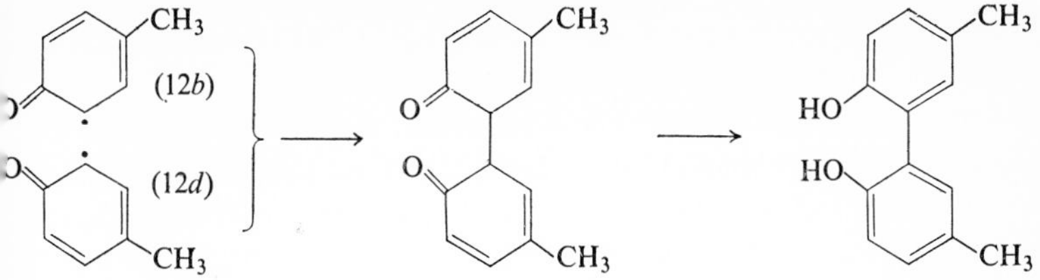

(40) (41)

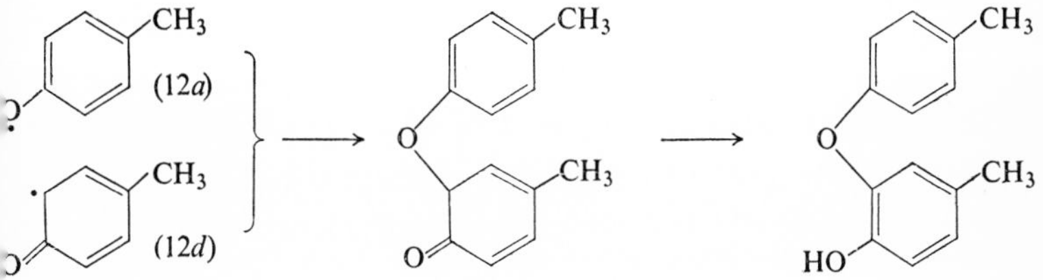

(42) (43)

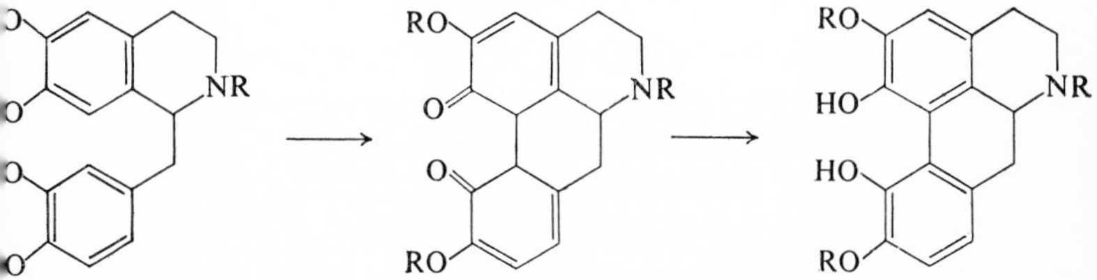

(44) (45) (46)

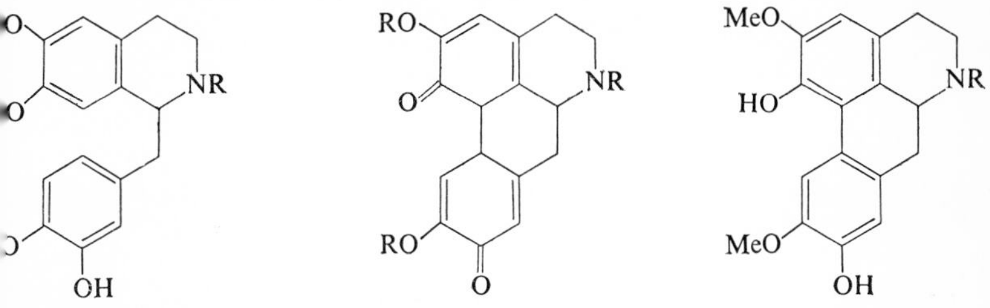

(44a) (45a) (46a)

9

alkaloid isothebaine in the oriental poppy, but the evidence presented is quite unconvincing, and the transformation is most unlikely, particularly as the two bases appear to belong to antipodal stereochemical series.

The bisbenzylisoquinoline alkaloids

General biogenetic theory of the type set out above was most helpful in the elucidation of the structures of the bases of this group, though the detail of the oxidative coupling process was not understood at the time. The fundamental unit from which alkaloids of this type appear to be derived is the trihydroxy-alkaloid norco-claurine (48), which could be derived from the amine (3) and the aldehyde (47) obtained by the oxidation of tyrosine (1). This phenol could suffer oxidation with oxygen–carbon linkage of the form shown in formulae (42) and (43) in several different ways, of which only some examples need be given here. Linkage between the C-12 hydroxyl group and C-11 leads to the structure (49), in which further oxidation can lead to the product of coupling between the C-7 hydroxyl and C-8', namely the base (50) and further coupling in this base between the C-7' hydroxyl and C-8 is possible. (It is obvious that the last two couplings could occur in the reverse order giving the same final product but by way of a base isomeric in structure with the base (50).) As an alternative to 12-11' coupling in the first step the union can involve the C-12 hydroxyl of one molecule and the C-8 position of the other, and if this occurs twice the product is the base (51). Further ramifications of structure in this series are discussed in Chapter 8.

Cularine

Although the coupling of the C-12 hydroxyl and C-8 can occur between two molecules of the base (48) to give the base (51), it cannot occur inside a single molecule, since the product of such a reaction (51a) would be impossibly strained. An internal ether-linked alkaloid, cularine (52), is however known, and formally this could be derived from either diphenol (53) or (54), with *O-*

HO
HO
NH_2
(3)
CHO
OH
(47)
HO
HO
NH
8
11
12
OH
(48)
12/11′
12/8′
OH
OH
N
7
8
HO
HO
7′
8′
NH
O
HO
(49)
7/8′
OH
OH
HO
7′
N
8
O
N
H
O
OH
(50)
HO
HO
NH
O
CH_2
H_2C
O
HN
OH
OH
(51)

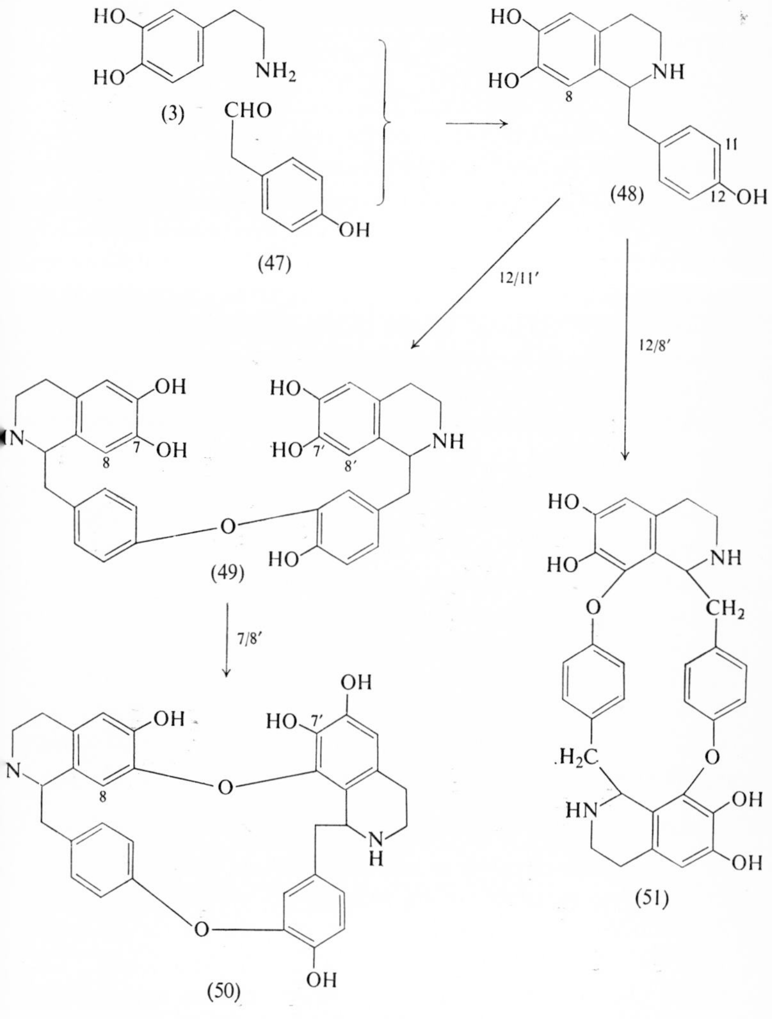

(53)

(54)

(52)

(55)

(51a)

(56)

methylation of the initial phenolic coupling product. The orientation of substituents in both of these possible precursors is, however, unusual, and the base most probably arises by oxidative coupling of a base of general structure (55), with subsequent removal of the unwanted C-6 substituent. In this connection it may be noted that only in *Corydalis claviculata* does cularine appear as a major alkaloid, and certain other *Corydalis* species elaborate the alkaloid capaurine (56), which has the same oxygen substitution pattern as the proposed cularine precursor (55).

A number of attempts have been made to effect the oxidative coupling of suitably substituted benzyltetrahydroisoquinolines to bases of the morphine, aporphine and bisbenzylisoquinoline groups in the laboratory. Working with norlaudanosine (57, R = Me), Robinson and Schöpf independently obtained in this way only the benzopyrrocolinium salts (58), and this process must also occur in Nature, since the Australian plant *Cryptocaria bowiei* Hook contains an alkaloid of this general structure. This nitrogen–carbon coupling has proved troublesome in the laboratory, and only by working with quaternary salts in which it cannot occur have the aporphine and bisbenzylisoquinoline structures been obtained in such a manner.

B. Condensation with formaldehyde

The tetrahydroberberine alkaloids doubtless arise in Nature from secondary bases of the benzyltetrahydroisoquinoline series (57, R = H) by condensation with formaldehyde or its equivalent. In the laboratory this process gives a mixture of the two possible products (59) and (59a) in the wholly phenolic series, but only the base (59a, R = Me) in the methylated series, whereas in Nature the substitution pattern shown in (59) is found almost exclusively, the base coreximine (59a, R = H) being the only natural base with the alternative pattern. It is probable that a phenolic hydroxy group *ortho* or *para* to which condensation can occur, is necessary for this reaction to take place in the plant, and the survival of corpaverine (60) in a plant that produces almost exclusively tetrahydro-

(59)

(58)

(57)

(61)

(59a)

(60)

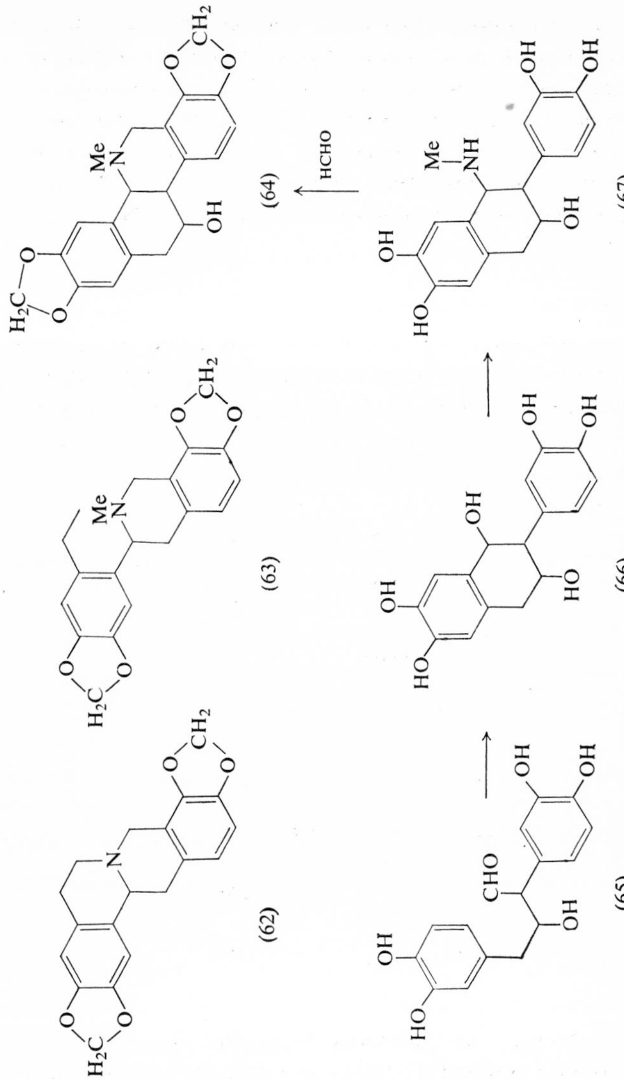

(62) (63) (64)

(65) (66) (67)

berberine alkaloids, as well as the proved structure of coreximine (59a, R = H) supports this view. The berberines clearly arise by the oxidation of the tetrahydro-bases. In support of these views it has been shown that the feeding of ^{14}C labelled tyrosine to berberine-producing plants results in the alkaloid being specifically labelled at the positions marked in formula (61) with an asterisk.

The other alkaloids of the isoquinoline group may all be regarded as being derived from those of the tetrahydroberberine series by oxidation.

α-*Naphthaphenanthridines*

These alkaloids, e.g. chelidonine (64) could arise from *N*-methylation, ring fission and recyclisation of a suitable tetrahydroberberine, e.g stylopine (62), but the details of such a process

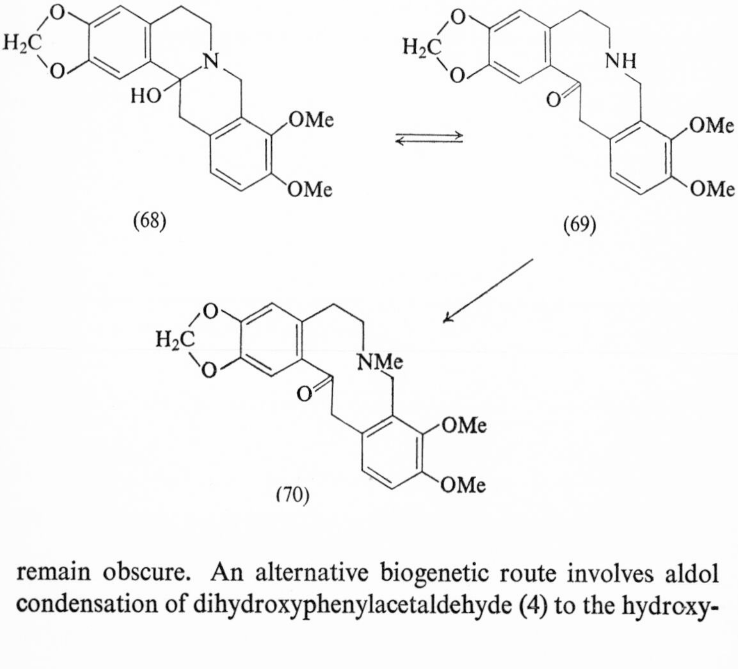

(68)   (69)

(70)

remain obscure. An alternative biogenetic route involves aldol condensation of dihydroxyphenylacetaldehyde (4) to the hydroxyaldehyde (65), cyclisation of this to the diol (66) and amination to give the base (67), followed by nitrogen–carbon bridging by formaldehyde as in the production of the tetrahydroberberine alkaloids. This process has the virtue that it leaves a hydroxyl group in the position in which one is actually found in chelidonine.

Alkaloids related to cryptopine

Bases such as cryptopine could quite simply arise by oxidation of the corresponding tetrahydroberberine to the carbinolamine (68), followed by methylation of the tautomeric secondary amine form (69); this process has been accomplished in the laboratory with the production of, for example, allocryptopine (70).

Rhoeadine and the phthalideisoquinoline alkaloids

Oxidation of the tetrahydroberberine alkaloids could also occur with attack at C-13 giving rise first to ophiocarpine (71), which is the only example of a hydroxytetrahydroberberine, and then by

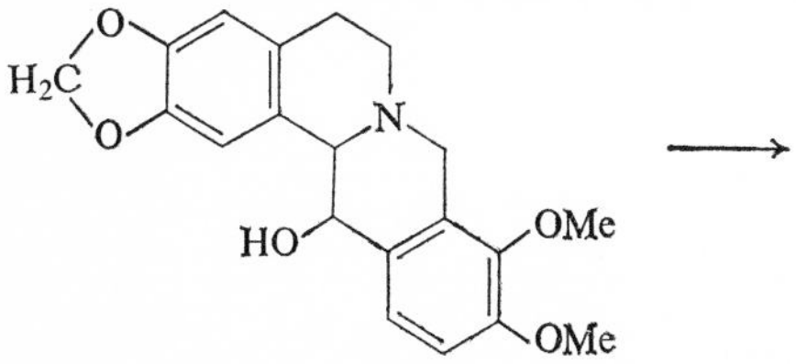

(71)

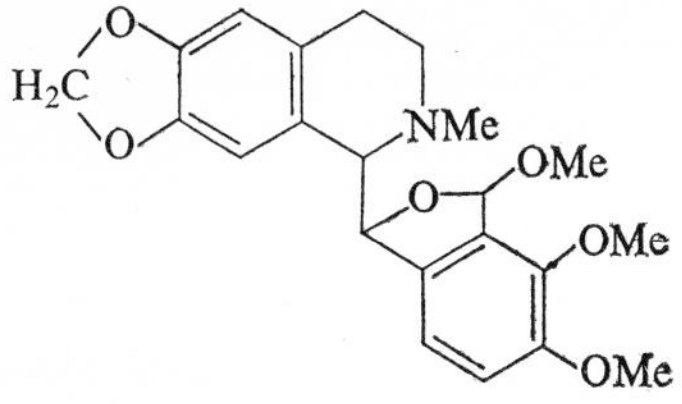

(72) 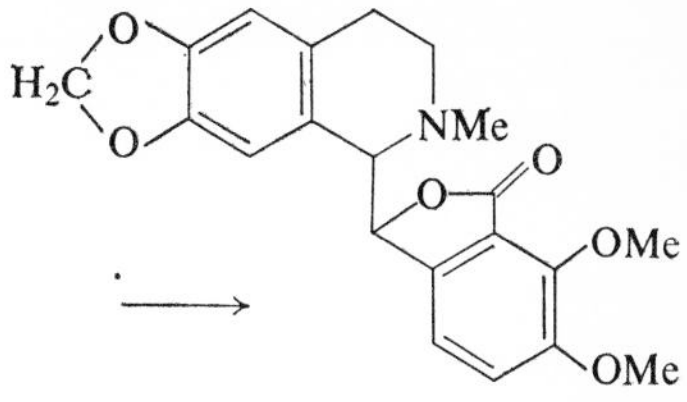   (73)

oxidation at C-8 and splitting of the C—N bond with prior or subsequent *N*-methylation to give successively the systems found in rhoeadine (72) and narcotine (73). If narcotine is derived in this manner from tyrosine by way of norlaudanosine and tetrahydroberberine, the feeding of ^{14}C labelled tyrosine to the opium poppy would be expected to give the alkaloid specifically labelled as indicated by asterisks in formula (73). This has indeed been found to be the case, and the same result has been obtained by feeding to the poppy norlaudanosoline labelled as in formula (5).

Emetine

In 1947 Woodward suggested that one of the steps in the biogenesis of strychnine (77) could be the fission of a catechol nucleus in an intermediate such as (74), leading to a hydroxyaldehyde such

as (75) that could then be converted into the alkaloid (77) via the base (76). At that time emetine was known to contain a simple tetrahydroisoquinoline unit and a second isoquinoline system in which the nitrogen atom was common to two rings, and Robinson suggested that this alkaloid could arise as the result of a similar fission of a suitable tetrahydroberberine base. Such a base (78) could suffer fission to the hydroxyaldehyde (79), and if this took

the place of the aldehyde (4) in a norlaudanosoline-like synthesis the product would have the skeleton (80), and its transformation into the structure (81), which is emetine, presents no problems. In this way the correct structure for emetine was deduced in advance of the chemical work set out in Chapter 13.

Index